Amino Acids, Proteins
and Cancer Biochemistry

JESSE PHILIP GREENSTEIN

1902-1959

Amino Acids, Proteins and Cancer Biochemistry

Papers presented at the
JESSE P. GREENSTEIN
MEMORIAL SYMPOSIUM
Division of Biological Chemistry
American Chemical Society, Sept. 16, 1959

With a biographical article on
Dr. Greenstein and a
bibliography of his writings
Edited by JOHN T. EDSALL

Preface by **SIDNEY W. FOX** *and* **JULIUS SCHULTZ**

1960

NEW YORK *and* **LONDON**  **ACADEMIC PRESS**

ACADEMIC PRESS INC.
111 FIFTH AVENUE
NEW YORK 3, N. Y.

United Kingdom Edition
Published by
ACADEMIC PRESS INC. (LONDON) LTD.
17 OLD QUEEN STREET, LONDON S.W. 1

Library of Congress Catalog Card Number 60-9069

PRINTED IN THE UNITED STATES OF AMERICA

612.015   J495

c. 1

CONTRIBUTORS

J. B. ALPERS, *Division of Nutrition and Physiology, The Public Health Research Institute of the City of New York, Inc., New York, New York*

SANFORD M. BIRNBAUM, *Laboratory of Biochemistry, National Cancer Institute, National Institutes of Health, Public Health Service, U. S. Department of Health, Education, and Welfare, Bethesda, Maryland*

C. Y. CHA, *Department of Chemistry, Cornell University, Ithaca, New York*

BRITTON CHANCE, *Johnson Research Foundation, University of Pennsylvania, Philadelphia, Pennsylvania*

JOHN T. EDSALL, *The Biological Laboratories, Harvard University, Cambridge, Massachusetts*

J. HERMANS, JR., *Department of Chemistry, Cornell University, Ithaca, New York*

SAUL KIT, *Department of Biochemistry, The University of Texas M. D. Anderson Hospital and Tumor Institute, Texas Medical Center, Houston, Texas*

ALTON MEISTER, *Department of Biochemistry, Tufts University School of Medicine, Boston, Massachusetts*

HANS NEURATH, *Department of Biochemistry, University of Washington, Seattle, Washington*

M. CLYDE OTEY, *Laboratory of Biochemistry, National Cancer Institute, National Institutes of Health, Public Health Service, U. S. Department of Health, Education, and Welfare, Bethesda, Maryland*

ELBERT A. PETERSON, *Laboratory of Biochemistry, National Cancer Institute, National Institutes of Health, U. S. Public Health Service, Department of Health, Education, and Welfare, Bethesda, Maryland*

E. RACKER, *Division of Nutrition and Physiology, The Public Health Research Institute of the City of New York, Inc., New York, New York*

EUGENE ROBERTS, *Department of Biochemistry, City of Hope Medical Center, Duarte, California*

JOHN A. RUPLEY, *Department of Biochemistry, University of Washington, Seattle, Washington*

H. A. SCHERAGA, *Department of Chemistry, Cornell University, Ithaca, New York*

C. L. SCHILDKRAUT, *Department of Chemistry, Cornell University, Ithaca, New York*

DAISY G. SIMONSEN, *Department of Biochemistry, City of Hope Medical Center, Duarte, California*

HERBERT A. SOBER, *Laboratory of Biochemistry, National Cancer Institute, National Institutes of Health, U. S. Public Health Service, Department of Health, Education and Welfare, Bethesda, Maryland*

TAKASHI SUGIMURA, *Laboratory of Biochemistry, National Cancer Institute, National Institutes of Health, Public Health Service, U. S. Department of Health, Education, and Welfare, Bethesda, Maryland*

BERT L. VALLEE, *Biophysics Research Laboratory of the Department of Medicine, Harvard Medical School, Peter Bent Brigham Hospital, Boston, Massachusetts*

SIDNEY WEINHOUSE, *The Institute for Cancer Research, Philadelphia, Pennsylvania*

MILTON WINITZ, *Laboratory of Biochemistry, National Cancer Institute, National Institutes of Health, Public Health Service, U. S. Department of Health, Education, and Welfare, Bethesda, Maryland*

R. WU, *Division of Nutrition and Physiology, The Public Health Research Institute of the City of New York, Inc., New York, New York*

Preface

AFTER THE DEATH of Jesse P. Greenstein in February 1959, the Executive Committee of the Division of Biological Chemistry of the American Chemical Society decided unanimously to schedule a memorial symposium. A full day was to be devoted exclusively to this purpose, in view of the magnitude of Dr. Greenstein's contributions to biochemistry and his close association with the Division. It was also unanimously agreed that Dr. John Edsall would be the appropriate chairman. His willingness to accept the assignment and the ready response of invited participants are testimony to the warmth of feeling for the late Dr. Greenstein. All of the contributions in this volume reflect the influence of Greenstein's work. Some of the contributors were his close associates and collaborators over many years, whereas others have worked quite independently but in their work were deeply influenced by him. We believe that this book, which includes all of the papers given at the Symposium, will make an important contribution in portraying some of the major current developments in amino acid and protein chemistry and in the biochemistry of cancer—the two great fields in which Greenstein's work was preeminent. The volume opens with an account of his life and work, written by his long-time friends and associates, Drs. Edsall and Meister. This tribute is a combined and extended version of the earlier obituary articles by Alton Meister in the *Archives of Biochemistry and Biophysics* **82,** i (1959) and by J. T. Edsall in *Science* **130**, 83 (1959). The volume is concluded with a comprehensive bibliography of Greenstein's writings.

Dr. Greenstein's contributions, both scientific and professional, were made in large part through this Division of which he was chairman in 1954–1955. His research was oriented toward problems of great biochemical and medical interest and was characterized throughout by skill in the use of the principles and methods of physical, inorganic, and organic chemistry. His close affiliation with the American Chemical Society was therefore most appropriate.

No one can measure the full impact of the contributions of an outstanding scientist. It is hoped, however, that the contents of this volume will serve to illuminate some of the many fields of research which were enriched by Greenstein's ability and insight, and that the problems here set forth will stimulate further active research by outstanding investigators. If this volume promotes the advancement of our knowledge of amino acids and proteins and of cancer biochemistry it will serve at least in part as a fitting memorial to Jesse P. Greenstein.

SIDNEY W. FOX, Chairman,
1958-59
JULIUS SCHULTZ, Secretary

Division of Biological Chemistry,
American Chemical Society
December, 1959

CONTENTS

CONTRIBUTORS v

PREFACE vii

Jesse Philip Greenstein, 1902-1959
    JOHN T. EDSALL and ALTON MEISTER 1

Quantitative Nutritional and *In Vivo* Metabolic Studies with
    Water-Soluble, Chemically Defined Diets
    MILTON WINITZ, SANFORD M. BIRNBAUM, TAKASHI SUGIMURA,
    and M. CLYDE OTEY 9

Internal Hydrogen Bonding in Ribonuclease
    H. A. SCHERAGA, C. Y. CHA, J. HERMANS, JR., and
    C. L. SCHILDKRAUT 31

Considerations of the Structure and Function of Carboxypeptidase A
    HANS NEURATH, JOHN A. RUPLEY, and BERT L. VALLEE . 43

Chromatographic Evaluation of Protein Mixtures
    HERBERT A. SOBER and ELBERT A. PETERSON 61

Observations on the Activation of Amino Acids and the Biosynthesis
    of Peptide Bonds
    ALTON MEISTER 85

Enzyme Activities and Tumor Progression
    SIDNEY WEINHOUSE 109

Free Amino Acids and Related Substances in Normal and Neoplastic
    Tissues
    EUGENE ROBERTS and DAISY G. SIMONSEN 121

The Nucleic Acids of Normal Tissues and Tumors
    SAUL KIT 147

Carbohydrate Metabolism in Ascites Tumor and HeLa Cells
    E. RACKER, R. WU, and J. B. ALPERS 175

A Digital Computer Representation of Chemical and Spectroscopic
    Studies on Chemical Control of Ascites Tumor Cell
    Metabolism
    BRITTON CHANCE 191

Bibliography of the Published Work of Jesse P. Greenstein . . . 213

AUTHOR INDEX 229

SUBJECT INDEX 237

JESSE PHILIP GREENSTEIN
1902–1959

JOHN T. EDSALL and ALTON MEISTER

*The Biological Laboratories, Harvard University,
Cambridge, Massachusetts, and Department of Biochemistry,
Tufts University School of Medicine, Boston, Massachusetts*

JESSE GREENSTEIN died suddenly on February 12, 1959. At the time of his death he was actively engaged in research and in writing; he was the scientific and administrative leader of a group of distinguished scientists. He will long be remembered and honored for his contributions to science and to his fellow men. His passing brought to an untimely close one of biochemistry's most active and productive careers; he had achieved eminence in his extensive work on the chemistry of amino acids, peptides, proteins, and the biochemistry of cancer. The bibliography of his published work, which is printed at the end of this volume, will convey to the reader some idea of the extraordinary breadth and scope of his activities. Here we shall attempt a brief portrayal of his character and personality and of the major events of his career and will discuss some of the chief landmarks in his work.

He was born on June 20, 1902 in New York. His scientific interests developed early, while he attended public elementary and high schools in New York, and while he worked in the Food and Drug Laboratory of the New York City Department of Health. He received the B.S. degree, *cum laude* in chemistry, from the Polytechnic Institute of Brooklyn in 1926, and the Ph.D. degree in 1930 from Brown University, where he worked with C. A. Kraus and P. H. Mitchell on the dissociation constants of glycine and certain simple peptides containing glycine (see reference 1).* The character of this first study foreshadowed much of his later work during the following decade. In 1930-1931 he was a National Research Council

---

* References to the bibliography of Dr. Greenstein's work at the end of this volume are cited by number in parentheses throughout the remainder of this article.

fellow at Harvard, under Edwin J. Cohn, where he continued and extended his studies on the ionization constants of peptides (2-4). This was followed by a year's work in Dresden under Max Bergmann, who was just developing the carbobenzoxy method of peptide synthesis. Greenstein's experience in Bergmann's laboratory profoundly influenced his subsequent career. With Bergmann and Zervas he was the first to apply the new methods to the synthesis of lysylglutamic acid and lysylhistidine (5), and he developed a mastery of both organic and physical chemistry, particularly in relation to the study of peptides and proteins, which was exceptional among the biochemists of his generation.

After a year in Berkeley in the laboratory of C. L. A. Schmidt, where he carried out further studies on the peptides of trivalent amino acids (6), he returned to Harvard for six years (1933-1939). During this period he was active as a tutor in Biochemical Sciences at the college and was also research associate at Harvard Medical School, in Cohn's laboratory. His zeal and devotion to both teaching and research, and his extraordinary energy and enthusiasm, were strikingly displayed then as later. As tutor in Biochemical Sciences he looked after a larger number of students than any other member of the board has ever been responsible for, and served as an inspiring and effective teacher in frequent personal conferences with students. He also served as head assistant to L. J. Henderson in the latter's course in biological chemistry; indeed, as Henderson's major interests were shifting from biochemistry toward sociology, Greenstein for several years was largely responsible for the general management of the course. At the same time he was astonishingly productive in research. He continued to synthesize new peptides and to determine their ionization constants and correlate these with their structure, and, in collaboration with J. Wyman, T. L. McMeekin, and others, he studied their dipole moments, solubility, and other physical properties (8-15, 19, 24, 26, 27). During these years he began those important studies of the peptides of cystine and cysteine (20, 21, 23, 25, 28, 33, 35) to which he frequently returned, with new points of view, and new techniques, in the course of the next twenty years (see for instance 98-101, 114, 224, 225).

In 1937 he published the first synthesis of L-cysteinyl-L-cysteine (23). This unique peptide was prepared by condensing dicarbobenzoxycystyl chloride with two molecules of cysteine ethyl ester to give dicarbobenzoxycystyldicysteinyl ethyl ester, which was cleaved with phosphonium iodide to cysteinylcysteine ethyl ester hydroiodide. The latter compound was converted in ethanol saturated with ammonia to the crystalline diketopiperazine anhydro-L-cysteinyl-L-cysteine, which on treatment with concentrated hydrochloric acid gave the hydrochloride of L-cysteinyl-L-cysteine. Oxidation of the L-cystine. The relationship of these studies on oxidation of cys-dipeptide at weakly alkaline reaction gave crystalline L-cystinyl-teinylcysteine to later work on proteins and naturally occurring peptides (such as insulin or oxytocin) led Greenstein to return to the problem in 1956. With Wade and Winitz (236) he investigated the oxidation of L-cysteinyl-L-cysteine at various values of pH and isolated a number of products of oxidation including the cyclic disulfide derivative of L-cysteinyl-L-cysteine, which he designated "cyclo-L-cystinyl":

$$\begin{array}{c} \text{}^+\text{H}_3\text{NCH—CONH—CHCOO}^- \\ | \qquad\qquad | \\ \text{CH}_2\text{—S—S—CH}_2 \end{array}$$

The crystalline dimeric product was shown to consist mainly of parallel cystinylcystine, with the two free amino groups adjoining one disulfide linkage, and the two free carboxyl groups adjoining the other:

$$\begin{array}{l} \text{SCH}_2\text{CH(NH}_3{}^+)\text{CONHCH(COO}^-)\text{CH}_2\text{S} \\ | \qquad\qquad\qquad\qquad\qquad\qquad | \\ \text{SCH}_2\text{CH(NH}_3{}^+)\text{CONHCH(COO}^-)\text{CH}_2\text{S} \end{array}$$

L-Cystinyl-L-cystine (parallel)

$$\begin{array}{l} \text{SCH}_2\text{CH(COO}^-)\text{NHCOCH(NH}_3{}^+)\text{CH}_2\text{S} \\ | \qquad\qquad\qquad\qquad\qquad\qquad | \\ \text{SCH}_2\text{CH(NH}_3{}^+)\text{CONHCH(COO}^-)\text{CH}_2\text{S} \end{array}$$

L-Cystinyl-L-cystine (antiparallel)

Although the formation of small amounts of the antiparallel isomer could not be unequivocally excluded, these studies clearly demonstrated preferential formation of one isomer, and represent a potentially important model system for the study of this type of cyclic structure. In one of his last papers (269) he studied the difficult problems involved in preparing unsymmetrical open-chain derivatives of cystine, and the complications introduced by disulfide interchange reactions; as a simple example of such a derivative, pure monoglycyl-L-cystine was prepared for the first time.

About 1937 he turned also to the study of protein structure and denaturation, making use of porphyrindin, which had recently been synthesized by Richard Kuhn, for the determination of protein sulfhydryl groups, in native and denatured proteins. He discovered the powerful action of guanidinium salts as denaturing agents for proteins and made extensive use of them and of concentrated urea solutions in studying the titratable sulfhydryl groups of egg albumin, edestin, excelsin, globin, myosin, and other proteins (29, 31, 34, 36, 37).

In 1939 his career entered a new phase when he became a member of the National Cancer Institute at Bethesda. Here again his extraordinary energy and vitality displayed themselves. He threw himself into an extremely active program for the study of the biochemistry of tumors, and in particular set about the determination of the activities of a variety of enzymes—arginase, amylase, catalase, xanthine dehydrogenase, and many others—in normal and cancerous tissue. This long series of studies, which extended over many years and involved numerous collaborators, represents probably the most extensive work of its kind yet carried out on cancer tissue. From this he evolved the concept of the "biochemical uniformity of tumors," the near-uniformity of tumors being due to the loss in a normal tissue, when it becomes malignant, of those specific functional characteristics which distinguish it from other normal tissues. The tumors which so emerge bear little or no physiological resemblance to their normal tissues of origin and appear to converge to a common type of tissue. Thus, normal hepatic and gastric tissues are very distinctly different, but biochemically the hepatoma and the gastric adenocarcinoma are closely similar. These researches were summarized, together with a comprehensive and critical survey of the whole field, in Greenstein's outstanding monograph, "Biochemistry of Cancer," first published (154) in 1947 and extensively revised in a second edition (221) which appeared in 1954. The findings and general concepts set forth in this monograph are discussed by Sidney Weinhouse later in this volume, and in the other papers which follow Weinhouse's contribution.

During his first years in Bethesda he also devoted himself vigorously to the study of nucleoproteins in normal and cancer tissue. This work (48-52, 55, 56, 58, 75, 77, 83 and later papers) was begun at a time when relatively few biochemical studies on nucleic acids were in progress. He published a number of papers on the enzymatic deamination and dephosphorylation of RNA and DNA (105, 106, 121, 122, 124). He was very much aware of the potential significance of nucleic acids for the structures of viruses and chromosomes and of their probable relationship to transforming factor. In his paper at the Cold Spring Harbor Symposium on Nucleic Acids in 1947 (143) he pointed out that "knowledge of the metabolic fate of the nucleic acids within tissues is of fundamental importance in the understanding of the phenomena presumed to be elicited by these substances." He also carried out work on the effect of radiation on DNA (144, 151) on the cation activation of deoxyribonuclease, and on the very interesting and remarkable effect of DNA in protecting ovalbumin and serum albumin against heat coagulation (117, 119, 178).

His interest in the study of protein denaturation remained unabated. With Neurath, Putnam, and Erickson he published in 1944 a review of this subject which has become one of the classics in the field (84).

In 1946 he was appointed chief of the newly created Laboratory of Biochemistry of the National Cancer Institute, a position which imposed upon him an increasing burden of administrative responsibility. His breadth of vision, his enthusiasm, and his patient good humor and understanding of many diverse types of people were of great importance in the development of the research activities of the Institute and in attracting workers to it from all over the United States and from the rest of the world.

These heavy administrative responsibilities, however, did not prevent him from continuing with an extraordinarily active program of research; indeed, the last dozen years of his career were probably the most productive of all. He made intensive studies of dehydropeptides and dehydropeptidases (see 161), of many cellular peptides, of the enzymatic desulfuration of cystine peptides, of the deamidation of glutamine and asparagine, and of other problems too numerous to mention here.

His outstanding contribution to the chemistry of the amino acids, and thereby to biochemistry and nutrition, lay perhaps in his superb researches on the preparation of optically pure L- and D-amino acids, in which he utilized the asymmetric hydrolytic or oxidative specificity of the amino acid acylases and oxidases to prepare the optical enantiomorphs in better than 99.9% purity.

Greenstein's work on the resolution of amino acids emphasized the problem of the optical purity of amino acids. In his classic review (223) in 1954 on the resolution of racemic α-amino acids, he summarized in elegant and thorough fashion the literature of the development of this area of research as well as his own important contributions to the problem up to that time. He pointed out that polarimetric measurement was not a sufficiently sensitive test of optical purity, and emphasized the value of employing enzymes— for instance the D- and L-amino acid oxidases and decarboxylases —as test reagents to detect minute amounts of optical isomers present as impurities, and also for obtaining preparations of high optical purity by destruction of the undesired isomer (267, 269). It is evident that this work has an important bearing on the problem of optical homogeneity of synthetic peptides. The work on resolution led directly to a major series of studies on the stereochemical configuration of diasymmetric amino acids. Greenstein and his collaborators devised procedures for the preparation of the possible isomers of isoleucine (192, 229), threonine, hydroxyproline (202), β-phenylserine, γ-hydroxyglutamic acid (259), β-methylaspartic acid (270), and β-hydroxy-β-methylaspartic acid (271). The studies on the three isomeric forms of α, ϵ-diaminopimelic acid (232, 254) gave much impetus to microbiological and enzymatic studies of this amino acid. The preparation (226) of the four isomers of α-amino-tricarballylic acid (Greenstein (11, 19) had prepared one of the racemic diastereoisomeric forms of this amino acid in 1935) and their conversion to the corresponding isocitric acids (227), made it possible to conclude that the α-carbon atom of the natural form of isocitric acid has the L-configuration. Greenstein and his collaborators succeeded in correlating information derived from rotatory dispersion studies, enzymatic work, and chemical investigations, and by these means were able to clarify in a most elegant way important aspects of the stereochemistry of the naturally occurring amino acids. An approach to the problem of the stereochemistry of α-substituted amino acids (e.g. isovaline) was made using enzymatic techniques.

In the last years of his life he initiated an extensive series of nutritional researches with diets containing mixtures of optically pure amino acids (272-274 and earlier papers). His work also demonstrated the toxic effect of injecting amino acid mixtures lacking in arginine, and the protective effect of the addition of arginine to these mixtures, which was clearly shown to be due to the function of arginine in the Krebs urea cycle, whereby the toxic ammonia released from other amino acids was rapidly converted to urea (266). A further discussion of the progress of this work will be found in the immediately following paper by Winitz et al. in this volume.

At the time of his death he was engaged, with M. Winitz, in the writing of a comprehensive treatise in three volumes on the chemistry of the amino acids (281). This great work has now been completed and will shortly be published. Several experts who have had the opportunity of examining the manuscript in advance of publication believe that it will stand for many years as the most authoritative discussion of the amino acids in existence.

Greenstein was awarded the Neuberg medal in 1950, the Distinguished Service award of the Department of Health, Education, and Welfare in 1952, and the Hillebrand award in 1958. In 1954 he served as chairman of the Division of Biological Chemistry of the American Chemical Society. He was for several years an editor of the *Archives of Biochemistry and Biophysics,* and, with A. Haddow, was editor of *Advances in Cancer Research.* He served as visiting professor of biochemistry at the University of California in 1948, and in 1957 he became a member of the Committee on Biochemistry of the National Research Council and served as the chairman of the Subcommittee on Amino Acids. In 1949 he was a member of the American delegation of the Cancer Colloquium called by Pope Pius XII at the Vatican, and in 1956 he was a visiting lecturer at several Japanese universities and became an honorary member of the Japanese Chemical Society and the Japanese Foundation for Cancer Research.

He led an arduous life as an investigator, administrator, and writer. In the course of his career he collaborated with more than 60 scientists. His influence on those with whom he worked was profound and lasting. He took a constant and active part in every piece of research that was published under his name and was personally responsible for writing all of the papers to which his name was attached. His hours of work were long. After dinner at home he would, several times each week, return to the laboratory quite early in the evening, where he could write or experiment uninterruptedly until one or two o'clock in the morning. Yet with all of this activity he was accessible, friendly, and relaxed when anyone came to see him and talk things over with him.

His interests were broad and ranged far beyond the sciences. He was always a prolific reader. One of us can well recall how, in his Harvard days, he delighted in Dickens, and especially in "Pickwick Papers." He read widely in philosophy, theology, and biography and was something of an expert on the history of the Civil War —its battles, issues, and great men. Undoubtedly the breadth of his reading and his appreciation of literature had much to do with the high quality of his own writings.

He married Lucy Mitchell in 1933. They had two children, a daughter, Louise Brill, and a son Michael. The latter had already worked during his school days for a summer in his father's laboratory on nutritional problems relating to the amino acids (268). During the last few years of his life Jesse Greenstein had become a boating enthusiast. Starting originally with a small outboard motor he had purchased in 1958 a 22-foot cabin cruiser. With his usual enthusiasm and intensity of purpose he had engaged in a thorough study of navigation and had received several certificates from the Washington Area Power Squadron. In this activity also his son Michael joined him.

Jesse Greenstein was outstanding in scientific skill, learning, energy, and devotion to his work. He inspired numerous young men, who came to work at the National Cancer Institute, with much of his own ardent enthusiasm for science. He was proud to be a servant of the United States Government, in a position of great responsibility, and his service went far beyond the allotted duties of his post. He was a loyal friend, whose wisdom and courage were a source of inspiration to his colleagues. Men with his inspiring qualities are rare, even unique. He will be sorely missed, but the inspiration which he and his work have imparted lives and continues.

Quantitative Nutritional and *In Vivo* Metabolic Studies with Water-Soluble, Chemically Defined Diets

MILTON WINITZ, SANFORD M. BIRNBAUM, TAKASHI SUGIMURA, and M. CLYDE OTEY

Laboratory of Biochemistry, National Cancer Institute, National Institutes of Health, Public Health Service, U.S. Department of Health, Education, and Welfare, Bethesda, Maryland

OVER THE PAST DECADE, a sizeable portion of Jesse P. Greenstein's research program was devoted to the development of resolution procedures (Greenstein, 1954; Greenstein and Winitz, 1960) which would permit the large-scale preparation of optically pure α-amino acids for primarily two reasons: first, to make the optical antipodes of amino acids readily available as starting materials for the synthesis of peptides to be employed as substrates in *in vitro* studies of peptidase specificity; second, to provide the amino acid components for a completely synthetic diet which would be suitable for long-term nutritional studies with experimental animals and appropriate for parenteral administration to human beings. It is the aspect of synthetic diets with which the present discussion will be primarily concerned. However, before embarking on this subject, some of the methods customarily employed to procure the optically active amino acids, which constitute a major portion of these synthetic diets, will be briefly reviewed.

Large-Scale Preparation of Optically Pure Amino Acids

At the present time, optically active amino acids in large amount are obtained essentially by three different techniques, namely, by isolation from acid or enzymatic hydrolyzates of proteins, by microbial synthesis, or by enzymatic resolution of the racemic form of the amino acid. With respect to the first technique, it should be noted that a given protein hydrolyzate may contain some eighteen or nineteen different amino acids. Although each of these amino acid components should, theoretically, be isolable in chemically pure form, the large-scale isolation of each of these un-

9

contaminated by any of the others poses, in practice, a rather formidable task. Indeed, such isolations have proven practical only in those cases where the amino acid precipitates from the aqueous hydrolyzate by virtue of its insolubility, as do tyrosine and cystine, or where the separation of the amino acid is facilitated as a result of its conversion to a salt or a derivative which exhibits unusual solubility properties, as do the mercury salt of histidine, the flavianate or benzylidine derivative of arginine, and the copper salt of proline. Although the large-scale separation of amino acids from protein hydrolyzates by column chromatography is a potentially important tool, this means has not yet found extensive commercial use. The second technique, that of microbial synthesis, is presently limited to the preparation of L-lysine and is based, for the most part, on the observation that L-lysine can arise from the enzymatic decarboxylation of α,ϵ-diaminopimelic acid, an amino acid which accumulates in the culture media of certain bacterial strains (Dewey and Work, 1952; Davis, 1952). In this same category might also be placed L-glutamic acid, which is produced in quantity as a side product in various fermentation processes. L-Asparagine, which occurs in the free state in various plant tissues, is conveniently isolated from these natural sources (Vickery et al., 1942), while L-glutamine is readily secured by synthesis from L-glutamic acid via the corresponding γ-hydrazide (Akabori and Narita, 1953). However, with the exception of the amino acids already mentioned, the L-isomers of most amino acids, and the D-isomers of all of them, are best obtained by some sort of resolution procedure.

The resolution of racemic compounds, as initially developed by Louis Pasteur, consisted of three independent methods: the first, that of mechanical separation of those crystals capable of showing hemihedrism; the second, that of employing an optically active acid or base which would transform the racemate into a diastereomeric mixture wherefrom the more insoluble diastereomeric salt would separate; and the third, that of utilizing a biological agent which would preferentially metabolize one or the other isomeric form of the racemate. In the search for a general resolution procedure that would permit the ready preparation in the laboratory not of grams but of kilograms of each of the optical isomers of a wide variety of amino acids, Dr. Greenstein in 1948 turned to the third of Pasteur's methods, that of the use of biological agents (Greenstein, 1954; Greenstein and Winitz, 1960). Such search culminated in the isolation from hog kidney of two separate enzymatic preparations which possessed the desired characteristics. The first, designated as renal acylase I, was capable of hydrolyzing asymmetrically only the L-isomers of N-acylated DL-amino acids; the second, designated as renal amidase, was capable of hydrolyzing asymmetrically only the L-isomers of DL-amino acid amides, thus:

$$\text{DL-RCO—NHCHR'CO}_2\text{H} \xrightarrow{\text{acylase}}$$
$$\text{L-NH}_2\text{CHR'CO}_2\text{H} + \text{RCO}_2\text{H} + \text{D-RCO—NHCHR'CO}_2\text{H}$$

$$\text{DL-NH}_2\text{CHR'CO—NH}_2 \xrightarrow{\text{amidase}}$$
$$\text{L-NH}_2\text{CHR'CO}_2\text{H} + \text{NH}_3 + \text{D-NH}_2\text{CHR'CO—NH}_2$$

Because of the optical specificity of the enzymes involved, the method of resolution is extremely simple. This is carried out as follows: The pertinent racemic amino acid is either N-acetylated or N-chloroacetylated, generally by treatment with acetic anhydride in boiling glacial acetic acid or with chloroacetyl chloride under Schotten-Baumann conditions. The resulting N-acylated amino acid is dissolved in 0.1 M concentration in water, the pH adjusted to 7.0, and the solution treated with the appropriate amount of purified enzyme and then incubated at 37°. Hydrolysis, which may be checked by Van Slyke ninhydrin-CO_2 measurements on aliquots, proceeds to exactly 50% of the racemate and goes no further, irrespective of how long the digest stands. Upon completion of the hydrolysis, the digest is condensed and the free L-amino acid is separated from the N-acyl-D-amino acid by precipitation with ethanol. Such separation can be alternatively achieved by a procedure which involves passage of the digest over an ion exchange resin (Baker and Sober, 1953).

The general utility of the enzymatic resolution procedure just outlined is strikingly revealed in Table I, which lists the variety of amino acids to which it was successfully applied in Dr. Greenstein's laboratory. With the exception of the aromatic amino acids, tyrosine, tryptophan, and β-phenylserine, which are best resolved through the use of pancreatic carboxypeptidase, the renal acylase system is effective in the resolution of all the α-amino acids shown. On the other hand, proline, whose N-acyl derivative is resistant to acylase because of the lack of hydrogen atom on the peptide nitrogen, is resolved as the amide with the aid of the renal amidase system. Tertiary leucine, whose acyl derivative is resistant to acylase because of steric factors, in addition to dodecyline and α,ϵ-diaminopimelic acid, are also best resolved through the renal

TABLE I

L- AND D-ISOMERS OF α-AMINO ACIDS OBTAINED BY ENZYMATIC RESOLUTION
WITH ACYLASE, AMIDASE, OR CARBOXYPEPTIDASE

Amino acid	Derivative employed	Enzyme employed
Alanine	Acetyl	Acylase I
Butyrine	Acetyl	Acylase I
Valine	Acetyl	Acylase I
Norvaline	Acetyl	Acylase I
Isovaline	Chloroacetyl	Acylase I
Leucine	Acetyl	Acylase I
Norleucine	Acetyl	Acylase I
Isoleucine	Acetyl	Acylase I
Alloisoleucine	Acetyl	Acylase I
Heptyline	Chloroacetyl	Acylase I
Capryline	Chloroacetyl	Acylase I
Nonyline	Chloroacetyl	Acylase I
Decyline	Chloroacetyl	Acylase I
Undecyline	Chloroacetyl	Acylase I
Dodecyline	Amide	Amidase
Serine	Chloroacetyl	Acylase I
Homoserine	Chloroacetyl	Acylase I
δ-Hydroxynorvaline	Chloroacetyl	Acylase I
ε-Hydroxynorleucine	Chloroacetyl	Acylase I
Threonine	Chloroacetyl	Acylase I
Allothreonine	Chloroacetyl	Acylase I
O-Methylthreonine	Chloroacetyl	Acylase I
O-Methylallothreonine	Formyl	Acylase I
Methionine	Acetyl	Acylase I
Ethionine	Acetyl	Acylase I
Cystine	Acetyl	Acylase I
S-Benzylcysteine	Acetyl	Acylase I
S-Benzylpenicillamine	Acetyl	Acylase I
S-Benzylhomocysteine	Acetyl	Acylase I
Aspartic acid	Acetyl	Acylase II
β-Methylaspartic acid	Acetyl	Acylase II
Glutamic acid	Carbobenzoxy	Acylase I
α-Aminoadipic acid	Chloroacetyl	Acylase I
α-Aminopimelic acid	Chloroacetyl	Acylase I
β-Aminoalanine	α,β-Diacetyl	Acylase I
γ-Aminobutyrine	α,γ-Dichloroacetyl	Acylase I
Ornithine	α,δ-Dichloroacetyl	Acylase I
Lysine	α,ε-Dichloroacetyl	Acylase I
Histidine	α-Acetyl	Acylase I
Arginine	α-Acetyl	Acylase I
β-Phenylalanine	Chloroacetyl	Acylase I

TABLE I—(Continued)

Amino acid	Derivative employed	Enzyme employed
Tyrosine	Chloroacetyl	Carboxypeptidase
Tryptophan	Chloroacetyl	Carboxypeptidase
Proline	Amide	Amidase
α-Phenylglycine	Chloroacetyl	Acylase I
α-Cyclohexylglycine	Chloroacetyl	Acylase I
β-Cyclohexylalanine	Chloroacetyl	Acylase I
β-Phenylserine	Trifluoroacetyl	Carboxypeptidase
Allo-β-phenylserine	Trifluoroacetyl	Carboxypeptidase
Tert-Leucine	Amide	Amidase
δ-Hydroxylysine	α-Chloroacetyl, ϵ-carbobenzoxy	Acylase I
Allo-δ-hydroxylysine	α-Chloroacetyl, ϵ-carbobenzoxy	Acylase I
α-Methylserine	Chloroacetyl	Acylase I
α,ϵ-Diaminopimelic acid	α,ϵ-Diamide	Amidase

amidase system. However, irrespective of the enzyme employed, the enzymatic resolution procedures just described lead to yields of the L- and D-isomers of the amino acids which vary from 60 to 90% of the theoretical. In addition, each enantiomorph, when checked for its optical purity by testing it against the appropriate amino acid oxidase (Meister *et al.*, 1951), reveals that the degree of optical contamination of one isomer by the other is invariably less than one part in one thousand.

The power of the general enzymatic resolution approach just outlined is evidenced by the fact that it has been responsible for the resolution of a larger variety of amino acids than all other resolution procedures combined. That it is capable of permitting an assembly line operation on the laboratory scale is attested to by the fact that, at the present time, we routinely employ this procedure in our laboratory to obtain between 1 and 2 kilograms of both optical antipodes of a different amino acid each day.

Formulation of Water-Soluble, Chemically Defined Diets

The commercial availability of certain L-amino acids in quantity, and of others by the enzymatic resolution procedures just described, led us some 4 years ago to develop a chemically defined diet which could be administered to experimental animals under conditions of high quantitative precision. Water solubility was deemed an essential feature of such a diet, since the use of a diet that could be provided in liquid form allows for precise measurement of intake and hence permits nutritional and metabolic studies on a quantitative basis. In the construction of such liquid diets, it was considered desirable to employ as high a concentration as possible in order to avoid the possibility of an overintake of water; furthermore, a highly concentrated and viscous solution could be safely employed in inverted drinking tubes without danger of spillage. A 50% clear aqueous solution was the goal aimed for, and it was with this in mind that diets composed of crystalline L-amino acids, glucose, vitamins, and the required salts were formulated. Such formulation led to the basal medium shown in Table II (Greenstein *et al.*, 1957). Quantities denoted refer to the amount of each component per kilogram of diet on a dry weight basis.

The ten essential L-amino acids listed in Table II were present in very nearly the same relative proportions as recommended by Rose and his associates in their classic studies on the amino acid requirements of the rat (Rose *et al.*, 1949). In addition, a source of 15.7 grams of nonessential nitrogen was provided either in the form of a single nonessential amino acid or as a mixture of nonessential amino acids. Since the type of nonessential nitrogen plays an important role in growth response, this aspect will be more fully discussed later. Although the amino acid and water-soluble vitamin components presented no obstacle toward the attainment of the desired 50% solution, the inability of certain cations and anions to coexist in solution in the required concentration did pose a severe problem. This problem was met, in the case of calcium and phosphate ions, by supplying the phosphate in an organically bound form as the very soluble monocalcium fructose-1:6-diphosphate. The anions of the other metals were also chosen with care so as to permit the use of highly soluble salts which would exhibit no tendency to cause precipitation of other components of the mixture. The pH of the diet solutions as constituted was invariably in the vicinity of 5.

The fat-soluble vitamins in corn oil or in ethyl linoleate were offered to the animals as a separate supplement or could, with the aid of Tween 80, be incorporated into the water-soluble portion of the diet to form a stable, crystal-clear emulsion (Greenstein *et al.*, 1960). In either case, the diet solutions remain water-clear after several weeks of standing in closed containers at 5°. Since the con-

TABLE II

The Basal Chemically Defined, Soluble Diet[a]

Amino acids	Weight (grams)	N (grams)	Vitamins	Weight (mg.)	Salts	Weight (grams)	Fats and fat-soluble vitamins	
L-Lysine·HCl	12.4	1.9	Thiamine·HCl[b]	5.0	Sodium chloride	7.0	Vitamin A acetate	1.0 mg.
L-Histidine·HCl·H$_2$O	5.4	1.1	Riboflavin	7.5	Potassium hydroxide Gluconolactone }	6.17 19.64	Calciferol	0.7 µg.
L-Arginine·HCl	7.5	2.0	Pyridoxine·HCl	6.3	Magnesium oxide Gluconolactone }	0.73 6.45	α-Tocopherol[c]	5.0 mg.
L-Tryptophan	2.0	0.3	Niacin	37.5			2-Methyl-1,4-naphthoquinone	0.42 mg.
L-Phenylalanine	9.0	0.8	Inositol	250.0	Ferrous ammonium sulfate	1.40		
L-Leucine	8.0	0.9	Choline·HCl	2500.0	Potassium iodide	0.03	Corn oil or ethyl linoleate[d]	2.0 ml.
L-Isoleucine	5.0	0.5	Ca pantothenate	50.0	Manganese acetate·4H$_2$O	0.26		
L-Threonine	5.0	0.6	Biotin	0.3	Zinc benzoate	0.022		
L-Methionine	6.0	0.6	Folic acid	0.5	Copper acetate·H$_2$O	0.015		
L-Valine	7.0	0.8	Ascorbic acid	500.0	Cobalt acetate·4H$_2$O	0.009		
[Nonessential nitrogen]	—	15.7	B$_{12}$	0.1	Ammonium molybdate·4H$_2$O	0.006		
			p-Aminobenzoic acid	300.0	Monocalcium fructose 1,6-diphosphate	50.0		
Total	67.3	25.2						

[a] Total weight brought to 1 kg. by addition of glucose. Each gram equivalent to 4 cal.
[b] This dose level multiplied by 2 at time of mating.
[c] This dose level multiplied by 4 at time of mating.
[d] Fat-soluble vitamins dissolved in this volume and fed in equally divided doses three times a week per animal. Alternatively, the fats and fat-soluble vitamin components were incorporated into the aqueous 50% diet solution with the aid of Tween 80. In this latter case, 4 g. of ethyl linoleate, 6.0 g. of Tween 80 and 10 times the quantity of fat-soluble vitamins listed above were employe[b] per kilogram of diet (on a dry weight basis).

stituents which compose the diet are carefully purified prior to mixing, and since the diet solutions are quite hypertonic, bacterial counts are negligible and remain so even after prolonged storage. This is strikingly illustrated by the fact that diet solutions, after incubation at 37° for 4 weeks, revealed a bacterial count of about 1.5 microorganisms per milliliter of solution. The final solutions possess a light golden hue, which does not darken if stored in a closed container in the refrigerator, or if the solution is frozen at − 18°. However, a slight but progressive change of color through light yellow to light brown does occur after exposure to air for several days at room temperature, probably as a result of some interaction of glucose with amino acids. No change in the nutritive effectiveness of the diet solutions appears to accompany this change of color, even when, after several weeks of standing, the color becomes a pronounced brown. In any event, no solution employed in the feeding studies to be presented was ever allowed to stand long enough to change color appreciably.

Feeding experiments were invariably begun with weanling Sprague-Dawley rats of both sexes. Each animal was housed in a separate metal cage with a wire mesh bottom. The pertinent diet solution was placed in inverted drinking tubes and the animals were allowed to feed ad libitum; water tubes were also provided.

Initial experiments involved the study of an individual L- or D-amino acid as the sole source of nonessential nitrogen in the previously described basal diet (Table II). Figure 1 indicates the various sources of nonessential nitrogen employed as well as the averaged daily gains on each regimen over a three-week period (Birnbaum et al., 1957b). Nonessential nitrogen in each case was added to the amount of 15.7 grams per kilogram of dry diet. The best growth response was between 2 and 3 grams per day, and was shown where the L-form of alanine, asparagine, glutamine, or proline served as the source of nonessential nitrogen. Lesser gains of between 1 and 2 grams per day were noted where urea, glycine, D-alanine, or ammonium acetate was employed. However, as is shown in curves C, D, and E of Fig. 2, the like use of L-butyrine, L-serine, or L-hydroxyproline as the single nonessential nitrogen source was accompanied by a loss in weight. Since a small but significant gain was noted with animals maintained on a diet completely devoid of a nonessential nitrogen source, as is shown by curve B, a toxic effect is indicated with these latter amino acids. As reflected by the growth of weanling rats, it would appear that

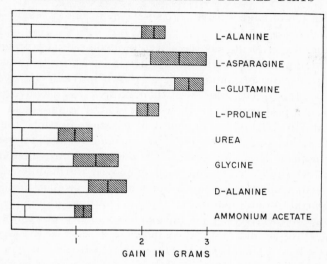

FIG. 1. Growth responses of weanling male rats when individual compounds were added to the basal diet as the sole source of nonessential nitrogen. All diets were isonitrogenous.

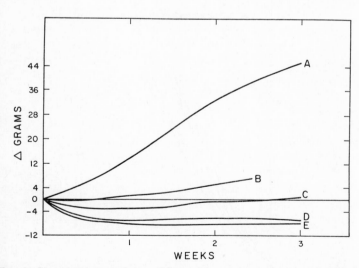

FIG. 2. Growth curves of weanling male rats when individual compounds were added to the basal diet as the sole source of nonessential nitrogen. All diets were isonitrogenous. Curve A, L-Alanine; curve B, No nonessential nitrogen; curve C, L-Butyrine; curve D, L-Serine; curve E, L-Hydroxyproline.

the utilization of nonessential nitrogen in the form of a single source varies very considerably.

Further experiments on the effect of nonessential nitrogen on growth were undertaken with diets wherein such nitrogen was provided by mixtures of amino acids, as shown in Table III (Greenstein *et al.*, 1957). Although all of the mixtures were isonitrogenous, the relative proportions of their nonessential amino acid components differed. The diets studied included those in which the nonessential amino acids were present in the same relative proportions as they appear in casein, in muscle protein, and in ovalbumin. In addition, a modified casein diet was employed which differed from the first-cited mixture in that a portion of the proline, glutamate, and aspartate was replaced by hydroxyproline, glutamine, and asparagine, respectively. Cysteine was used in lieu of cystine, and both the tyrosine and cysteine components in each of the mixtures were present as their respective ethyl ester hydrochlorides in order to ensure water solubility. Growth responses on each of these diets are shown in Fig. 3. The growth curves reveal that the best growth,

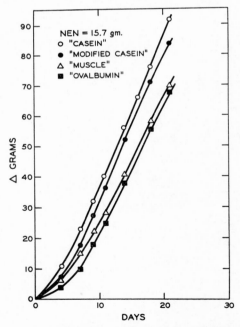

Fig. 3. Growth curves of male weanling rats on diets containing various mixtures of nonessential amino acids. These are averaged gain values of six animals on each diet.

TABLE III

"Nonessential" Amino Acids (all to 15.7 grams N) Added to Identical Basal Diet

No. 26 (Casein)	Amount in grams	No. 27 (Muscle)	Amount in grams	No. 28 (Ovalbumin)	Amount in grams	No. 34 (Modified casein)	Amount in grams
L-Proline	29.9	L-Proline	14.6	L-Proline	18.1	L-Proline	19.9
L-Tyrosine ester·HCl	19.8	L-Tyrosine ester·HCl	13.2	L-Tyrosine ester·HCl	12.7	L-Hydroxyproline	11.4
L-Glutamate (Na)	60.2	L-Glutamate (Na)	43.0	L-Glutamate (Na)	41.0	L-Tyrosine ester·HCl	19.8
L-Aspartate (Na)	19.0	L-Aspartate (Na)	22.8	L-Aspartate (Na)	24.1	L-Glutamate (Na)	30.1
L-Cysteine ester·HCl	0.9	L-Cysteine ester·HCl	2.9	L-Cysteine ester·HCl	5.4	L-Glutamine	13.0
L-Serine	15.5	L-Serine	14.6	L-Serine	19.0	L-Aspartate (Na)	9.6
L-Alanine	7.5	L-Alanine	18.0	L-Alanine	16.5	L-Asparagine (anhydr.)	3.9
Glycine	4.8	Glycine	12.2	Glycine	8.0	L-Cysteine ester·HCl	0.9
						L-Serine	15.5
						L-Alanine	7.5
						Glycine	4.8

by far, was achieved on the diet wherein the nonessential amino acids were present in the proportions in which they occur in casein. Indeed, animals on this diet gained steadily and in linear fashion, with an average growth of 4 to 5 grams per day. It was this diet, which was designated as diet No. 26, that was adopted for long-term nutrition studies, including those bearing on longevity, reproduction, lactation over several generations (Greenstein *et al.*, 1957), and various pathologic conditions (Sugimura *et al.*, 1959a, b, c).

Although time does not permit discussion of these studies in detail, certain features are nonetheless worthy of comment. Thus, long-term nutrition studies with diet No. 26 revealed that growth was progressive until a normal adult weight of over 400 grams was attained. The adult animals were carried to maturity and bred to produce satisfactory litters which were nursed to weaning, reared to maturity on the same synthetic diet, and again bred to give satisfactory second generation litters. Since no bulk is added to the synthetic diet, excretion of fecal material was scanty and infrequent. Sacrifice of a few animals and examination of their intestinal contents revealed about one-fourth to one-fifth the weight of such contents as compared with rats of the same age and the same sex reared on laboratory chow pellets. Autopsies of mature animals of both sexes revealed no pathology of any tissues, either gross or microscopic. No dental caries or any dental pathology was evident which, in view of the fact that these animals at no time ever used their teeth, was of considerable interest. In this connection, it should be noted that adult animals reared only on a liquid diet, and themselves arising from parents that had been reared on the liquid diet, fared well when provided with a laboratory chow diet and, indeed, were able to undergo the normal processes of elimination with no apparent untoward responses. Substitution of sucrose or fructose for glucose in the diet made no difference in the rate of growth (Winitz *et al.*, 1957a).

As the L-isomers of certain amino acids are several times more expensive than their racemic counterparts, appreciable financial savings could accrue from the substitution, in diet No. 26, of the less costly racemic forms. With an eye toward such financial economy, two diets (designated as diet Nos. 40 and 44) were formulated which were patterned after diet No. 26 but which contained certain of the amino acid components as the economically less expensive forms. These are depicted in Table IV. Thus, the composition of

TABLE IV

COMPARISON DIETS FOR TESTING GROWTH PROMOTION
WITH L- AND DL-AMINO ACIDS

Diet no.	Essential amino acids[a]	Grams N per kg. diet	Nonessential amino acids[b]	Grams N per kg. diet	Total N per kg. diet
26	All L-isomers	9.5	All L-isomers	15.7	25.2
40	All DL-isomers except leucine and arginine	13.3	All L-isomers	15.7	29.0
44	All DL-isomers except leucine and arginine	13.3	All L-isomers except serine, alanine, and aspartic acid	20.7	34.0

[a] Leucine, isoleucine, valine, phenylalanine, tryptophan, threonine, methionine, arginine, histidine, and lysine.

[b] Tyrosine, proline, glutamic acid, alanine, serine, glycine, cysteine, and aspartic acid.

diet No. 40 was identical with that of diet No. 26, except that here twice the amount of the racemic essential amino acids was employed when these were found to be less costly than the corresponding L-forms. In the case of the still more economically satisfactory diet No. 44, both essential and nonessential amino acids were substituted for by twice the amount of their less expensive racemic counterparts. Thus, the essential amino acid nitrogen in diet No. 26 was only 9.5 grams, but in diet Nos. 40 and 44, utilizable and nonutilizable, it was 13.3 grams. Further, the nonessential amino acid nitrogen in diet Nos. 26 and 40 was 15.7 grams to give a total nitrogen per kilogram of diet of 25.2 and 29.0 grams, respectively, whereas that of diet No. 44 was 20.7 grams to give a total nitrogen per kilogram of diet of 34.0 grams. A comparison of the growth promoting abilities of each of these diets over a 21-day period is shown in Fig. 4. The curves reveal that diet Nos. 40 and 44, the economically less expensive diets, are dramatically less effective than is diet No. 26 in promoting growth, although the total nitrogen in both of these diets is greater. Actually, how much of the D-components in diet Nos. 40 and 44 is utilizable, how much is inhibitory and how much is indifferent, it is clearly impossible to say. Animal tissues are geared to handle metabolically the L-forms of the amino acids, and although some of the D-forms can be more or less rapidly

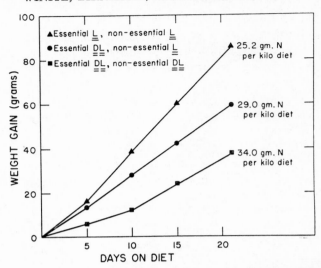

Fig. 4. Growth responses of male weanling rats on diets containing L- and DL-amino acids.

inverted, they may, in mixtures, interfere with each other's inversion. In any event, L-amino acids are now accessible in quantity, and there is no reason why racemates should be employed in nutritional experiments any longer. It should hardly be necessary to press this point, but the substitution of financial economy for quality of experiment has little to recommend it.

Applications of Chemically Defined Diets

Certain features possessed by water-soluble, chemically defined diets make them of potential practical application in a number of ways. Such applications include (a) use for quantitative metabolic studies in man and in laboratory animals, (b) food for germ free animals, (c) food supply in space travel, (d) treatment of patients with metabolic dysfunctions, (e) food for patients with ulcerative colitis, (f) parenteral feeding, (g) treatment of kwashiorkor, and (h) use for study of specific enzyme systems and metabolic processes in vivo. Thus, our own use of such diets for quantitative metabolic studies in laboratory animals has permitted the accumulation of data on nitrogen balance and nitrogen metabolism with a degree of precision and certainty not hitherto achieved (Birnbaum et al., 1957a). Comparable quantitative metabolic studies in man, using these same diets, are presently being carried out by our clinical associates. As a potential source of food for germ free animals, these diets possess a distinct advantage in that the whole diet can be sterilized by filtration, or the separate components can be sterilized by filtration or by autoclaving and subsequently admixed under sterile conditions. As a potential food supply in space travel, chemically defined diets afford complete and adequate nutriment in highly concentrated form. This is strikingly revealed by the fact that only one cubic foot of the diet, as a 50% solution in water, is sufficient to provide a man with the required amino acids, vitamins, salts, and essential fatty acids, in addition to 2000 calories per day, for a period of nearly a month. For the study and treatment of patients who suffer from kwashiorkor or from certain metabolic dysfunctions, such as oligophrenia phenylpyruvica, the diet possesses an advantage in that any component or group of components can be added to or eliminated from the diet at will. As the diet is rapidly absorbed in the upper portion of the gastrointestinal tract and contains no added bulk, it should also prove of value for the treatment of patients who suffer from ulcerative colitis.

Very recently, we have found that chemically defined diets also provide a potentially valuable tool for the study of specific enzymes and metabolic processes *in vivo*. In the final few moments, some of our experiences along these lines will be briefly discussed. Thus, earlier workers have shown that certain of the essential L-amino acids, such as arginine (Winitz *et al.*, 1957b), methionine (Jackson and Block, 1937-1938; Wretlind and Rose, 1950), tryptophan (du Vigneaud *et al.*, 1932; Berg, 1934) and leucine (Berg, 1953; Rechcigl *et al.*, 1958), may be replaced in whole or in part by their corresponding D-isomers in the diet of the rat. Some of our own results with chemically defined diets, as revealed in Fig. 5, reaffirm these early observations. In this case, the standard diet, designated as No. 3, contained the basal diet shown in Table II in addition to a mixture of L-proline, L-tyrosine ethyl ester·HCl, monosodium L-glutamate, and L-alanine as the source of nonessential nitrogen. The curves reveal that when D-methionine was employed instead L-methionine in diet No. 3, no change in the growth response of weanling rats was observed over a 10-day period. However, D-tryptophan was only partially effective in replacing its corresponding L-antipode, and D-leucine even less effective, since this latter amino acid had to be added at a level equivalent to 1.4 times its L-antipode before a significant growth response was observed. Evidently, the ability of the organism to utilize a given essential

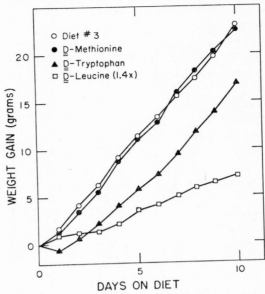

Fig. 5. Growth responses of male weanling rats on diets containing a specific D-amino acid *in lieu* of the L-form.

amino acid as its D-antipode varies considerably. In any event, it is generally accepted that the utilization of the D-amino acid results from its conversion to the corresponding L-isomer according to the following scheme:

$$\underset{\substack{\text{D-amino}\\\text{acid}}}{\overset{\substack{\text{CO}_2\text{H}\\|\\\text{H}-\text{C}-\text{NH}_2\\|\\\text{R}}}{}} \rightarrow \underset{\substack{\alpha\text{-keto}\\\text{acid}}}{\overset{\substack{\text{CO}_2\text{H}\\|\\\text{C}=\text{O}\\|\\\text{R}}}{}} \rightarrow \underset{\substack{\text{L-amino}\\\text{acid}}}{\overset{\substack{\text{CO}_2\text{H}\\|\\\text{NH}_2-\text{C}-\text{H}\\|\\\text{R}}}{}}$$

Thus, the D-amino acid is presumably first converted to its corresponding α-keto acid by the action of D-amino acid oxidase, and the α-keto acid, in turn, transformed to the corresponding L-amino acid by a process of transamination.

As the amounts of the enzyme systems responsible for this transformation are evidently present in the organism in limiting amounts, it became of interest to ascertain whether, in feeding experiments with synthetic diets, these enzyme systems could be provided with more substrate than they could effectively handle. The results of one such study are shown in Fig. 6. Thus, four diets were

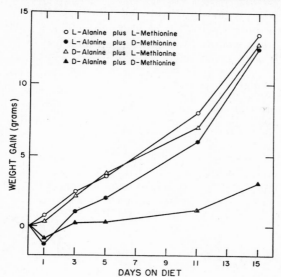

FIG. 6. Growth curves of male weanling rats on diets containing alanine and methionine in the L- and D-configuration.

prepared which were identical in all respects but for the exception that in the first, alanine and methionine were provided as their L-isomers; in the second, alanine was provided as the L-isomer and methionine as the D-isomer; in the third, alanine was provided as the D-isomer and methionine as the L-isomer; and in the fourth, both amino acids were provided as their D-forms. The growth curves on these diets over a 15-day period reveal that with the first three diets, that is, those containing at least one L-form of either methionine or alanine, the growth response was very nearly the same. On the other hand, the growth response with the diets containing the two D-isomers was very markedly diminished. It therefore appeared, in this latter case, that the D-amino acids were provided in an amount which was in excess of the ability of the organism to effectively convert them to their corresponding L-isomers commensurate with the needs for increased growth. However, from the data so far obtained, it was not possible to ascertain whether the rate-limiting step in the conversion of the D-amino acids to their corresponding L-isomers was due to the rate of oxidative deamination of the D-amino acids to the α-keto acids or to the rate of formation of the L-amino acids from the α-keto acids by transamination.

Now it was previously established (Bartlett, 1948) that sodium benzoate is a potent inhibitor of D-amino acid oxidase *in vitro*. If sodium benzoate would also behave as an inhibitor of D-amino acid oxidase in the whole organism, then a means would be at hand to pinpoint the rate-limiting step in the *in vivo* conversion of a D-amino acid to its corresponding L-isomer. Chemically defined diets were therefore formulated which were identical in every respect but with the exceptions noted in Fig. 7. Thus, the first diet contained

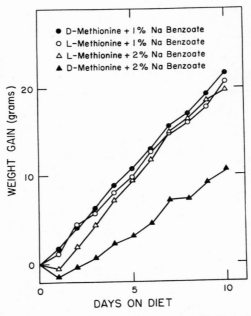

Fig. 7. Growth curves of male weanling rats on diets containing 1% and 2% sodium benzoate.

D-methionine as the source of this essential amino acid in addition to 1% sodium benzoate; the second diet was identical with the first but contained L-methionine instead of the D-isomer; the third diet likewise contained L-methionine as the source of this essential amino acid but, in addition, contained sodium benzoate in 2% concentration; the last diet was identical with the third but contained D-methionine instead of the L-isomer. The growth curves on each of these diets over a 10-day period reveal that groups on all diets displayed comparable growth except those receiving the diet containing

D-methionine plus 2% sodium benzoate, in which case growth was strikingly diminished. Such data thereupon pointed to the oxidative deamination step as the rate-limiting one. However, in order to establish this mechanism still more firmly, comparable feeding experiments are presently being carried out with the α-keto analog of methionine, which should undergo transamination directly to L-methionine, thereupon by-passing the need for the oxidative deamination step.

One further observation is worthy of note. It will be recalled that earlier workers established that the detoxification of sodium benzoate in the animal organism takes place as a result of the condensation of this

$$\langle\hspace{-0.3em}\bigcirc\hspace{-0.3em}\rangle\text{—CO}_2\text{H} + \text{NH}_2\text{CH}_2\text{CO}_2\text{H} \rightarrow \langle\hspace{-0.3em}\bigcirc\hspace{-0.3em}\rangle\text{—CO—NHCH}_2\text{CO}_2\text{H}$$

benzoic acid   glycine   hippuric acid

compound with glycine to form hippuric acid, which may then be eliminated in the urine as hippuric acid. Thus, if a means could be found to accelerate the conversion of sodium benzoate to hippuric acid in the whole organism, then it might be possible to reverse the inhibition of D-amino acid oxidase more effectively, due to the presence of large amounts of sodium benzoate in the diet. On the assumption that glycine was not provided by the body with sufficient rapidity to detoxify very large amounts of sodium benzoate, diets were prepared of the same constitution as those shown in Fig. 7 but in which a portion of the nonessential amino acid complement was replaced by glycine. Indeed, the inhibition of D-amino acid oxidase by the sodium benzoate was completely reversed, as was attested to by the fact that the diet which contained the D-methionine and the 2% sodium benzoate now supported the growth of weanling rats as well as did the other three diets. Whether the use of comparable experiments will permit us to ascertain the rate of glycine synthesis in the whole organism is presently under investigation. In any event, it might be presumed, from what has already been said, that the use of chemically defined diets, wherein the components can be changed at will, provides a potentially useful tool for studying metabolic interconversions in the whole animal organism.

Summary

The enzymatic resolution procedures, as developed by Jesse P. Greenstein and his associates, were based primarily upon the

L-directed asymmetric hydrolysis either by hog renal acylase I or carboxypeptidase of a suitable N-acyl-DL-amino acid, or by hog renal amidase of a DL-amino acid amide. Such resolution procedures were employed to obtain the L- and D-antipodes of a large variety of α-amino acids on the large scale, and permitted the formulation of water-soluble, chemically defined diets composed of crystalline essential and nonessential L-amino acids, the requisite vitamins and salts, glucose, and ethyl linoleate or mazola oil as the essential fatty acid component. Employment of chemically defined diets in long-term, quantitative nutrition studies with Sprague-Dawley rats is discussed, as is the potential application of these diets (a) for quantitative metabolic studies in man and in laboratory animals, (b) as a food for germ-free animals, (c) as a food supply in space travel, (d) for treatment of patients with metabolic dysfunctions, e.g. oligophrenia phenylpyruvica, or with ulcerative colitis, (e) for the study of kwashiorkor, (f) for parenteral feeding, and (g) as a tool for the study of specific enzyme systems and metabolic processes *in vivo*.

REFERENCES

Akabori, S., and Narita, K. (1953). *Proc. Acad. Sci. Japan* **29**, 264.

Baker, C. G., and Sober, H. A. (1953). *J. Am. Chem. Soc.* **75**, 4058.

Bartlett, G. R. (1948). *J. Am. Chem. Soc.* **70**, 1010.

Berg, C. P. (1934). *J. Biol. Chem.* **104**, 373.

Berg, C. P. (1953). *Physiol. Revs.* **33**, 145.

Birnbaum, S. M., Greenstein, J. P., and Winitz, M. (1957a). *Arch. Biochem. Biophys.* **72**, 417.

Birnbaum, S. M., Winitz, M., and Greenstein, J. P. (1957b). *Arch. Biochem. Biophys.* **72**, 428.

Davis, B. D. (1952). *Nature* **169**, 534.

Dewey, D. L., and Work, E. (1952). *Nature* **169**, 533.

du Vigneaud, V., Sealock, R. R., and Van Etten, C. (1932). *J. Biol. Chem.* **98**, 565.

Greenstein, J. P. (1954). *Advances in Protein Chem.* **9**, 121.

Greenstein, J. P., and Winitz, M. (1960). "Chemistry of the Amino Acids." Wiley, New York. In press.

Greenstein, J. P., Birnbaum, S. M., Winitz, M., and Otey, M. C. (1957). *Arch. Biochem. Biophys.* **72**, 396.

Greenstein, J. P., Otey, M. C., Birnbaum, S. M., and Winitz, M. (1960). *J. Natl. Cancer Inst.* **24**, 211.

Jackson, R. W., and Block, R. J. (1937-1938). *J. Biol. Chem.* **122**, 425.

Meister, A., Levintow, L., Kingsley, R. B., and Greenstein, J. P. (1951). *J. Biol. Chem.* **192**, 535.

Rechcigl, M., Loosli, J. K., and Williams, H. H. (1958). *Science* **127**, 1051; *J. Biol. Chem.* **231**, 829.

Rose, W. C., Smith, L. C., Womack, M., and Shane, M. (1949). *J. Biol. Chem.* **181,** 307.

Sugimura, T., Birnbaum, S. M., Winitz, M., and Greenstein, J. P. (1959a). *Arch. Biochem. Biophys.* **81,** 439.

Sugimura, T., Birnbaum, S. M., Winitz, M., and Greenstein, J. P. (1959b). *Arch. Biochem. Biophys.* **81,** 448.

Sugimura, T., Birnbaum, S. M., Winitz, M., and Greenstein, J. P. (1959c). *Arch. Biochem. Biophys.* **83,** 521.

Vickery, H. B., Pucher, G. W., and Deuber, C. G. (1942). *J. Biol. Chem.* **145,** 45.

Winitz, M., Birnbaum, S. M., and Greenstein, J. P. (1957a). *Arch. Biochem. Biophys.* **72,** 437 (1957).

Winitz, M., Greenstein, J. P., and Birnbaum, S. M. (1957b). *Arch. Biochem. Biophys.* **72,** 448.

Wretlind, K. A. and Rose, W. C. (1950). *J. Biol. Chem.* **187,** 697.

Internal Hydrogen Bonding in Ribonuclease[1,2]

H. A. SCHERAGA, C. Y. CHA, J. HERMANS, JR., and C. L. SCHILDKRAUT

Department of Chemistry, Cornell University, Ithaca, New York

So MUCH PROGRESS has been made in recent years in the determination of the amino acid sequences of polypeptide chains that it has become feasible to attempt to determine the complete internal structure (secondary and tertiary) of a protein. The method of attack employed here has been the location of interactions in the backbone chain and between side-chain R groups (Scheraga, 1959). Presumably, the complete structure will be determined when a sufficient number of such interactions has been located. With the recent determination of the sequence (Hirs *et al.*, 1960) and location of the disulfide bridges (Spackman *et al.*, 1960) of ribonuclease, this protein has become a logical one for structural studies. Accordingly, attempts have been made to detect the presence of internal hydrogen bonds in ribonuclease by several experimental methods, and the data have been used (in conjunction with information about the primary structure) to construct a three-dimensional model of the protein. The model may not necessarily be a unique one, but it is believed to be consistent with the data available at present. Also, it provides a basis for planning future experiments for the location of side-chain interactions in ribonuclease.

The reader is referred to the papers of Hirs and associates (1960) and Spackman *et al.* (1960) for the complete amino acid

[1] This investigation was supported by research grant E-1473 from the National Institute of Allergy and Infectious Diseases, of the National Institutes of Health, U.S. Public Health Service, and by research grant G-6461 from the National Science Foundation.

[2] This symposium paper is based on work reported in more detail elsewhere (Cha and Scheraga, 1960; Schildkraut and Scheraga, 1960; Scheraga, 1960; Hermans and Scheraga, 1960).

31

sequence of oxidized bovine ribonuclease and location of the disulfide bridges in the native molecule.

There are many indications in the literature that the native molecule is folded in a compact form and is held together not only by covalent bonds but also by hydrogen bonds. For example, Carlisle and Scouloudi (1951) obtained dimensions of $18 \times 30 \times 48$ Å. from X-ray studies of wet ribonuclease crystals. From studies on dilute solutions, Harrington and Schellman (1956) obtained a value of 2.09×10^6 for the hydrodynamic parameter β (Scheraga and Mandelkern, 1953), which suggests that the axial ratio may not be very different from unity. The native structure is considerably disrupted by a variety of treatments, e.g. heat, urea, or oxidation of the disulfide bridges (Harrington and Schellman, 1956). If the native molecule is heated to 60° at pH 6.5, it undergoes a transition from an ordered to a disordered structure, as deduced from optical rotation (Harrington and Schellman, 1956) and viscosity (Tanford and Weber, 1960) measurements. If the disulfide bridges are oxidized, the molecule is converted to a randomly coiled form (Harrington and Schellman, 1956) in which all of its hydrogens exchange instantaneously with deuterium (Hvidt, 1955). Finally, the native form is sufficiently folded to lead to abnormal ionization behavior of 3 of the 6 tyrosyl groups (Shugar, 1952; Tanford et al., 1955) and of an indeterminate number of the carboxyl groups (Tanford and Hauenstein, 1956). The examples cited here represent only some of the evidence to support the notion that the protein is compact, with the possibility of many internal interactions.

In order to obtain further evidence for the existence of internal hydrogen bonds, experiments have been carried out involving titrations in a denaturing solvent, kinetics of deuterium-hydrogen exchange, effect of deuterium-hydrogen substitution on the stability of hydrogen bonds, ultraviolet difference spectra, and optical rotation. The results of these experiments, and of those cited earlier, have enabled us to propose a model for the structure of ribonuclease.

Abnormal Tyrosyl and Carboxyl Groups

Measurements of the pH-dependence of ultraviolet (UV) difference spectra were interpreted in terms of tyrosyl-carboxylate ion hydrogen bonding with an abnormally low pK for the carboxyl ionization (Scheraga, 1957). Other measurements on UV difference spectra were similarly interpreted (Harrington and Schellman,

1956; Sela and Anfinsen, 1957; Sela *et al.*, 1957; Bigelow and Ottesen, 1959). The postulate of tyrosyl-carboxylate ion hydrogen bonding was consistent with the titration anomalies observed for tyrosyl and carboxyl groups (Tanford *et al.*, 1955; Tanford and Hauenstein, 1956). Attempts were, therefore, made to render the tyrosyl and carboxyl groups normal with the aid of a hydrogen-bond-breaking, or denaturing, solvent. For this purpose a study of hydrogen ion equilibria of ribonuclease in a denaturing solvent was carried out (Cha and Scheraga, 1960). A similar investigation had previously been carried out by Blumenfeld and Levy (1958) for the tyrosyl groups.

The solvent chosen was a mixture which was 5 *M* in guanidine hydrochloride and 1.2 *M* in urea (designated as GU). In this solvent acetic acid has the same pK as it has in 0.15 *M* KCl, and the pK's of imidazole, phenol, and *n*-butylamine in GU differ very slightly from the corresponding values in 0.15 *M* KCl (Donovan *et al.*, 1959). By this choice of solvent it was possible to avoid large solvent effects on the pK's. A similar use had been made of GU in structural studies of lysozyme (Donovan *et al.*, 1959). At this concentration of guanidine hydrochloride and urea, ribonuclease is denatured (Anfinsen *et al.*, 1955; Anfinsen, 1957). Complete titration curves, as well as spectrophotometric ones in the alkaline pH range, were therefore obtained for ribonuclease in GU in order to determine whether the carboxyl and tyrosyl groups behave normally in this denaturing solvent. Details of the experiments have been reported by Cha and Scheraga (1960).

The experimental titration curve for ribonuclease in GU agrees with a theoretical one computed with the parameters given in Table I and the theory of Linderstrøm-Lang (1924). The values of the intrinsic dissociation constants in GU, pK'_{int}, and the electrostatic factor w, were computed from plots of $(pH - \log x/(1 - x))$ versus Z, according to the equation

$$pH - \log \frac{x}{1 - x} = pK'_{int} - 0.868\, w\, Z \qquad (1)$$

for the data on the carboxyl and tyrosyl groups, respectively, where x is the fraction of the groups of the given kind which have dissociated protons at the given pH, and Z is the net charge of the protein at the same pH. Similarly, the spectrophotometric titration data for all 6 tyrosyl groups agreed with a theoretical titration curve computed from the tyrosyl parameters of Table I. The data

TABLE I

PARAMETERS[a] USED TO CALCULATE TITRATION CURVE[b]
($w = 0.056$)

Group	pK'_{int}
Carboxyl	4.6
Imidazole	6.5
α-Amino	7.8
Tyrosyl	10.0
ϵ-Amino	10.2
Guanidine	>12

[a] The values for carboxyl and tyrosyl groups were determined from plots according to Eq. 1. The values for the other groups, being the same in GU as in 0.15 M KCl, were taken from Tanford and Hauenstein (1956).

[b] Cha and Scheraga (1960).

in GU and in 0.15 M KCl are listed in Table II. From these data, compared with those of Table III for model compounds (Donovan *et al.*, 1959), it may be seen that all 11 carboxyl and 6 tyrosyl groups of ribonuclease titrate normally in GU. This is in contrast to the low pK for the 11 carboxyl groups and inaccessibility of 3 tyrosyl groups of the native molecule in 0.15 M KCl. As a further indication of the normality of the carboxyl and tyrosyl groups in GU, and of the absence of significant pH-dependent configurational changes of ribonuclease in this solvent, it is seen that the w-values for both kinds of groups are identical. It thus seems valid to conclude that internal interactions, which render the carboxyl and half of the tyrosyl groups of native ribonuclease in 0.15 M KCl

TABLE II

EXPERIMENTAL PARAMETERS FOR IONIZATION OF CARBOXYL
AND TYROSYL GROUPS IN RIBONUCLEASE[a]

	pK'_{int} (in 0.15 M KCl)	pK'_{int} (in GU)	w (in 0.15 M KCl)	w (in GU)
Carboxyl				
11 groups	4.1	4.6	0.061	0.057
Tyrosyl				
3 groups	9.95	10.0	0.061	0.056
3 groups	inaccessible	10.0	—	0.056

[a] Cha and Scheraga (1960).

TABLE III

EXPERIMENTAL PARAMETERS FOR THE IONIZATION
OF MODEL COMPOUNDS[a]

	pK (in 0.15 M KCl)	pK (in GU)
Acetic acid	4.62	4.62
Imidazole	7.07	7.20
Phenol	9.92	10.03
n-Butylamine	10.79	10.74

[a] Donovan et al. (1959).

abnormal, are removed in the denaturing solvent GU. While these titration data indicate the breakdown of internal interactions, they do not prove that it is tyrosyl-carboxylate ion hydrogen bonds which are ruptured. However, further evidence on this point will be presented below in the discussion of UV difference spectra.

Kinetics of Deuterium–Hydrogen Exchange

Since there appear to be internal interactions in ribonuclease it was important to determine whether these involved hydrogen bonds and, if so, how many hydrogen bonds. For this purpose kinetic studies of deuterium-hydrogen exchange were carried out (Schildkraut and Scheraga, 1960) by the method of Linderstrøm-Lang (1955).

In this technique a deuterated protein is placed in H_2O at a given pH and temperature, aliquots are withdrawn at various times, and the D_2O—H_2O mixture removed from each aliquot by cryosublimation. The density of the sublimate (and, thereby, the composition) is determined in a density gradient column and the extent of exchange computed for each aliquot. Rapidly exchangeable hydrogens (within 30 sec.) are considered to be non-hydrogen-bonded ones. Those hydrogens which exchange more slowly are considered to be involved in hydrogen bonds.

At pH 4.8 there are 245 exchangeable hydrogens in ribonuclease. At 0° at this pH approximately 175 exchange instantaneously (within 30 sec.).[3] Therefore, this number of hydrogens is probably

[3] It should be noted that in some experiments this number dropped as low as 160 (Schildkraut and Scheraga, 1960). This discrepancy arises, of course, from the difficulty of making measurements within 30 sec.

not involved in hydrogen bonding. Of the remaining 70 hydrogens approximately 25 exchange in about 6 hr. and the remaining 45 do not exchange to any significant extent at 0°C. up to 24 hr. If the temperature is raised to about 38°C. an additional 25 exchange, but the remaining 20 do not exchange unless the original deuteration and the back exchange are both carried out above the transition temperature (60°C.) found from optical rotation studies (Harrington and Schellman, 1956). The hydrogens may thus be grouped in four sets of 175, 25, 25, and 20 each. The 70 hydrogens of the last three sets are considered to be involved in hydrogen bonding of different bond strengths, the last set of 20 presumably being most tightly bound. In view of the discrepancy in the number of rapidly exchangeable hydrogens (175 compared with 160), cited earlier,[3] the first set of 25 could be a larger set, possibly as large as 40. This would mean that the total number of hydrogen bonds could be as high as 85. Further work is in progress to try to determine which of these 70-85 hydrogen bonds are in the backbone chain and which in the side-chains. For the present, we shall assume that essentially all of them are in the backbone, i.e. secondary structure.

Effect of Deuterium on the Transition Temperature

If deuterium is substituted for hydrogen, and the latter is involved in a hydrogen bond, then the bond strength will be affected. As a consequence one would expect a deuterated helical macromolecule to have a different stability from a hydrogen-containing one, using the random coil as a reference state. This altered stability should manifest itself in a change in the transition temperature between the helix and random coil. Indeed, such an effect was found in solutions of poly-γ-benzyl-L-glutamate in mixtures of dichloroethane and dichloroacetic acid, where a change of 11° in the transition temperature upon deuteration was observed (Calvin *et al.*, 1959). Since ribonuclease shows a transition with increasing temperature (Harrington and Schellman, 1956), the effect of deuterium substitution on the transition temperature was investigated by means of optical rotation measurements in order to obtain additional evidence for the existence of internal hydrogen bonds in ribonuclease.

As in the case of poly-γ-benzyl-L-glutamate, the transition temperature of deuterated ribonuclease in D_2O is different (about 4° higher in this case) from that of hydrogen-containing ribonuclease in H_2O (Hermans and Scheraga, 1959). Further, the free energy of formation of a peptide hydrogen bond was found to be smaller in the deuterated molecule than in the hydrogen-containing one by an amount of the order of 50 cal./mole. This difference lies in the predicted range of ± 100 cal./mole. These results provide additional evidence that hydrogen bonds stabilize the structure of ribonuclease in aqueous solutions.

It should be mentioned that the results reported in this section in no way vitiate those reported in the previous section on kinetics, since the kinetics experiments were carried out at 0°, far below the transition, where the effect of deuterium on the stability of the hydrogen bonds would not be observed (Calvin et al., 1959).

Ultraviolet Difference Spectra and Optical Rotation

In this section we report additional data on the thermally induced transition in ribonuclease. At the present time we have not yet realized all of the implications of the experimental results, which will be reported soon in more extensive form (Hermans and Scheraga, 1960).

The thermally induced transition has been investigated at a series of pH's from 0.9 to 6.8, using both ultraviolet difference spectra and optical rotation measurements. Both properties change in such a way with increasing temperature as to indicate a transition from an ordered to a disordered state. Further, if the data are plotted as "fraction converted" at any pH versus temperature, then S-shaped curves are obtained at all pH's, with an increase in the transition temperature as the pH is raised. In addition, the curve at any given pH, obtained from the UV difference spectrum, is completely superimposable on the curve obtained from optical rotation measurements.[4] It therefore seems that if tyrosyl-carboxylate ion hydrogen bonds are present (and are responsible for the UV difference spectrum), these bonds are ruptured in the general configuration change which gives rise to the changes in optical rotation when the temperature is increased.

The pH-dependence of reversible denaturation provides a means of detecting hydrogen bonds between ionizable side-chain groups (Scheraga, 1958). An analysis of the pH-dependence of the UV difference spectrum and optical rotation in terms of equilibria be-

[4] Tanford and Weber (1960) also noted a lower transition temperature at low pH, using optical rotation and viscosity measurements, and also found a parallelism between these two properties.

tween native and denatured forms in different states of ionization suggests that 2 groups in the native molecule in 0.15 M KCl have a pK of about 1.5. As the temperature is raised at a given pH or the pH is lowered at a given temperature these groups acquire normal ionization properties. From the direct titration curves at 25° and 45° a difference curve was computed which paralleled the curve representing the fraction of unfolded ribonuclease as a function of pH at 45°. This difference curve corresponded to the titration of 2 groups, presumably carboxyls. It seems that the interactions which are removed by heating may be the same as those removed by GU in the experiments cited earlier. Since these abnormal carboxyls also are detectable in UV difference spectra of tyrosine, it seems that possibly two tyrosyl-carboxylate ion hydrogen bonds may be present in the native molecule in 0.15 M KCl at

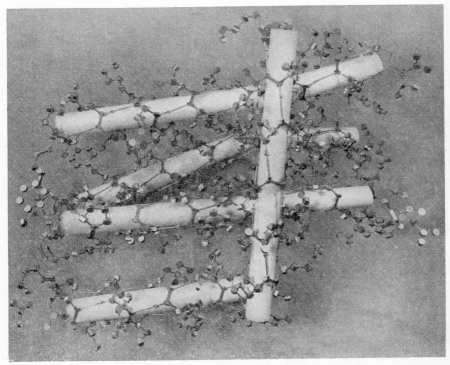

Fig. 1. Model of ribonuclease showing parallel array of all helical portions except the N-terminus which is perpendicular to the other chains. (Scheraga, 1960.)

25°. Further studies on the kinetics and thermodynamics of the denaturation of ribonuclease are in progress.

A Model for Ribonuclease

On the basis of the results discussed here, and also those reported in the literature, we have constructed a model which is believed to be consistent with the experimental data. Two views are shown in Figs. 1 and 2. Further details are presented elsewhere (Scheraga, 1960). The model consists of 6 α-helical portions with 6 nonhelical breaks. The N-terminus is close to the C-terminus and

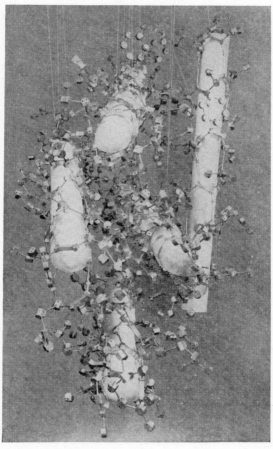

Fig. 2. End view of the model showing the ends of the helical portions and the vertical N-terminus. (Scheraga, 1960.)

the remainder of the molecule is essentially a parallel array of helical chains. The model is consistent with the primary structure, the evidence cited above for internal hydrogen bonding (including the number of hydrogen bonds from deuterium-hydrogen exchange), and provides for a large number of side-chain interactions (including tyrosyl-carboxylate ion hydrogen bonds). Its over-all dimensions are consistent with those deduced from X-ray and hydrodynamic measurements. It remains for further experimentation, both on the crystalline material and on the molecule in solution, to establish the correct model. The one proposed here not only reconciles the data available at present, but also provides a basis for planning such further experiments.

Summary

Experimental data have been presented to provide evidence for the existence of internal hydrogen bonds in ribonuclease. These data were obtained from titrations in a denaturing solvent, kinetics of deuterium-hydrogen exchange, effect of deuterium-hydrogen substitution on the stability of hydrogen bonds, ultraviolet difference spectra, and optical rotation. A three-dimensional model has been proposed to account for these and other observations, and also to provide a basis for further experimentation.

REFERENCES

Anfinsen, C. B. (1957). *Federation Proc.* **16**, 783.
Anfinsen, C. B., Harrington, W. F., Hvidt, A., Linderstrøm-Lang, K., Ottesen, M., and Schellman, J. (1955). *Biochim. et Biophys. Acta* **17**, 141.
Bigelow, C. C., and Ottesen, M. (1959). *Biochim. et Biophys. Acta* **32**, 574.
Blumenfeld, O. O., and Levy, M. (1958). *Arch. Biochem. Biophys.* **76**, 97.
Calvin, M., Hermans, J., Jr., and Scheraga, H. A. (1959). *J. Am. Chem. Soc.* **81**, 5048.
Carlisle, C. H., and Scouloudi, H. (1951). *Proc. Roy. Soc.* **A207**, 496.
Cha, C. Y., and Scheraga, H. A. (1960). *J. Am. Chem. Soc.* **82**, 54.
Donovan, J. W., Laskowski, M., Jr., and Scheraga, H. A. (1959). *J. Molecular Biol.* **1**, 293-296.
Harrington, W. F., and Schellman, J. A. (1956). *Compt. rend. trav. lab. Carlsberg, Sér. chim.* **30**, 21.
Hermans, J., Jr., and Scheraga, H. A. (1959). *Biochim. et Biophys. Acta* **36**, 534.
Hermans, J., Jr., and Scheraga, H. A. (1960). *J. Am. Chem. Soc.* to be submitted.
Hirs, C. H. W., Moore, S., and Stein, W. H. (1960). *J. Biol. Chem.*, in press.
Hvidt, A. (1955). *Biochim. et Biophys. Acta* **18**, 306.
Linderstrøm-Lang, K. (1924). *Compt. rend. trav. lab. Carlsberg* **15**, No. 7.
Linderstrøm-Lang, K. (1955). *Chem. Soc.* (London), *Spec. Publ. No.* **2**, 1.

Scheraga, H. A. (1957). *Biochim. et Biophys. Acta* **23**, 196.

Scheraga, H. A. (1958). *Abstr. 134th Meeting Am. Chem. Soc.*, Chicago, Illinois, Sept. 1958, p. 51C.

Scheraga, H. A. (1959). *Ann. Rev. Phys. Chem.* **10**, 191.

Scheraga, H. A. (1960). *J. Am. Chem. Soc.*, in press.

Scheraga, H. A., and Mandelkern, L. (1953). *J. Am. Chem. Soc.* **75**, 179.

Schildkraut, C. L., and Scheraga, H. A. (1960). *J. Am. Chem. Soc.* **82**, 58.

Sela, M., and Anfinsen, C. B. (1957). *Biochim. et Biophys. Acta* **24**, 229.

Sela, M., Anfinsen, C. B., and Harrington, W. F. (1957). *Biochim. et Biophys. Acta* **26**, 502.

Shugar, D. (1952). *Biochem. J.* **52**, 142.

Spackman, D. H., Stein, W. H., and Moore, S. (1960). *J. Biol. Chem.*, in press.

Tanford, C., and Hauenstein, J. D. (1956). *J. Am. Chem. Soc.* **78**, 5287.

Tanford, C., and Weber, R. E. (1960), in press.

Tanford, C., Hauenstein, J. D., and Rands, D. G. (1955). *J. Am. Chem. Soc.* **77**, 6409.

Considerations of the Structure and Function of Carboxypeptidase A[1]

HANS NEURATH, JOHN A. RUPLEY, and
BERT L. VALLEE

*Department of Biochemistry, University of Washington, Seattle,
Washington, and the Biophysics Research Laboratory of the Department of Medicine, Harvard Medical School, Peter Bent Brigham Hospital, Boston, Massachusetts*

AN IMPORTANT PHASE of Jesse Greenstein's scientific work has dealt with the action of stereospecific enzymes on isomeric amino acids and peptides. The substrates involved were mainly α-halogenacylated amino acids and simple peptides, and the enzymes included a group of acylases of renal tissue, and pancreatic carboxypeptidase (Greenstein, 1954, 1956). Since in these systems the stereospecificity of the enzymes was practically absolute, this work has led to a new and powerful practical method for the resolution of amino acids by asymmetric hydrolysis. By use of renal acylases I and II, all but four N-acylamino acids could be resolved to within one part in 1000 or better, whereas pancreatic carboxypeptidase, which in this sense is likewise an acylase, was effectively employed for the resolution of phenylalanine, tyrosine, tryptophan, and β-phenylserine. Greenstein's interest in proteolytic enzymes has extended far beyond their practical use just alluded to, and it seems fitting and appropriate, as part of the present contribution, to review recent progress in the study of one of these acylases, i.e., the pancreatic carboxypeptidase, first isolated in crystalline form by Anson (1937) from the drip juice of freshly collected beef pancreas glands. The more recent identification of carboxypeptidase as a metalloenzyme (Vallee and Neurath, 1954, 1955), and the elucidation of some of the steps involved in its formation from the parent zymogen, procarboxypeptidase (Keller *et al.*, 1956, 1958a), have elicited renewed interest in this enzyme, and have opened new avenues in the correlative investiga-

---

[1] "Carboxypeptidase A" denotes the enzyme originally described by Anson (1937), and will be referred to in the text simply as "carboxypeptidase."

tion of the chemical structure and biological function of this protein.

In general terms, and as background information, crystalline carboxypeptidase (A) may be characterized as follows. The enzyme is a zinc-metalloprotein, having a molecular weight of 34,300 (see Neurath, 1957) and containing one gram atom of zinc per mole (Vallee and Neurath, 1954, 1955). The primary structure consists of a single polypeptide chain, of known composition (Smith and Stockell, 1954) but unknown sequence, containing 310 amino acid residues, with an asparagine residue at each end (Thompson, 1953; Ando et al., 1959). The protein has an isoelectric point near pH 6.0 (Putnam and Neurath, 1946) and a net negative charge at the pH of crystallization (near pH 8.0). These properties, and others to be discussed, are summarized in Table I.

TABLE I

Some Properties of Carboxypeptidase[a]

Molecular weight	34,300
Number of amino acid residues	310
Metal content	1 gm. atom of Zn per mole
N-terminal	Asparagine
C-terminal	Asparagine
Isoelectric Point	
Ionic Strength 0.2	6.0
Ionic Strength 0.3	5.6
$[\alpha]_D^{0°}$	−18°

[a] For references, see the text.

The substrate specificity of this enzyme has been the subject of extensive investigations in various laboratories, and has been reviewed on several occasions (Neurath and Schwert, 1950; Smith, 1951; Green and Neurath, 1954). Suffice it to state that carboxypeptidase hydrolyzes the C-terminal peptide bond of peptides and proteins, provided that the carboxyl group of the C-terminal amino acid is free. Substrates are particularly susceptible to hydrolysis by carboxypeptidase if the C-terminal residue, in the L-configuration, is contributed by aromatic or branched aliphatic amino acids, whereas no hydrolysis ensues if arginine, lysine, or proline are C-terminal. Carboxypeptidase has been used successfully for the determination of C-terminal groups of proteins and polypeptides (Harris, 1955; Neurath et al., 1954), but the extent of degradation beyond the C-terminal amino acid depends on the secondary structure of the protein substrate.

Carboxypeptidase occurs *in vivo*, as the zymogen in the exocellular secretions of the pancreas (Keller *et al.*, 1958b), specifically in the zymogen granules of the acinar cells (P. J. Keller, unpublished experiments). Recent studies of the chemical and enzymatic characterization of the components of bovine pancreatic juice (Keller *et al.*, 1958b, 1959) and of aqueous extract of acetone powder of beef pancreas glands have identified procarboxypeptidase within the spectrum of pancreatic proteins. The elution profile of freshly collected bovine pancreatic juice, subjected to chromatography on DEAE cellulose (Fig. 1) reveals procarboxypeptidase

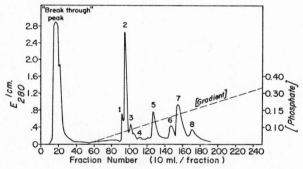

FIG. 1. Chromatographic resolution of the anionic proteins of bovine pancreatic juice on DEAE-cellulose. Procarboxypeptidase is associated with the last two effluent peaks. (From Keller *et al.*, 1958b.)

as two well-resolved components (peaks 7 and 8 in Fig. 1) which, together with carboxypeptidase A (peak 6), formed by spontaneous activation, comprise 28% of the total proteins of bovine pancreatic juice (Keller *et al.*, 1958b). Procarboxypeptidase is preparatively isolated from aqueous extracts of acetone powder of beef pancreas glands, by a process involving fractional precipitation with ammonium sulfate, followed by either isoelectric precipitation or by chromatography on DEAE cellulose columns (Keller *et al.*, 1956, 1958b). The purified zymogen has a molecular weight approximately three times greater than that of carboxypeptidase (approximately 96,000) and a considerably lower isoelectric point (less than pH 4.5). Activation of procarboxypeptidase involves the participation of trypsin, which in low concentrations elicits the formation from procarboxypeptidase of an endopeptidase which is

active toward acetyl-L-tyrosine ethyl ester and is inhibited by
DFP; the action of this endopeptidase, together with relatively
high concentrations of trypsin, is required to convert the "activated"
procarboxypeptidase into carboxypeptidase and a number of peptides having an average molecular weight of approximately 1500.
The dual nature of procarboxypeptidase as a precursor of enzymatic activity is illustrated in Fig. 2. Significantly, crystalline
carboxypeptidase has no endopeptidase activity, suggesting that
this activity is associated with a different region of the zymogen
than the carboxypeptidase activity. Zinc, the metal of carboxypeptidase, is preexistent in the zymogen molecule (quoted by
Neurath, 1955), together with significant quantities of iron and

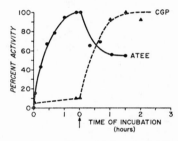

Fig. 2. Appearance of enzymatic activity toward acetyl-L-tyrosine ethyl
ester and toward carbobenzoxyglycyl-L-phenylalanine upon activation of procarboxypeptidase by trypsin (1×10^{-4} mg. N per ml.) at 0°. At the time
indicated by the arrow, the trypsin concentration was raised 100-fold. (From
Keller *et al.*, 1958a.)

nickel (Vallee, Keller, and Neurath, unpublished experiments).
The role of these metals in the activation process is being investigated. The nature of the peptides, and the kinetics of their formation, are likewise subjects of a current study.

In 1954, Vallee and Neurath demonstrated that pancreatic
carboxypeptidase contains one gram atom of zinc per mole of
protein, and provided proof that the enzyme conforms to the
operational criteria of a metalloenzyme. The specificity of association between zinc and protein in the native enzyme has been recently further corroborated by the isolation and crystallization
of a biosynthetically labeled, radioactive carboxypeptidase
[(CPD)Zn^{65}], obtained from bovine and canine pancreatic secretions collected from the live animals through fistulae (J. A. Rupley
and H. Neurath, in preparation). In these experiments, Zn^{65}, as the

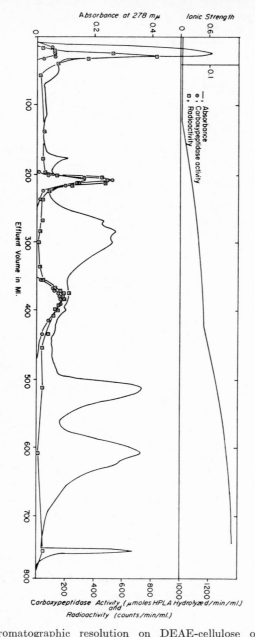

Fig. 3. Chromatographic resolution on DEAE-cellulose of the anionic components of activated canine pancreatic juice collected after the administration of Zn^{65}. Carboxypeptidase activity is associated with the second radioactive peak (effluent volume 200-300 ml.). (From Rupley and Neurath, in preparation.)

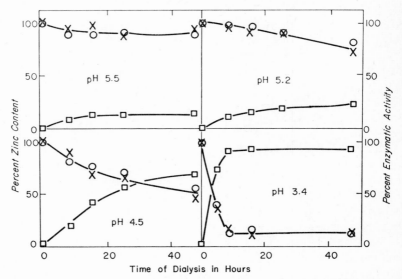

FIG. 4. Rates of loss of zinc and enzymatic activity on dialysis of carboxypeptidase against buffers of low pH. The circles denote per cent zinc inside the dialysis bag, the squares per cent zinc in buffer outside the dialysis bag, and the crosses per cent peptidase activity inside the dialysis bag. (From Vallee *et al.*, 1960.)

chloride, was administered intravenously to the experimental animals, and the radioactive pancreatic juice collected at various intervals thereafter. A typical chromatogram, representing the protein and the radioactive components of spontaneously activated canine pancreatic juice is shown in Fig. 3, which reveals the radioactivity to be associated with the component which enzymatically and chemically has been identified as carboxypeptidase. Like the bovine enzyme, carboxypeptidase from canine pancreatic juice can be isolated in pure, crystalline form.

While zinc is sufficiently firmly bound to native carboxypeptidase to accompany the protein through successive crystallizations in stoichiometrically constant proportions (Vallee and Neurath, 1954, 1955), the metal can be removed either by dialysis against buffers of pH below 5.5, or at neutral pH, by dialysis against 1,10-phenanthroline. In either instance, the loss of enzymatic activity is directly proportional to the loss of metal (Vallee *et al.*, 1958 and 1960). The effects of pH on zinc content and enzymatic activity, as a function of time, are shown in Fig. 4. The effect of pH on removal of metal after 48 hours' dialysis is shown in Fig. 5. Within the limits of measurement, removal of zinc is complete at pH 3.4 after approximately 10 hours.

The resultant metal-free protein is homogeneous, stable, and enzymatically inactive. However, enzymatic activity may be regained by the addition of zinc to the apoenzyme. The reactivation again is directly proportional to the amount of zinc bound by the enzyme, up to one gram atom per mole of protein. Zinc in excess of this amount may be bound but without any accompanying increase in activity, as shown by the bar diagrams of Fig. 6. Dialysis against buffer readily removes loosely bound, extraneous zinc, but neither firmly bound zinc nor enzymatic activity is affected by this procedure. The reconstituted apoenzyme may be crystallized and is enzymatically and chemically indistinguishable from native carboxypeptidase.

It is of considerable significance that activity can be restored to the metal-free protein not only by zinc but also by certain ions of the first transition period, i.e., Cr^{+++}, Mn^{++}, Fe^{++}, Co^{++}, and Ni^{++} (Vallee et $al.$, 1958 and 1960). No other ion has yet been found to similarly restore activity. Under identical conditions of

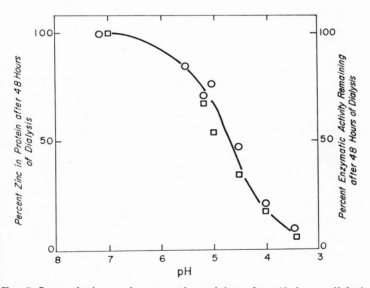

FIG. 5. Loss of zinc and enzymatic activity after 48 hours dialysis of carboxypeptidase against buffers of varying pH. The circles refer to zinc content and the squares to peptidase activity. (From Vallee et $al.$, 1960.)

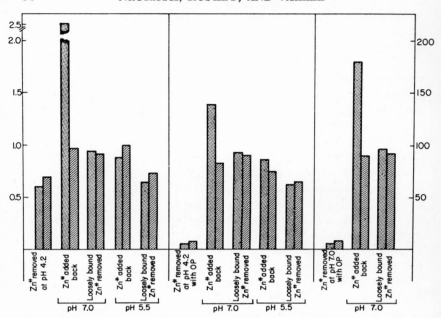

FIG. 6. Reconstitution of zinc-depleted carboxypeptidase with zinc. Cross-hatched bars denote gram atoms of zinc bound per mole of protein; diagonally shaded bars denote per cent peptidase activity. (From Vallee *et al.*, 1960.)

these enzymatic assays (0.02 *M* substrate concentration), the different metals restore activity toward the peptide substrate, carbobenzoxyglycyl-L-phenylalanine, to varying degrees; the cobalt enzyme was found to be most active. Representative data are shown in Fig. 7. In this context, it is important to recall Greenstein's observations that the addition of Co^{++} to acylase I causes acceleration of hydrolysis of some substrates, and inhibition of enzymatic action on others. An effect of the metal on enzyme specificity was also indicated by the finding that some nearly resistant substrates, such as acetyl-D-alanine, became hydrolyzed in the presence of Co^{++} at an appreciable rate (quoted in Greenstein, 1956). It is worthy of note that in the case of Ni^{++} and Fe^{++}, in contrast to Co^{++}, removal of loosely bound metal by dialysis results in a significant increase in specific activity. Hence, the lack of activity observed on the addition of a metal to apocarboxypeptidase does not necessarily indicate that the restoration of an active carboxypeptidase was not achieved, unless the fraction of the metal which is *extrinsic* and inhibitory has first been removed. Each of these metal carboxypeptidases, containing one gram atom of metal per mole of protein, has been crystallized (Coleman *et al.*, 1960); representative crystals are shown in Fig. 8. The formation of the cobalt enzyme is accompanied by the appearance of an absorption maximum at 530 mμ, reflected by a distinctive, reddish color of the crystalline enzyme (Coleman and Vallee, in press).

The metal in cobalt-carboxypeptidase is more loosely bound than in zinc-carboxypeptidase. Whereas zinc remains firmly bound and activity remains unchanged during 6 days of dialysis against metal-free buffer at neutral pH, the cobalt enzyme, under these conditions, loses 40% of bound metal and of its activity.

The apparent dissociation constants of these two metal carboxypeptidases have been estimated from equilibrium dialysis measurements at pH 8.0, 4° as being 5×10^{-9} M for the zinc enzyme and 1.5×10^{-6} M for the cobalt enzyme. The two forms of the enzyme are interconvertible, dialysis of the cobalt enzyme against a solution of zinc ions resulting in complete replacement of cobalt by zinc (Coleman and Vallee, in press). The resultant

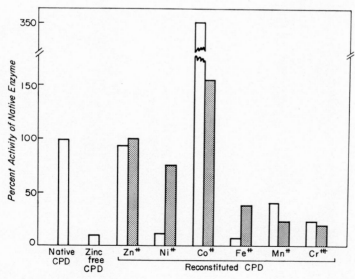

FIG. 7. Reactivation of zinc-free apocarboxypeptidase with metal ions. The peptidase activity is shown after dialysis against 1×10^{-4} M metal ions (open bars) and after further dialysis against metal-free buffer (shaded bars). (From Vallee *et al.*, 1960.)

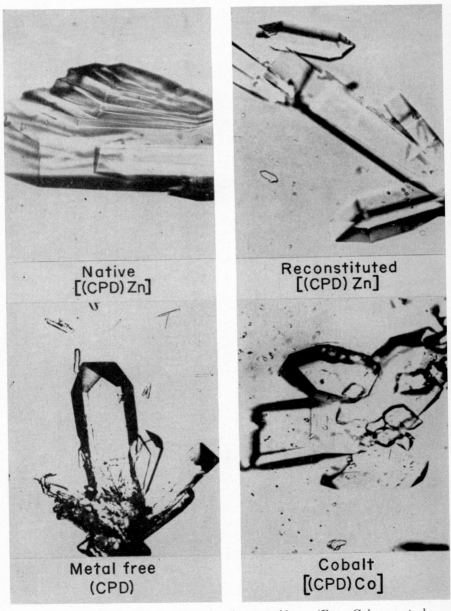

FIG. 8. Crystals of various metal carboxypeptidases. (From Coleman *et al.,* 1960.)

decrease in enzymatic activity as a function of time is exactly as predicted on the basis of the mole fraction of cobalt and zinc enzyme present at any one time (Fig. 9). The reverse reaction, i.e., the displacement of zinc by cobalt, requires dialysis against solutions of higher cobalt concentrations (100-fold molar excess), and longer periods of time, as indicated by the corresponding plots of Fig. 9, the increase in enzymatic activity being exactly as predicted from the metal composition of the mixture. It is clear, therefore, that the metals responsible for enzymatic activity, zinc and cobalt,

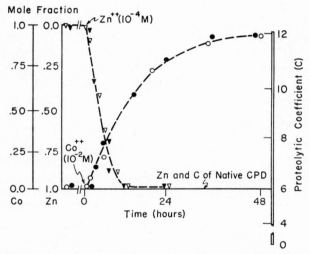

Fig. 9. Replacement of radiocobalt bound to carboxypeptidase by stable zinc and the replacement of radiozinc bound to carboxypeptidase by stable cobalt. The calculated activities are represented by the dashed lines. (From Coleman and Vallee, in press.)

are bound at the same site on the protein, which, however, is different from the site or sites responsible for the binding of extraneous, nonfunctional metal ions.

Carboxypeptidase fits the operational definition of a metalloenzyme in which one metal species bears a specific and somewhat unique relationship to the structure and function of the protein, zinc being the metal of the native enzyme. Metal-enzyme complexes, in contrast, exhibit a specific, functional relationship to several rather than one specific metal ion, and are often isolated without a metal which must be restored *in vitro* to observe catalytic activity. Since in carboxypeptidase the characteristic metal, however, can be replaced by certain other metal ions of the first transition series, this enzyme occupies an intermediate position in a hypothetical scale which extends from the metalloenzymes on one end to the metal-enzyme complexes on the other. The mutual replacement of these metals thus permits a clear differentiation of the mechanisms which operate biologically from those which are chemically possible; also, the activation by a number of metals permits a wide range of experimental approaches to the study of the functional role of the metal in enzymatic activity, and various investigative avenues, resulting from this general concept, are now being explored both at Harvard and in Seattle.

With a view toward elucidating the spatial environment and function of zinc in the structural organization of carboxypeptidase, a comparison was recently undertaken of several physical properties of metal-free and native carboxypeptidase (J. A. Rupley and H. Neurath, in press). To this end, the metal-free apoenzyme was prepared by dialysis of the native enzyme against 1,10-phenanthroline, followed by removal of the chelating agent by dialysis against buffer, and the metal-free protein was crystallized. In this as in all similar studies, special precautions were mandatory to avoid metal contamination from all solutions and glassware.

Electrophoretic analysis in the moving-boundary apparatus failed to indicate any differences in the electrophoretic mobilities of the native enzyme and of the major component of the metal-free apoenzyme, within the pH range of 6.6 to 10.5. In LiCl solutions of 0.3 ionic strength, the common isoelectric point is 5.60 (Fig. 10). The metal-free enzyme contained a minor electrophoretic component which was identified as denatured protein. It was capable of binding zinc, in the same proportions as the main component, however, without concomitant restoration of enzymatic activity. Sedimentation analysis of native and metal-free carboxypeptidase at pH 4.5 and 7.0 revealed both proteins to behave as homogeneous products with identical sedimentation constants, as shown in Fig. 11. The absence of any change in sedimentation constant upon removal of the zinc was also confirmed by analysis of native carboxypeptidase in the presence of 1,10-phenanthroline, after prior exposure to the chelating agent for times ranging from 1 hour to 7 days. No change in sedimentation behavior was observed, in contrast to similar studies with other metalloenzymes such as glutamic dehydrogenase, studied by Frieden (1958), and yeast alcohol de-

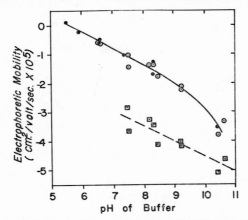

Fɪɢ. 10. Electrophoretic mobilities of native (filled circles) and metal-free (open circles) carboxypeptidase in monovalent buffers of 0.3 ionic strength. The open squares denote the minor component of the metal-free protein. (From Rupley and Neurath, in press.)

hydrogenase, studied by Kägi (1959), who, under these conditions, found dissociation of these metalloenzymes into smaller components.

Measurements of the optical rotation over a wide pH range have likewise failed to reveal significant differences between native and metal-free protein. The data shown in Fig. 12 attest to the unusually low specific levorotation and to its insensitivity to changes in pH. On the basis of the estimates of Yang and Doty (1957), carboxypeptidase, native or metal-free, would be approximately 70% in a helical configuration.

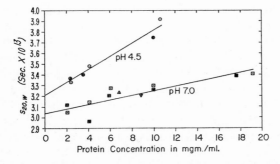

Fɪɢ. 11. Concentration dependence of the sedimentation constants of native (open symbols) and metal-free (filled symbols) carboxypeptidase at pH 7.0 and 4.5, respectively. (From Rupley and Neurath, in press.)

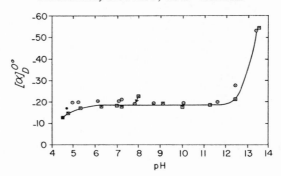

Fig. 12. Specific optical rotation of crystalline native (open symbols) and metal-free (filled symbols) carboxypeptidase, at various pH, at 0°. The solid line is drawn through the values obtained with the native enzyme. (From Rupley and Neurath, in press.)

With a further view of examining the structures of native carboxypeptidase, and of the metal-free apoenzyme, single crystals of each, in equilibrium with their mother liquor, were compared by X-ray diffraction. The two crystals were found to be essentially isomorphous to within approximately 1% change at a 6 Angstrøm unit resolution. Such changes in unit cell parameters as were observed are probably real and may be ascribed alternatively to small changes in hydration and salt content, or to a relatively larger change within a small region of the molecule. We are indebted to Dr. Joseph Kraut for the performance and interpretation of the X-ray diffraction measurements.

The measurements thus far discussed reflect the over-all structure of the protein but do not portray configurational changes which are limited to a discrete region of the structure surrounding the metal atom. It is significant, in this latter respect, that the metal-free protein fails to bind an inhibitory structural analog of a specific substrate for carboxypeptidase, i.e., phenylacetate (Elkins-Kaufman and Neurath, 1949). This compound belongs to a group of bifunctional competitive inhibitors of carboxypeptidase which contain a free carboxyl group and an aromatic or heterocyclic ring (Neurath and Schwert, 1950). Equilibrium dialysis measurements with native and metal-free carboxypeptidase, respectively, and C^{14}-phenylacetate are presented in Fig. 13 which shows that the apoenzyme does not bind phenylacetate to any significant extent, whereas the binding by the native enzyme is of the order to be expected from kinetic studies if one mole or inhibitor were max-

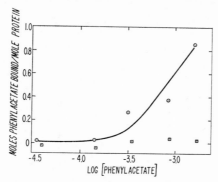

FIG. 13. A plot of the moles of phenylacetate-1-C[14] bound per mole of crystalline native (O) and metal-free (□) carboxypeptidase as a function of the logarithm of the phenylacetate concentration, at 0°. (From Rupley and Neurath, in press.)

imally bound per mole of enzyme. On this basis, the dissociation constant is 0.8×10^{-3} M at 0° as compared to 0.4×10^{-3} M previously obtained at 25° from inhibition studies (Elkins-Kaufman and Neurath, 1949).

This all-or-none difference in behavior toward phenylacetate suggests that in native carboxypeptidase the metal either coordinates with the inhibitor, or confers a configuration to the enzyme which is essential for the formation of the protein-inhibitor complex. No decision between these alternatives can be made on the basis of the present data. However, regardless of interpretation, these findings strongly suggest that in carboxypeptidase the metal may not only contribute to the catalytic step but is also essential for the formation of the enzyme-substrate complex.

The metal-free apoenzyme shows one additional characteristic which differentiates it chemically from the native enzyme, i.e., a greater susceptibility to denaturation. This has been observed in the half-times of denaturation in the alkaline pH region, above pH 10, and in the appearance of a second electrophoretic component, previously alluded to. In this respect, carboxypeptidase is similar to other metalloenzymes such as the α-amylase from *Bacillus subtilis* (Fischer *et al.*, 1959).

No information is yet at hand to delineate the nature of the group or groups on the protein involved in the binding of zinc. The circumstance that activity results only from the interaction of the apoenzyme with zinc and certain transition elements suggests the participation of sulphur or nitrogenous ligand groups for which these elements show a marked preference (Williams, 1959). The effects of carefully controlled modifications of the apoenzyme on its recombination with metal, and on the restoration of enzymatic activity, are now being explored toward an elucidation of this problem. The effects of limited proteolysis on the activity of the native enzyme, and on the recombination of the apoenzyme with the metal, are other experimental approaches now in progress.

Summary

Recent evidence concerning the relation of structure and function of pancreatic carboxypeptidase A has been reviewed. The enzyme occurs in the exocellular secretions of bovine and canine pancreas as procarboxypeptidase, which is the zymogen for carboxypeptidase as well as for an endopeptidase. Native carboxypeptidase is a zinc metalloenzyme, removal of zinc resulting in a proportionate loss of metal and of enzymatic activity. Activity can be restored to the metal-free apoenzyme by the addition of zinc and certain other ions of the first transition series, leading to the formation of various crystallizable metalloenzymes, each containing one gram atom of metal per mole of protein.

Metal-free apocarboxypeptidase is indistinguishable from the native enzyme in electrophoresis, sedimentation, optical rotation and single-crystal X-ray analysis. However, it is more susceptible to denaturation and, even more significantly, it fails to bind the competitive inhibitor of the native enzyme, phenylacetate. These experimental findings are related to the functional role of the metal in carboxypeptidase.

REFERENCES

Ando, T., Fujioka, H., and Kawanishi, Y. (1959). *Biochim. et Biophys. Acta* **34**, 296.

Anson, M. L. (1937). *J. Gen. Physiol.* **20**, 663.

Coleman, J. E., and Vallee, B. L. (1960). *J. Biol. Chem.*, in press.

Coleman, J. E., Allan, B. J., and Vallee, B. L. (1960). *Science* **131**, 350.

Elkins-Kaufman, E., and Neurath, H. (1949). *J. Biol. Chem.* **178**, 645.

Fischer, E. H., Sumerwell, W., Junge, B., and Stein, E. A. (1959). *In* "Symposium on Proteins, IVth International Congress of Biochemistry." Pergamon Press, New York.

Frieden, C. (1958). *Biochim. et Biophys. Acta* **21**, 431.

Green, N. M., and Neurath, H. (1954). *In* "The Proteins" (H. Neurath and K. Bailey, eds.), Vol. II, p. 1057. Academic Press, New York.

Greenstein, J. P. (1954). *Advances in Protein Chem.* **9**, 121.

Greenstein, J. P. (1956). *In* "Cancer and Biochemistry." Japanese Biochem. Soc., p. 1.

Harris, I. J. (1955). *Chem. Soc.* (London), *Spec. Publ.* No. **2**, p. 71.

Kägi, J. H. R. (1959). *Federation Proc.* **18**, 484.

Keller, P. J., Cohen, E., and Neurath, H. (1956). *J. Biol. Chem.* **223**, 457.

Keller, P. J., Cohen, E., and Neurath, H. (1958a). *J. Biol. Chem.* **230**, 905.

Keller, P. J., Cohen, E., and Neurath, H. (1958b). *J. Biol. Chem.* **233**, 344.

Keller, P. J., Cohen, E., and Neurath, H. (1959). *J. Biol. Chem.* **234**, 311.

Neurath, H. (1955). *Discussions Faraday Soc.* **20**, 257.

Neurath, H., and Schwert, G. W. (1950). *Chem. Revs.* **46**, 69.

Neurath, H., Gladner, J. A., and Davie, E. W. (1954). *In* "The Mechanism of Enzyme Action" (W. D. McElroy and B. Glass, eds.), p. 50. Johns Hopkins Press, Baltimore, Maryland.

Neurath, H. (1957). *Advances in Protein Chem.* **12**, 319.

Putnam, F. W., and Neurath, H. (1946). *J. Biol. Chem.* **166**, 603.

Rupley, J. A., and Neurath, H. (1960). *J. Biol. Chem.*, in press.

Smith, E. L. (1951). *In* "The Enzymes" (J. B. Sumner and K. Myrbäck, eds.), Vol. I, p. 793. Academic Press, New York.

Smith, E. L., and Stockell, A. (1954). *J. Biol. Chem.* **207**, 501.

Thompson, E. O. P. (1953). *Biochim. et Biophys. Acta* **10**, 633.

Vallee, B. L., and Neurath, H. (1954). *J. Am. Chem. Soc.* **76**, 5006.

Vallee, B. L., and Neurath, H. (1955). *J. Biol. Chem.* **217**, 253.

Vallee, B. L., Rupley, J. A., Coombs, T. L., and Neurath, H. (1958). *J. Am. Chem. Soc.* **80**, 4750.

Vallee, B. L., Rupley, J. A., Coombs, T. L., and Neurath, H. (1960). *J. Biol. Chem.* **235**, 64.

Williams, R. J. P. (1959). *In* "The Enzymes" (P. D. Boyer, H. Lardy, and K. Myrbäck, eds.), 2nd ed., Vol. I, p. 391. Academic Press, New York.

Yang, J. T., and Doty, P. (1957). *J. Am. Chem. Soc.* **79**, 761.

Chromatographic Evaluation of Protein Mixtures

HERBERT A. SOBER and ELBERT A. PETERSON

Laboratory of Biochemistry, National Cancer Institute, National Institutes of Health, Public Health Service, U.S. Department of Health, Education and Welfare, Bethesda, Maryland

We FEEL IT TO BE particularly appropriate that the chromatographic evaluation of protein mixtures be discussed at this Jesse P. Greenstein Memorial Symposium. His interest in enzymes as molecular parameters in disease and as preparative and analytical reagents, his insistence on the most rigorous scrutiny of the purity of all "biochemical reagents," his enthusiasm for the development of new approaches, and the stimulation and encouragement which he gave generously made it possible for us to explore this field at a time when it was beset with difficulties.

As these were overcome, the utilization of chromatographic techniques for the separation of protein mixtures steadily increased, despite a lack of concrete information concerning the factors involved in the discrimination between protein components. As a result of the high resolving power now attainable, we are being confronted with an ever-increasing number of specific biological and biochemical activities which apparently reside in macromolecules with different physical and chemical properties. In each case, consideration must be given to the verification of the indicated chromatographic differences and their interpretation in terms of molecular differences. The chromatographic heterogeneity observed may be of considerable biological interest or it may be superficial, in that minor and biologically insignificant differences were responsible for the chromatographic distinctions. Heterogeneity introduced as a result of experimental procedures employed in isolation is another possibility that must be taken into account.

Evaluation of the biological significance of observed heterogeneity is a matter of conducting special investigations designed for the particular case. On the other hand, the validation of chromatographically detected heterogeneity and its interpretation in molecular terms are considerably aided by a general knowledge of the mechanisms involved and the factors influencing the separation. With such knowledge, experiments can be designed to minimize or eliminate artifactitious heterogeneity, and important clues as to the molecular characteristics of the established components can be derived.

Progress in the chromatographic fractionation of proteins has depended upon the selection of adsorbents having properties somewhat different from those usually employed in the chromatography of smaller molecules. With few exceptions, the successful adsorbents have been ion exchangers, but organic ion exchange resins have failed to qualify as generally useful adsorbents in spite of the remarkable success attained in certain cases with Amberlite IRC-50 (or XE-64), a carboxyl-containing resin (Moore and Stein, 1956).

Perhaps the most important limitation of the resins is their irreversible binding of many proteins. In some cases this may be due to a denaturation of the protein on the surface of the resin, but, in general, it is probably the result of the formation of too many bonds with the adsorbent, so many that simultaneous dissociation of all does not occur except under conditions destructive to the native configuration of the molecule. Presumably, these bonds are electrostatic in nature, but van der Waals' forces and hydrogen bonding undoubtedly are also involved. It is to be anticipated, moreover, that some proteins, initially adsorbed by electrostatic forces, might tend to become denatured by a subsequent van der Waals' bonding of amino acid side chains to lipophilic regions on the surface of the adsorbent, with a concomitant opening of noncovalent bonds. The lability of the secondary and tertiary structure of the protein is an important factor and one which varies over a wide range.

These considerations have led to the development of two substantially different types of adsorbent for the chromatography of typical proteins: calcium phosphate gels and cellulosic ion exchangers. Although both types offer the advantages of a large, well hydrated surface, and ionic interaction appears to be the major adsorptive process in each, their chromatographic selectivity for proteins is fortunately not the same. Both appear to have general applicability.

Calcium phosphate gels have for some time been widely used in the purification of enzymes by batch procedures, but, in column work, the extremely high resistance imposed by such materials to the flow of aqueous buffers has been a serious handicap. However, higher flow rates have been made possible by mixing the gel with Super-Cel (Swingle and Tiselius, 1951) or by forming the gel in the presence of cellulose (Price and Greenfield, 1954; Black and Wright, 1955). Recently, methods have been developed for the preparation of calcium phosphate in forms [brushite (Tiselius, 1954) or hydroxylapatite (Tiselius et al., 1956)], which permit adequate flow without the addition of a filter aid.

The cellulosic adsorbents (Fig. 1) are available as either anion

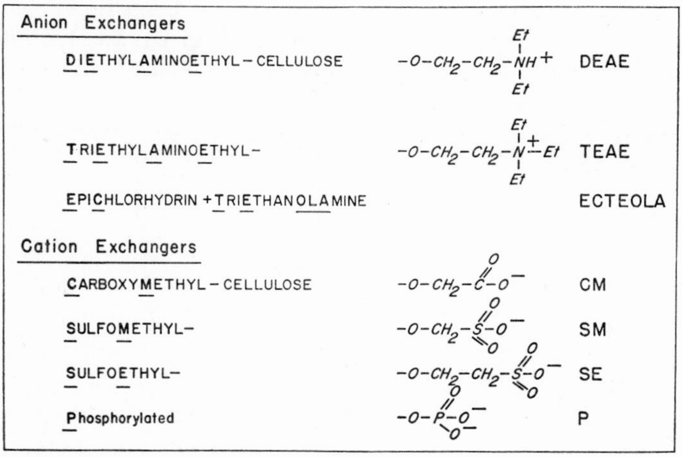

FIG. 1. Diagrammatic representation of the cellulosic ion exchangers.

or cation exchangers (Peterson and Sober, 1956) and both types have been used (Peterson and Sober, 1960; Sober et al., 1956; Sober and Peterson, 1958). Sulfomethylcellulose (SM), sulfoethylcellulose (SE), and triethylaminoethylcellulose (TEAE) are promising adsorbents, introduced by Porath (1957), that retain their charges at more extreme pH values.

General Considerations of Mechanism

Although basic studies of the adsorption of proteins on ion exchange surfaces are lacking, the formation of multiple electrostatic bonds between the protein and the adsorbent is undoubtedly involved (Boardman and Partridge, 1955; Moore and Stein, 1956; Peterson and Sober, 1956). Both the protein and the ion exchanger are polyelectrolytes, and they are therefore capable of interacting at several points, provided intercharge distances are favorable. Moreover, experience shows that the adsorbed protein is more tightly bound than a singly charged substance under the same conditions but can be eluted from a suitable ion exchanger if the pH is changed to reduce the number of charges on the protein or adsorbent, or if the salt concentration is raised to compete for the existing charges. In accord with the concept of multiple bonding is the observation that a homologous series of polynucleotides emerges from a cellulosic anion exchange column in the order of increasing size (Tener *et al.*, 1958; Staehelin *et al.*, 1959).

In Fig. 2 is shown a chromatogram of a digest resulting from the exhaustive hydrolysis of polyadenylic acid by an *Azotobacter* enzyme of Stevens and Hilmoe (1959). Partial hydrolysis experi-

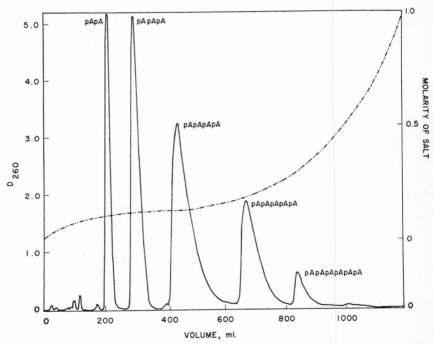

Fig. 2. Chromatographic separation of oligonucleotides. DEAE-cellulose (230-325 mesh, 0.9 meq. N per gm.), 0.9 × 30 cm. Eluted with concave gradient from 0.01 M NH$_4$-bicarbonate (adjusted to pH 8.6 with NH$_4$OH) to 1.0 M NH$_4$-bicarbonate (pH 8.6 when diluted M/20). Temp., 5°. Solid line, D$_{260}$; broken line, salt molarity. (From Staehelin *et al.*, 1959.)

ments yielded a chromatogram which showed no di- or tri-nucleotide, small amounts of tetra- and penta-nucleotide, and considerable amounts of incompletely resolved higher homologs. Thus, the separation of the digestion products on the basis of molecular size enabled these authors to conclude that larger fragments of the polynucleotide chain were produced first and were subsequently degraded to smaller units.

The conditions required for elution of a given molecule from a given adsorbent depend upon the number of bonds that can be formed between them. Therefore, a molecule having the same net surface charge density as another (and hence a similar electrophoretic mobility) but exceeding it significantly in size, would require a stronger eluting condition because it would be capable of forming more bonds with the adsorbent. Similarly, proteins with appreciably different net surface charge densities might emerge from the column at the same position because of compensating differences in size. Moreover, the spatial arrangement of ionizable groups on the molecule can be expected to be a factor in their effectiveness in establishing bonds with the adsorbent. Consequently, a simple relationship between elution conditions and electrophoretic mobility will not always be maintained, even at constant pH. The numerous departures from correspondence with electrophoretic order that have been observed (Fahey *et al.*, 1958; Hjertén, 1959; Sober *et al.*, 1956) actually enhance the usefulness of chromatography, for subsequent electrophoresis of the eluted fractions provides resolution not otherwise attainable. Whether nonionic binding forces contribute to the observed departures, even on ion exchange surfaces, has not yet been established, but their participation is not unlikely.

Figure 3 demonstrates the electrophoretic characterization of a consecutive series of fractions from a serum chromatogram. On the whole, there is a trend toward higher electrophoretic mobilities in successive fractions, as one would expect if ion exchange were playing a dominant role. The proteins with high isoelectric points (the γ-globulins) lose their negative character earlier than those with lower ones as the eluting solution becomes more acid. However, the fractions emerging in the last third of the chromatogram, after the major albumin peak, are complex electrophoretically, and some include proteins representing every electrophoretic category.

When a mixture of proteins in an appropriate buffer is applied to an ion exchange column, some of the proteins become tightly

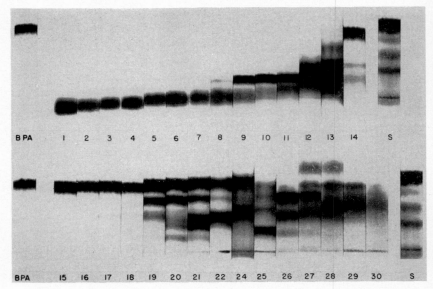

Fig. 3. Paper electrophoretic patterns from fractions of a serum chromato-gram. Concentrated fractions (0.01-0.03 ml.) in 0.075 μ veronal, pH 8.6, on Whatman 3 MM at 6 milliamps and 8 strips per cell, 68-72 volts at room temperature. Strips stained with bromphenol blue. Control strips with un-fractionated serum (S) and bovine plasma albumin (BPA) were run in each cell. The numbers refer to the fractions of Fig. 5.

bound to the exchanger through the formation of many electrostatic bonds. These proteins will not move so long as the initial con-ditions are maintained. Other protein components of the mixture, because they lack sufficient charges of appropriate sign to form multiple bonds with the exchanger, move through the column without being retarded.

A third group of proteins may possess charges in such number and sign that under the existing conditions, the number of electro-static bonds formed with the adsorbent permits a reasonable probability, at a given instant, for the simultaneous dissociation of all those restraining a given molecule. At the moment of release the molecule moves, only to be held again at another site as electrostatic bonds are momentarily reestablished. Such molecules are undergoing "true chromatography," which depends upon a series of successive adsorptive and desorptive processes for its high resolving potential. The rate of migration is, then, determined by the instantaneous probability of such release, and differences in this probability (in turn dependent upon the number and sign of the charges as well as their extension in space) are the basis for the differential migration of those proteins under fixed conditions. These molecules can be said to be in finite equilibrium with the adsorbent.

After the initial moving bands have emerged from the column, a suitable increase in the eluting power of the buffer will result in the movement of some of the proteins which were initially immobilized. If the change in eluting power is a continuous one, the bound proteins will be exposed to conditions increasingly favorable for simultaneous dissociation of the restraining bonds, and when the instantaneous probability for the occurrence of this event reaches a reasonable value, noticeable movement of the band results. In its early stages this movement is actually a widening of a still immobile band, presumably because some of the binding sites require a somewhat lower eluting condition than others, and the protein released from these sites is bound tightly at more densely charged sites below them. However, as the eluting power of the mobile phase increases, a point is reached where the requirements of all the sites are satisfied and the band moves slowly down the column. Because the movement of the liquid phase is faster than that of the band, the eluting power of the liquid environment of the protein band is constantly increasing, with a consequent acceleration of the band movement. Ultimately, if the column is long enough, the band will move at the same rate as the mobile phase when the eluting power of its milieu is such as to make the instantaneous probability of simultaneous dissociation of all the restraining bonds equal to unity.

If the change in eluting power is not a continuous one, a situation will be created resembling that described for the initial application of the sample. Some of the proteins will move with the new eluent front, some more slowly than the eluent, and the rest will remain immobile.

Stepwise Elution

An example of a discontinuous procedure is provided in Fig. 4 which shows the separation of egg white proteins on the cation exchanger, CM-cellulose (Rhodes *et al.*, 1958). These authors found that stepwise elution, in this case, gave better results than elution with the gradients they tried. In all cases, the proteins were eluted in the order of and near their reported isoelectric points.

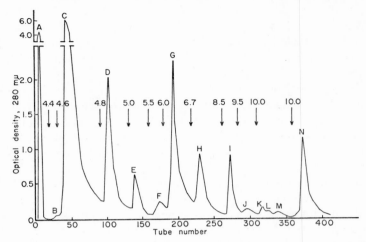

FIG. 4. Separation of egg-white proteins. Dialyzed egg-white (30 ml.) on a 2.2 × 14.0 cm. column of CM-cellulose. Fractions (15 ml.) collected at a rate of 2.5 ml. per min. Eluting buffer was 0.1 M NH$_4$-acetate with stepwise changes in pH as indicated by the *arrows*. In addition, 0.025 M Na$_2$CO$_3$ was added at tube 310 and 0.2 M Na$_2$CO$_3$ at tube 359. Room temperature. Peaks identified as follows: A, mixture of ovomucoid and flavoprotein; B, ovomucoid; C, ovalbumin A_1; D, ovalbumin A_2; E, ovalbumin A_3; G and H, conalbumin; L, avidin; N, lysozyme; F, I, J, K, unidentified "globulins." (From Rhodes *et al.*, 1958.)

Ovalbumin A_1 and A_2 (peaks C and D) were electrophoretically homogeneous after crystallization. The avidin peak, L, contained small amounts of other egg white proteins as measured by specific assay.

However, resolution can generally be expected to be less than that attainable by gradient elution, because stepwise elution of a complex mixture of proteins is likely to be predominantly a single stage process, rather than the multistage process which is characteristic of what might be called "true chromatography" and is responsible for the high resolving power achieved in many chromatographic systems. The application of each new eluent results in the more or less simultaneous desorption of all the proteins having elution requirements in the range between the new eluent and the preceding one. However, a few components may have properties which result in their being in finite adsorption equilibrium with the adsorbent under the new conditions, and these will move down the column at different rates, permitting separation. (Note peaks

K, L, Fig. 4.) Unfortunately, the concomitant widening (and often tailing) of such a slowly moving band may result in its appearance in two peaks if the next change of eluent is injudiciously made (Alm *et al.,* 1952), which may have been the case with peaks *G* and *H,* both of which were identified as conalbumin, and *I* and *J* which were labeled "globulin." Moreover, the change in conditions may have reduced the capacity of the adsorbent for some of the proteins which remain "tightly" adsorbed, so their bands may widen. If the column is too small, this increase in the width of the bands may result in the spilling over of some of the leading component into the effluent under conditions in which the rest of that protein remains firmly bound to the column. This can be clearly seen in the behavior of the colored bands resulting from the application of an excessive quantity of human serum protein to a small column of DEAE-cellulose. A similar effect with serum albumin on Dowex-2 has been reported by Boman and Westlund (1956).

Thus, artifactitious distribution of protein can occur as the result of either premature application of new eluent or the initial application of a given protein in an amount exceeding the capacity of the adsorbent for that protein under conditions just inadequate for elution.

However, when relatively simple mixtures are chromatographed, it is possible to devise stepwise elution schedules that provide, at appropriate times, conditions under which components are released from the column separately. This may include the favorable situation in which two or more protein species, in finite equilibrium with the adsorbent under the conditions imposed by one of the eluents, move simultaneously down the column at rates sufficiently different to effect separation.

Gradient Elution

An inclusive scan of complex mixtures in which all the protein is distributed into as many chromatographically distinct peaks as possible by a single passage through a column is of value in investigations where the nature of the protein or proteins involved may be unknown, as in the study of normal transport mechanisms or in the examination of pathological sera for quantitative or qualitative abnormalities (Reisfeld *et al.,* 1959). It has the advantage of permitting the examination of all the proteins that may be involved in a complex system and is potentially capable of revealing molecular heterogeneity in the agents responsible for a given biological activity. Such a scan will usually require gradient elution in order to obtain reliable detection of unknown components as peaks in a protein profile.

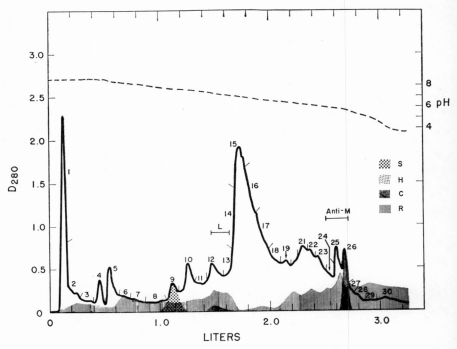

Fig. 5. Effluent diagram of normal human serum. Pooled, clarified serum (30 ml., 2 gm. protein) applied to 25 gm. DEAE-cellulose (1.0 meq. N per gm.; finer than 325 mesh). Eluted with concave gradient from "Tris" phosphate, pH 8.6 (0.005 M in phosphate), to 0.35 M "Tris" H_2PO_4. Flow rate 35 ml. per hr. Temp., 5°. L represents lipoprotein; S, siderophilin; H, absorption at 405 mμ; and C, ceruloplasmin distribution. "Anti-M" designates the location of that blood group factor. R is a plot of the ratio of carbohydrate to absorption at 280 mμ as a measure of carbohydrate content per unit of protein.

In Fig. 5 is shown a chromatogram of normal human serum protein eluted by a gradient of increasing molarity and decreasing pH that was selected to produce a relatively uniform distribution of the protein within the arbitrary limits of the buffer volume employed. Fractions 1-7 contained only γ-globulins with progressively increasing mobilities, as evidenced by paper electrophoresis (see Fig. 3). The shaded area at Fraction 9 represents siderophilin (S), the ironbinding β-globulin. Lipoprotein (L) was found in Fractions 12 and 13. Albumin was by far the major component of the large peak (Fractions 14-18). The peak of 405 mμ adsorption (H, at Fraction 12) is due to the presence of a complex of hemoglobin with haptoglobin, an α_2-globulin. The shaded area at Fraction 26 represents ceruloplasmin (C), a blue copper-containing α_2-globulin. A number of other proteins have been localized in such chromatograms (Sober $et\ al.$, 1956; Peterson and Sober, 1960).

Protein having electrophoretic mobility in the albumin range appears in fractions covering a wide section of the chromatogram (see Fig. 3). It is likely that a high degree of heterogeneity is responsible for this behavior, rather than an inherent difficulty in the chromatography of albumin, $per\ se$. That complexes of albumin with fatty acids and other small molecules may account for much of this heterogeneity is suggested by the observation, in this Laboratory, that the addition of oleic acid to serum or to purified mercaptalbumin results in the formation of a number of overlapping chromatographic components having higher affinity than the original albumin for the adsorbent. This indicates, moreover, the need for avoiding the contact of serum protein with extraneous sources of lipid, such as stopcock grease. Recently, progressive changes of a similar nature occurred upon repeated rechromatography of fractions, under the original conditions (Sober and Peterson, 1958). Except for one peak, the rechromatographed fractions emerged in their original positions. The anomalous fraction, consisting almost entirely of albumin, did show increased retardation on rechromatography. This has been traced to an unknown, presumably lipid, substance contaminating the cellophane membranes used for dialysis between experiments. The effect is shown in Fig. 6 where highly purified mercaptalbumin showed this altered chromatographic behavior after extensive dialysis.

Albumin has yielded multiple peaks when chromatographed on Dowex 2 (Boman, 1955) and on calcium phosphate (Tiselius $et\ al.$, 1956). In the latter case, the validity of the three components obtained by stepwise elution of bovine serum albumin was established by rechromatography.

A suitably designed gradient brings the tightly bound proteins gradually into adsorption equilibrium by reducing the number of attracting charges on the protein through a change in pH or by

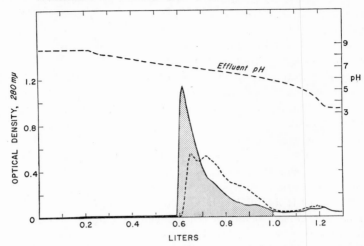

FIG. 6. Effect of exhaustive dialysis on the chromatographic behavior of purified human mercaptalbumin. DEAE-cellulose (0.9 meq. N per gm.; 100–230 mesh). Eluted with concave gradient from 0.005 M "Tris" phosphate, pH 8.6, to 0.5 M "Tris" H_2PO_4; flow rate 45 ml. per hour. Temp. 5°. Solid line presents pattern obtained with fresh mercaptalbumin; broken line gives that obtained upon rechromatography of the shaded fractions after dialysis vs. the pH 8.6 buffer for 54 hours at 5°.

promoting the dissociation of existing bonds as a result of increasing salt concentration. At times, it is advantageous to change *both* simultaneously in order to reduce the required range of each. The fraction of the total migration which occurs under conditions of adsorption equilibrium will be determined by the gradient, for the more rapid the increase in eluting power during the migration, the quicker the attainment of conditions which prevent further readsorption.

When two or more substances are chromatographed under conditions of finite adsorption equilibrium with an eluent of constant composition, increasing the length of the adsorbent column will improve the separation. This is not necessarily true, however, when gradient elution is employed. An increase in column length will effect no improvement if the gradient is such that the milieu of the bands emerging from the shorter column prevents readsorption. If, on the other hand, the gradient is adjusted to permit the use of a longer portion of the column in multistage adsorption, an improvement in resolution can be expected. For an inclusive scan, the most effective gradient can be considered to be one which is relatively flat in regions where many proteins having similar affinities for the adsorbent are eluted and steep where the affinities of the migrating proteins are widely different. The elution requirements of the individual protein components are distributed differently in different mixtures, and the shapes of the appropriate gradients vary accordingly. For some purposes, a simple linear (Parr, 1954) or exponential gradient (Alm *et al.*, 1952; Bock and Ling, 1954) is satisfactory, but an inclusive scan of a complex mixture of proteins such as whole serum is likely to require a compound gradient. In any case, the most suitable gradient for a given mixture can be determined only by a series of chromatographic trials, and this process is greatly aided by the use of devices which permit small, systematic changes in the gradient (Peterson and Sober, 1959).

The usefulness of gradient elution is not restricted to inclusive scans of complex mixtures. In the last stages of purification of a given protein, the remaining impurities are likely to resemble the protein of interest so closely as to make conditions for separation extremely critical. Stepwise elution, in this case, may be too coarse a procedure to provide an unambiguous separation. Gradient elution, on the other hand, not only automatically encompasses the elution requirements of the mixture, but does so in a manner which permits a less equivocal interpretation of evidence of heterogeneity.

For an example of the separation of very similar proteins, let us again turn to albumin. Radioiodine-labeled albumin has become an important research tool for the determination of the rate of metabolic breakdown of albumin, and such use is based on the assumption that the labeled protein which is administered is degraded at the same rate as the endogenous protein. However, it has been demonstrated (Fahey and Steinfeld, 1958) that the radioactive label and the albumin, determined electrophoretically, do not coincide when chromatographed on a cellulosic anion exchanger. That this discrepancy is largely a result of self-irradiation is shown very nicely in Fig. 7 (Cohen, 1959). Trace amounts of labeled, chromatographically purified albumin were added to human serum after storage for 7, 14, and 22 days to provide self-irradiation doses of 44, 68, and 85 kilo rads., respectively. Note that protein and radioactivity coincide in the fresh sample.

A rather impressive example of heterogeneity is shown in Fig. 8, which presents the chromatographic pattern obtained from ammonium sulfate-fractionated, lyophilized horse hemoglobin, on the cation exchange adsorbent. This degree of complexity is artifacti-

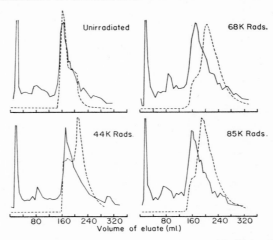

Fig. 7. Effect of irradiation on the chromatographic behavior of human albumin labeled with iodine-131 and prepared by chromatography. Tracer amounts of the labeled solution which contained 650 μc. I^{131} per ml. and 2.5 mg. albumin per ml. were added to normal human serum immediately after iodination and after storage for 7, 14, and 22 days, which provided self-irradiation doses of 44 k. rads, 68 k. rads, and 85 k. rads, respectively. The analysis was performed on DEAE-cellulose columns with 0.005 M phosphate buffer, pH 7.1, using gradient elution to 0.30 M NaH$_2$PO$_4$. Protein distribution is indicated by solid lines and radioactivity by broken lines. (From Cohen, 1959.)

tious; clearly a result of the isolation procedure and storage, since unpurified hemoglobin from freshly lysed cells presents a much simpler picture (Gutter et al., 1959). However, no apparent differences in the effluent fractions could be found by spectrophotometric, electrophoretic, and ultracentrifugal techniques.

On the other hand, it is well known that slightly altered hemoglobins (Itano, 1957) occur in various diseases, some of them genetically determined. It is clear, moreover, that even normal hemoglobin is not homogeneous, an observation reported from several laboratories (Kunkel and Wallenius, 1955; Morrison and Cook, 1955) and based on results obtained with different techniques. The subunit structure of hemoglobin is now generally accepted (Singer and Itano, 1959; Vinograd and Hutchinson, 1959) and a dissociation-association equilibrium of these subunits (Field and O'Brien, 1955; Gutter et al., 1956, 1957) would serve to explain some of the chromatographic heterogeneity observed.

That the forces maintaining the integrity of the hemoglobin

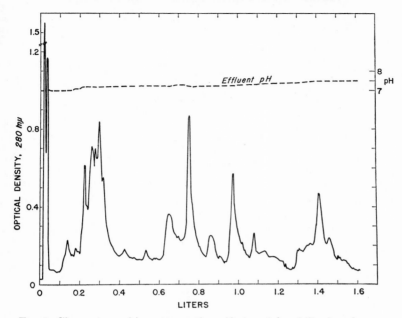

FIG. 8. Chromatographic pattern of purified and lyophilized carbon monoxide horse hemoglobin. CM-cellulose (0.7 meq. per gm.; finer than 325 mesh). Eluted with pH gradient (7.0 to 7.6) at constant molarity of phosphate (0.01 M); flow rate 4 ml. per hour. Temp., 5°.

molecule vary with the species has been indicated by sedimentation experiments in 4 M urea wherein it was found that horse hemoglobin dissociates into smaller units, human hemoglobin merely unfolds, and dog hemoglobin is essentially unchanged (Gutter *et al.*, 1959). The species difference in hemoglobin can be shown in another way. Figure 9 provides a chromatographic comparison of unpurified human and horse hemoglobins. Unlike the human COHb, which gave a simpler pattern, horse carbon monoxide hemoglobin showed a marked increase in heterogeneity when chromatographed at room temperature. Whereas the components obtained at 5°, the upper pair, were electrophoretically distinguishable, absorption spectra and sedimentation studies revealed no differences between material applied to the column and fractions obtained after chromatographic separation. However, differences in sedimentation rate between eluted components were observed if the components were subsequently exposed to 4 M urea or when chromatography was performed in the presence of urea.

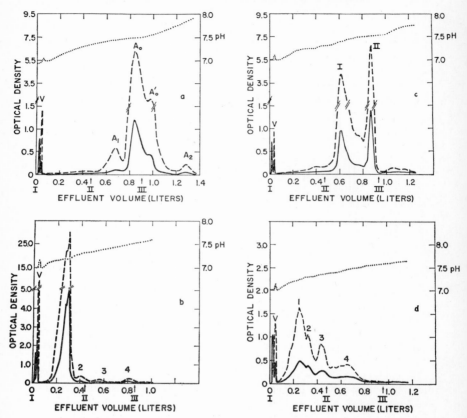

Fig. 9. Effluent diagrams of normal adult human and horse carbon monoxide hemoglobin (COHb). One hundred mg. applied to 50×0.9 cm. CM-cellulose (8 gm., 0.72 meq. per gm., finer than 325 mesh). Flow rate 7–9 ml. per hr. Starting buffer: 0.01 M Na-phosphate, pH 7.0, in 200 ml. mixing chamber. I, gradient to 0.01 M Na-phosphate, pH 7.3; II, gradient to 0.01 M Na-phosphate, pH 7.5; III, gradient to 0.01 M NaH$_2$PO$_4$. Solid line, D$_{280}$; broken line, D$_{420}$; dotted line, effluent pH.

    a: Human COHb at 5°, b: human COHb at 25°, c: horse COHb at 5°, and d: horse COHB at 25°. (From Gutter *et al.*, 1959.)

The chromatographic pattern of horse hemoglobin in urea was considerably more complex than in the absence of urea. Moreover, significantly different sedimentation values, as low as 2.6, were obtained for several peaks in this medium (Table I), whereas unfractionated material gave values of 3.2. Absorption spectra were still indistinguishable. Human hemoglobin in urea showed less ex-

TABLE I[a]

SEDIMENTATION COEFFICIENTS OF FRACTIONS OF HORSE, HUMAN, AND DOG COHb OBTAINED BY CHROMATOGRAPHY IN 4 M UREA[b]

	Horse			Human			Dog	
Chromatographic peak	Chromatographic effluent pH	$S_{20,w} \times 10^{13c,d}$	Chromatographic peak	Chromatographic effluent pH	$S_{20,w} \times 10^{13c,d}$	Chromatographic peak	Chromatographic effluent pH	$S_{20,w} \times 10^{13c,d}$
Before chromatography V	—	3.2	Before chromatography 3	—	3.3	Before chromatography	—	3.9
	7.17	3.2		7.52	3.3	Major component	7.43	3.7
2	7.24	3.7	4	7.76	4.3	Minor component	7.57	3.6
3	7.32	3.4	5	7.87	3.5			
4	7.49	3.3						
5	7.59	2.6						
6	7.79	2.6						
7	7.84	2.8						
8	7.95	3.1						
Weighted av. of all fractions	—	3.1						

[a] From Gutter et al. (1959).
[b] All fractions were concentrated by ultrafiltration to 0.2% Hb before sedimentation.
[c] All fractions were dialyzed overnight against 100 volumes of the following buffer before sedimentation studies were performed: 0.0238M K$_2$HPO$_4$—0.0287M KH$_2$PO$_4$—4M urea, pH 7.0.
[d] $S_{20,w}$ values are significant to ±0.1 S unit.

tensive change. The sedimentation constant of the unfractionated hemoglobin in urea, as well as those of peaks 3 and 5, was lowered to 3.3. However, the sedimentation constant for peak 4 remained at 4.3, the value for native hemoglobin, indicating resistance of part of the hemoglobin even to a change in shape. Dog hemoglobin was relatively homogeneous when chromatographed in 4 M urea. Thus chromatographic evidence paralleled that obtained in sedimentation studies with respect to the relative susceptibilities of the three species to dissociation by urea.

The nature and origin of the heterogeneity found in normal hemoglobin is still obscure, although its validity is well established. The normal components observed may be genetically determined and may all exist together within the red cell, or they may exist separately in different cells as a consequence of different sites of origin or varying ages of the circulating red blood cells. This is now amenable to investigation since techniques are available for the differential lysis of cells (Sterling *et al.*, 1958). On the other hand, the heterogeneity observed might be the result of changes in a single native molecule, presumably occurring *after* lysis of the cell. Chemical examination of the isolated individual components would be of crucial importance in evaluating such an explanation.

The chromatography of proteins is becoming an increasingly useful tool in the study of enzymes. An interesting interaction relationship of two proteins catalyzing the final step in tryptophan biosynthesis in *Escherichia coli*, reported by Crawford and Yanofsky (1958), is shown in Fig. 10. These proteins, A and B, apparently form a complex with new catalytic as well as chromatographic properties. Since neither was active alone in the conversion of indole + serine to tryptophan, A was assayed in the presence of an excess of B, and B in an excess of A.

Chromatography of partially purified tryptophan synthetase (TSase) on DEAE-cellulose, employing a gradient of NaCl resulted in the pattern shown in section A of the figure. The position of the active complex at 17 was revealed by assay without additions. The presence of component A at 8 and component B at 21 was made evident by addition of the complementary component to the assay medium. The appearance of a small additional A peak at 4 was variable and may have resulted from overloading with respect to A. Rechromatography of the fractions containing the active complex (16-19) demonstrated its partial dissociation into components A and B, as shown in section C, and mixing the chro-

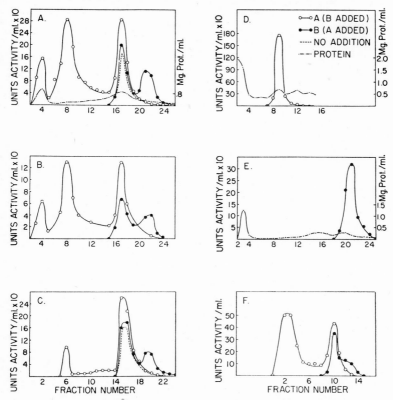

Fig. 10. Chromatography of partially purified *Escherichia coli* preparations on DEAE-cellulose. Gradient from 0.01 M K-phosphate, pH 7, to same buffer made 0.5 M in NaCl. (A) T-3 tryptophan synthetase (TSase) assayed by indole → tryptophan. (B) T-3 TSase assayed by indoleglycerol phosphate → tryptophan. (C) Rechromatography of center (combined) peak fractions. (D) Partially purified T-3 component A. (E) Partially purified T-8 component B. (F) Mixture of chromatographically purified T-3 component A and T-8 component B. C-F assayed by indole → tryptophan. (From Crawford and Yanofsky, 1958.)

matographically purified (sections D and E) components resulted in the formation of the active complex, as seen in section F.

Another very interesting example of a different type of enzymatic heterogeneity can be drawn from some work done in conjunction with Dr. Maver (see Maver *et al.*, 1959). Nuclease preparations purified by conventional fractionation techniques produced, when examined chromatographically, the pattern shown in Fig. 11.

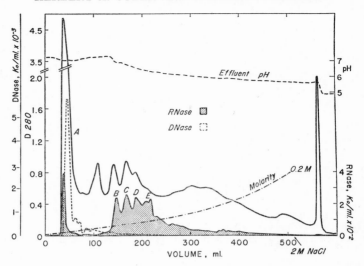

Fig. 11. Elution pattern of spleen nuclease preparations from the cellulosic anion exchanger. Spleen nuclease preparation applied to DEAE-cellulose (0.9 meq. N per gm.; 230–325 mesh). Eluted with concave gradient from 0.005 M Na-phosphate, pH 7.0, to 0.2 M Na-phosphate, pH 5.5; flow rate 18 ml. per hour; temp. 5°. (From Maver et al., 1959.)

Peak A contained all of the cathepsin, most of the deoxyribonuclease (DNase) and some of the ribonuclease (RNase). By using a variety of substrates, it could be established that more than one phosphodiesterase activity was present in A, cyclic nucleotides being hydrolyzed to give both 2′ and 3′ nucleotides. However, peaks $B, C, D,$ and E only produced 2′ nucleotides. They were less resistant to heat and had lower pH optima than the RNase of peak A. Only very small differences in activity toward several substrates, in heat stability, in pH optima, etc., could be found between the components in $B, C, D,$ and E. However, rechromatography under the original conditions, of a mixture of peaks B and E, established the validity of the separation.

Figure 12 shows further subdivision of the previously unadsorbed RNase and DNase fraction on CM-cellulose, the cation exchanger. Clear differences in heat stability as well as in pH optima of RNase activities were found. Several enzyme activities were separated that can serve as reagents in investigations of nucleic acid structure. These activities had been previously attributed to one enzyme. Moreover, a rather extensive heterogeneity

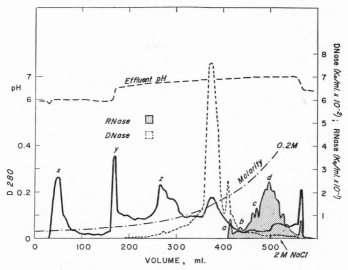

FIG. 12. Rechromatography of fraction A of Fig. 11 on the cation exchanger. CM-cellulose (0.74 meq. per gm., 100–230 mesh). Eluted with concave gradient from 0.015 M Na-phosphate, pH 6.0 to 0.02 M Na-phosphate, pH 7.0. Remainder as in Fig. 11. (From Maver et al., 1959.)

among RNase-active proteins was found. It is important to emphasize, however, that DNase-active protein did not show this phenomenon.

The origin or physiological significance of the heterogeneity remains to be explained. Whether the observed differences represent structural variations established during their synthesis and reflecting certain, as yet undetermined, special functions, whether the differences arose as a result of metabolic or chemical degradation thereafter, or whether they simply represent a combination of enzymatically active protein with diverse small and large molecules, is a subject for further investigations. It may develop, however, that we were dealing with a still unresolved complex mixture of enzymes with overlapping substrate specificities.

Åqvist and Anfinsen (1959) have reported a similar extensive heterogeneity in RNase prepared from sheep pancreas. Eight fractions having ribonuclease activity were obtained by a combination of CM- and DEAE-cellulose chromatography. Four of these, separated on the cation exchanger, maintained their chromatographic properties even after deionization on mixed bed ion exchangers. A difference other than net charge must be invoked since these components showed essentially the same isoionic point. The remaining 4 components, which passed through the cation exchanger and were separated on the anion exchanger, were absent after treatment with IRC-50. A combination with acidic substances, stable to CM-cellulose but disrupted by IRC-50, was suggested as a possible causative factor in the establishment of these chromatographic differences. The origin or the biological significance of this multiplicity of components remains to be determined. Their existence, however, is clear.

Some knowledge of the quantitative as well as qualitative basis for chromatographic resolution would certainly be valuable. Preliminary experiments with polynucleotide fractionation have contributed some information on this point (Staehelin *et al.*, 1959).

Pancreatic RNase is believed to split only the 5′-phosphate linkage in ribonucleic acids. A chromatogram of such a partial digest of yeast RNA is shown in Fig. 13. Identification of the

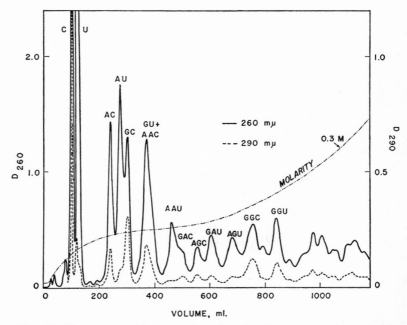

Fig. 13. Chromatographic separation of nucleotides in a pancreatic RNase digest of yeast RNA. Remainder as Fig. 2 except that the gradient limit was 0.40 *M*. (From Staehelin *et al.*, 1959.)

material in the peaks was accomplished by spectrophotometric examination, paper chromatography, and specific enzymatic hydrolysis. There is a regular increase in the molecular size of successively eluted components, as already mentioned, and within this size fractionation, there is separation based on nucleotide sequence: cytidylic precedes uridylic and adenylic precedes guanylic, even when in polynucleotide form. There is even separation of isomeric pairs: GAC and AGC, and GAU and AGU. The overlapping of GU and AAC, and AAC and GAC, can be avoided in a longer column. Similar results have been obtained with DNA digests, and these preliminary experiments have confirmed the existence of a nonrandom distribution of nucleotides within the chain.

The point to be made, however, is that differences in size, charge, and arrangement appear to be detectable. The simultaneous interplay of all of these, however, precludes a simple interpretation of the molecular characteristics in an unambiguous manner. A means of deducing structure from chromatographic experiments, even aided by other measurements, is still beyond the horizon but not beyond our aspirations.

REFERENCES

Alm, R. S., Williams, R. J. P., and Tiselius, A. (1952). *Acta Chem. Scand.* **6,** 826.
Äqvist, S. E. G., and Anfinsen, C. B. (1959). *J. Biol. Chem.* **234,** 1112.
Black, S., and Wright, N. G. (1955). *J. Biol. Chem.* **213,** 51.
Boardman, N. K., and Partridge, S. M. (1955). *Biochem. J.* **59,** 543.
Bock, R. M., and Ling, N.-S. (1954). *Anal. Chem.* **26,** 1543.
Boman, H. G. (1955). *Nature* **175,** 898.
Boman, H. G., and Westlund, L. E. (1956). *Arch. Biochem. Biophys.* **64,** 217.
Cohen, S. (1959). *Nature* **183,** 393.
Crawford, I. P., and Yanofsky, C. (1958). *Proc. Natl. Acad. Sci. U.S.* **44,** 1161.
Fahey, J. L. and Steinfeld, J. L. (1958). *Proc. Soc. Exptl. Biol. Med.* **97,** 281.
Fahey, J. L., McCoy, P. F., and Goulian, M. (1958). *J. Clin. Invest.* **37,** 272.
Field, E. O., and O'Brien, J. R. P. (1955). *Biochem. J.* **60,** 656.
Gutter, F. J., Sober, H. A., and Peterson, E. A. (1956). *Arch. Biochem. Biophys.* **62,** 427.
Gutter, F. J., Sober, H. A., and Peterson, E. A. (1957). *Arch. Biochem. Biophys.* **71,** 342.
Gutter, F. J., Peterson, E. A., and Sober, H. A. (1959). *Arch. Biochem. Biophys.* **80,** 353.
Hjertén, S. (1959). *Biochim. et Biophys. Acta* **31,** 216.
Itano, H. A. (1957). *Advances in Protein Chem.* **12,** 216.
Kunkel, H. G., and Wallenius, G. (1955). *Science* **122,** 288.
Maver, M. E., Peterson, E. A., Sober, H. A., and Greco, A. (1959). *Ann. N.Y. Acad. Sci.* **81,** 599.

Moore, S., and Stein, W. H. (1956). *Advances in Protein Chem.* **11**, 191.

Morrison, M., and Cook, J. L. (1955). *Science* **122**, 920.

Parr, C. W. (1954). *Biochem. J.* **56**, xxvii.

Peterson, E. A., and Sober, H. A. (1956). *J. Am. Chem. Soc.* **78**, 751.

Peterson, E. A., and Sober, H. A. (1959). *Anal. Chem.* **31**, 857.

Peterson, E. A., and Sober, H. A. (1960). *In* "The Plasma Proteins" (F. W. Putnam, ed.), Vol. I, Chapter 4, pp. 105-141. Academic Press, New York.

Price, V. E., and Greenfield, R. E. (1954). *J. Biol. Chem.* **209**, 363.

Porath, J. (1957). *Arkiv Kemi* **11**, 97.

Reisfeld, R. A., Bergenstal, D. M., and Hertz, R. (1959). *Arch. Biochem. Biophys.* **81**, 459.

Rhodes, M. B., Azari, P. B., and Feeney, R. E. (1958). *J. Biol. Chem.* **230**, 399.

Singer, S. J., and Itano, H. (1959). *Proc. Natl. Acad. Sci. U.S.* **45**, 174.

Sober, H. A., and Peterson, E. A. (1958). *Federation Proc.* **17**, 1116.

Sober, H. A., Gutter, F. J., Wyckoff, M. M., and Peterson, E. A. (1956). *J. Am. Chem. Soc.* **78**, 756.

Staehelin, M., Peterson, E. A., and Sober, H. A. (1959). *Arch. Biochem. Biophys.* **85**, 289.

Sterling, W. R., Greenfield, R. E., and Price, V. E. (1958). *Federation Proc.* **17**, 316.

Stevens, A. L., and Hilmoe, R. J. (1959). *Federation Proc.* **18**, 332.

Swingle, S. M., and Tiselius, A. (1951). *Biochem. J.* **48**, 171.

Tener, G. M., Khorana, H. G., Markham, R., and Pol, E. H. (1958). *J. Am. Chem. Soc.* **80**, 6223.

Tiselius, A. (1954). *Arkiv Kemi* **7**, 443.

Tiselius, A., Hjertén, S., and Levin, Ö. (1956). *Arch. Biochem. Biophys.* **65**, 132.

Vinograd, J., and Hutchinson, W. D. (1959). *Federation Proc.* **18**, 344.

Observations on the Activation of Amino Acids and the Biosynthesis of Peptide Bonds[1]

ALTON MEISTER

*Department of Biochemistry, Tufts University School of Medicine
Boston, Massachusetts*

ALTHOUGH the mechanism of protein synthesis is not yet known, considerable information has accumulated concerning the biosynthesis of certain low molecular weight compounds possessing peptide bonds. Thus, the major outlines of the enzymatic reactions leading to the synthesis of benzoylglycine (Borsook and Dubnoff, 1940, 1947; Cohen and McGilvery, 1947; Chantrenne, 1951; Schachter and Taggart, 1954; Moldave and Meister, 1957), pantothenic acid (Maas and Novelli, 1953), glutamine (Krebs, 1935; Speck, 1947, 1949; Elliott, 1948, 1951, 1953; Levintow and Meister, 1954), phenylacetylglutamine (Moldave and Meister, 1957), glutathione (Bloch, 1949; Snoke and Bloch, 1955; Mandeles and Bloch, 1955), carnosine, and anserine (Kalyankar and Meister, 1959a, b; Winnick and Winnick, 1959), have gradually taken shape. The biosynthesis of each of these compounds appears to involve activation of the carboxyl group of one reactant by adenosine 5'-triphosphate. In several instances synthesis is associated with conversion of adenosine 5'-triphosphate to adenosine 5'-diphosphate and inorganic phosphate (e.g., glutamine, glutathione), while in others (e.g., benzoylglycine, phenylacetylglutamine, carnosine) the evidence favors the view that adenosine 5'-triphosphate is converted to inorganic pyrophosphate and adenosine 5'-monophosphate. In general, the evidence suggests that formation of the peptide bond is initiated by a reaction involving the carboxyl group of one reactant, an enzyme, a metal ion (Mg^{++}), and adenosine 5'-triphosphate to form an enzyme-bound intermediate, which may react

[1] The author wishes to acknowledge the generous support of the National Science Foundation and of the National Institutes of Health, Public Health Service, Department of Health, Education, and Welfare.

with a specific acceptor to yield another carboxyl-activated intermediate, or to form a peptide bond. It would appear that the intermediate reacts with an acceptor in the absence of an external source of energy. These reactions are therefore somewhat analogous to those commonly employed by the synthetic organic chemist, which utilize such amino acid derivatives as acid chlorides, azides, and anhydrides. Although other types of activation in biological systems (including activation of the α-amino group of amino acids) have not been excluded unequivocally, there is now considerable experimental evidence for the occurrence of carboxyl activation, not only in peptide bond synthesis, but also in the activation of fatty acids. Thus, synthetic acetyl adenylate was found to react as an intermediate in acetate activation (Berg, 1955). Other studies indicated that not only acetate, but other fatty acids (Jencks and Lipmann, 1957; Moyed and Lipmann, 1957), and amino acids (Berg, 1955, 1956; Hoagland, 1955; Hoagland et al., 1956) may be activated by adenosine 5′-triphosphate to yield enzyme-bound acyl adenylates. The activation of amino acids to yield amino acyl adenylates has attracted attention because of the possibility that these anhydrides may be intermediates in protein synthesis. Recent studies provide evidence for the transfer of the amino acyl moieties of amino acyl adenylates to ribonucleic acid acceptors, in which the amino acids are bound by ester linkages to one of the ribose hydroxyl groups of the terminal adenosine residues (Holley, 1957; Ogata and Nohara, 1957; Zamecnik et al., 1958; Hoagland et al., 1958; Weiss et al., 1958a, b; Berg and Ofengand, 1958; Zachau et al., 1958; Schweet et al., 1958). It has been suggested that the amino acyl moieties of RNA-amino acid complexes are ultimately incorporated into protein (see reviews by Loftfield, 1957; Chantrenne, 1958; Meister, 1959). Although evidence for such a pathway of protein synthesis is still incomplete, information relating to the formation of amino acyl adenylates by specific amino acid-activating enzymes, and to the formation of RNA-amino acid complexes is more abundant.

This paper will be concerned with certain aspects of amino acid activation and peptide bond formation, and will review studies on the synthesis of glutamine, phenylacetylglutamine, benzoylglycine, and carnosine (and related peptides), and on the activation of tryptophan by pancreatic tryptophan-activating enzyme. Such a discussion seems appropriate on the occasion of this symposium not only because of Jesse Greenstein's deep interest in amino acids and peptides, but because certain of these studies (those on glutamine synthesis) were begun (in collaboration with Leon Levintow) in the stimulating environment of Greenstein's laboratory at the National Institutes of Health.

Synthesis of Glutamine

Although the enzymatic synthesis of glutamine has received much attention since the early studies of Krebs (1935), Speck (1947, 1949), and Elliott (1948, 1951, 1953), the mechanism of the reaction remains an intriguing enigma. The over-all reaction,[2]

(1)   L-glutamate + NH$_3$ + ATP $\underset{\phantom{Mg^{++}}}{\overset{Mg^{++}}{\rightleftharpoons}}$ L-glutamine + ADP + P$_i$

was shown to be reversible (Levintow and Meister, 1954), and it was also shown (Levintow et al., 1955) that the transfer reaction catalyzed by the glutamine synthesis enzyme,

(2)   L-glutamine + NH$_2$OH $\xrightarrow{\text{ADP, P}_i\text{, Mn}^{++}}$ L-γ-glutamylhydroxamic acid + NH$_3$

did not involve obligatory intermediate formation of glutamate. Thus, when the transfer reaction was carried out in the presence of C^{14}-glutamate, there was negligible incorporation of isotope into the hydroxamate formed.

Studies with O^{18} (Boyer et al., 1956; Kowalsky et al., 1956) have shown that glutamine synthesis is associated with transfer of an oxygen atom from the ω-carboxyl group to inorganic phosphate; this observation is consistent with the intermediate formation of γ-glutamyl phosphate. However, experiments in our laboratory (Levintow and Meister, 1956; Castelfranco and Meister, unpublished data) with synthetic γ-glutamyl phosphate (and also with γ-glutamyl phosphate labeled with P^{32}), have thus far failed to provide evidence for the participation of this compound in the reaction. In addition to the O^{18} data, other studies also suggest that a carboxyl-activated intermediate is formed. Thus, we found that although hydroxamic acids were formed from both isomers of glutamic acid at approximately the same rate, the synthesis of L-glutamine was about three times more rapid than that of its enantiomorph (Levintow and Meister, 1953). Furthermore, L-glutamine was several hundred times more active in the transfer reaction than was D-glutamine (Table I). The evidence suggests a two-step

---

[2] Abbreviations employed: Adenosine 5′-triphosphate, ATP; adenosine 5′-diphosphate, ADP; adenosine 5′-monophosphate, AMP; coenzyme A, CoA— SH or CoA; orthophosphate, P$_i$; pyrophosphate, PP.

TABLE I

SYNTHESIS OF THE OPTICAL ISOMERS OF GLUTAMINE
AND γ-GLUTAMYLHYDROXAMIC ACID[a]

Synthesis System[b]

Substrate	Hydroxamic acid formed (units/hour)	Amide formed (units/hour)
L-Glutamate	407	428
D-Glutamate	385	171

Transfer System[c]

Substrate	Hydroxamic acid formed (units/hour)
L-Glutamine	286
D-Glutamine	3.93

[a] From Levintow and Meister (1953).

[b] Units—μmoles formed/mg. enzyme N. The reaction mixtures contained 50 μmoles of $MgCl_2$, 100 μmoles of neutralized hydroxylamine hydrochloride or NH_4Cl, 50 μmoles of glutamate, 25 μmoles of β-mercaptoethanol, 10 μmoles of sodium ATP, 50 μmoles of imidazole buffer, pH 7.0. Incubated at 37° for 15 to 40 minutes, with sufficient pea enzyme to effect the synthesis of 2 to 4 μmoles of hydroxamic acid or amide with active substrates. Final volume, 1.0 ml.; pH 7.0. Values corrected by subtraction of blanks.

[c] The reaction mixtures contained 50 μmoles of $MgCl_2$, 1 μmole of sodium ADP, 50 μmoles of glutamine, 100 μmoles of neutralized hydroxylamine hydrochloride, 20 μmoles of β-mercaptoethanol, 5 μmoles of phosphate buffer, pH 6.6. Incubated at 37° for 15 to 30 minutes, with sufficient pea enzyme to effect the formation of 0.5 to 1.0 μmoles of hydroxamic acid. Final volume, 1.0 ml.; pH 6.5. Values corrected by subtraction of blanks.

mechanism: (1) activation of glutamate by reaction with adenosine 5′-triphosphate and the enzyme, and (2) reaction of the activated intermediate with ammonia. The second step would appear to be more optically specific than the first. Failure to detect free intermediates in the reaction implies that the intermediates formed are enzyme-bound. The apparent inability of added synthetic γ-glutamyl phosphate to serve as an enzymatically active intermediate when added to the system does not necessarily exclude formation of this compound as an enzyme-bound intermediate. However, the requirement for catalytic amounts of ADP in the transfer reaction, suggests that ADP must also be a constituent of the activated intermediate. Thus, the intermediate may include enzyme, Mg^{++}, glutamate, the terminal phosphate group of ATP, and ADP. It is abundantly evident that the nature of the glutamine synthesis reaction requires further study. Although much has been learned from kinetic and isotopic studies, these investigations have been carried out with relatively crude enzyme preparations. Perhaps further purification will permit new types of experiments. Studies with large quantities of pure enzyme may lead to more conclusive information concerning the mechanism of this reaction. The synthesis of both peptide bonds of glutathione is also accompanied by conversion of ATP to ADP (Snoke and Bloch, 1955; Mandeles and Bloch, 1955); these reactions may be similar to that involved in glutamine synthesis.

Synthesis of Phenylacetylglutamine and Benzoylglycine

In contrast to the synthesis of glutamine, the synthesis of phenylacetylglutamine and benzoylglycine appear to involve participation of acyl adenylate intermediates. The studies on phenylacetylglutamine, which have been described in detail elsewhere (Moldave and Meister, 1957), are consistent with the following scheme:

(3)   phenylacetic acid + ATP $\rightleftharpoons$ phenylacetyl adenylate + PP

(4)   phenylacetyl adenylate + CoA—SH $\rightleftharpoons$ phenylacetyl CoA + AMP

(5)   phenylacetyl CoA + glutamine $\rightleftharpoons$ phenylacetyl glutamine + CoA—SH

The participation of phenylacetyl adenylate (and of benzoyl adenylate in the benzoylglycine-forming system) is suggested by experiments in which synthetic acyl adenylates were incubated with glutamine, coenzyme A, and enzyme preparations obtained from human liver or kidney. The formation of phenylacetyl glutamine required both the presence of enzyme and of coenzyme A. Reactions (3) and (4) are analogous to those proposed for the activation of acetate and other fatty acids, in which pyrophosphate formation and ATP-pyrophosphate exchange were demonstrated. Although available information suggests that acyl adenylates are intermediates in the activation of fatty acids and in the synthesis of benzoylglycine and phenylacetylglutamine, the evidence for participation of these intermediates is incomplete, for their enzymatic formation has not yet been demonstrated.

The α-carboxyl activation of amino acids first observed by Berg (1955, 1956), and by Hoagland (1955) [Hoagland *et al.* (1956)] has been studied in a number of laboratories, and it is now fairly certain that the reaction leads to the formation of an enzyme-bound amino acyl adenylate according to the following reaction:

(6)   amino acid + enzyme + ATP $\overset{Mg^{++}}{\rightleftharpoons}$ enzyme-amino acyl adenylate + PP

In the presence of the specific amino acid, the enzyme catalyzes incorporation of inorganic pyrophosphate into ATP. When enzyme, ATP, Mg^{++}, and amino acid are incubated with relatively high concentrations of hydroxylamine, the corresponding amino acyl hydroxamate is formed. The formation of an amino acyl adenylate is suggested by analogy with the apparent mechanism of the acetate-activating system. DeMoss and Novelli (1956) found that leucyl adenylate reacted enzymatically with pyrophosphate to give ATP; this finding was interpreted as reversal of reaction (6). Further evidence consistent with the formation of an anhydride linkage between the phosphoric acid group of AMP and the carboxyl group of amino acids was obtained in studies in which transfer of O^{18} was observed from the carboxyl group of an amino acid to AMP during enzymatic activation (Hoagland *et al.*, 1957).

Studies on Amino Acyl Adenylates

Direct evidence for the enzymatic formation of amino acyl adenylates was first reported by Karasek *et al.* (1958a, b), who incubated DL-C^{14}-tryptophan with purified pancreatic tryptophan-

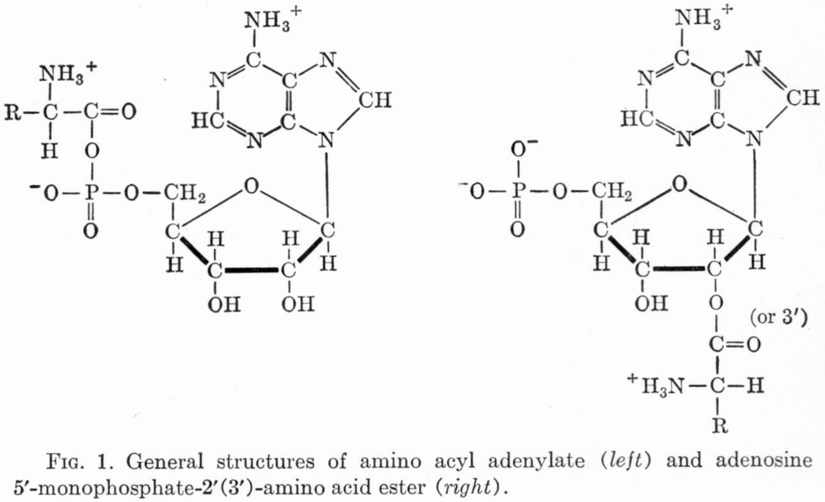

Fig. 1. General structures of amino acyl adenylate (*left*) and adenosine 5′-monophosphate-2′(3′)-amino acid ester (*right*).

activating enzyme [prepared according to Davie *et al.* (1956)], pyrophosphatase, magnesium ions, and ATP; tryptophanyl adenylate was isolated from the lyophilized reaction mixture by extraction and paper ionophoresis. In the initial studies, recovery of tryptophanyl adenylate was low; however, in subsequent experiments in which improved methods of isolation were employed, approximately 80% of the added radioactivity was accounted for, and about 50% of the recovered isotope was found (calculated as L-tryptophan) in the isolated tryptophanyl adenylate (Table II;

TABLE II

ISOLATION OF ENZYMATICALLY FORMED
C^{14}-TRYPTOPHANYL ADENYLATE[a]

	Per cent of initial C^{14}
Tryptophanyl adenylate	41[b]
Total recovery of C^{14}	82
Recovery of synthetic tryptophanyl adenylate added to system	60-80

[a] The reaction mixture consisted of tryptophan-activating enzyme (30 mg.), ATP (5 μmoles), crystalline yeast pyrophosphatase (50 μg), DL-tryptophan-3-C^{14} (0.127 μmole; 565,000 c.p.m.), $MgCl_2$ (10 μmoles), and 2-amino-2-(hydroxymethyl)-1, 3-propanediol-HCl buffer (pH 8; 100 μmoles) in a final volume of 2.0 ml.; incubated for 5 μmoles at 37°.
[b] Calculated on the basis of the L-isomer.

Krishnaswamy and Meister, 1960). Since 20 to 40% of added synthetic tryptophanyl adenylate was hydrolyzed during the isolation procedure, it seems probable that tryptophanyl adenylate represents the major tryptophan-containing enzymatic product. Enzymatically-formed tryptophanyl adenylate exhibited the properties of tryptophanyl adenylate prepared by organic synthesis. A procedure was developed for the preparation of amino acyl adenylates which involves reaction of adenylic acid with a carbobenzoxy amino acid in the presence of N,N'-dicyclohexylcarbodiimide in aqueous pyridine (Castelfranco *et al.*, 1958a, b; Moldave *et al.*, 1959). The resulting carbobenzoxy amino acyl adenylate is isolated and purified, and the carbobenzoxy group is removed by catalytic hydrogenation. We found that amino acyl adenylates are spontaneously converted under certain conditions (e.g., standing for several weeks at −15° to −20°) to the isomeric adenosine 5'-monophosphate-2'(3') amino acid esters, which can be separated from amino acyl adenylates by their more negative charge at pH 5.9 on paper ionophoresis. In the experiments described above in which tryptophanyl adenylate was isolated from an enzyme reaction mixture, no adenosine 5'-monophosphate-2'(3') tryptophanate was detected. On the other hand, a negatively charged radioactive band was consistently observed on paper ionophoresis at pH 4.5. This band may represent adenosine 5'-triphosphate-2'(3') tryptophanate, a compound whose formation in a similar system was reported by Weiss *et al.* (1958a). Kingdon *et al.* (1958) have independently observed enzymatic formation of tryptophanyl adenylate by the tryptophan-activating enzyme.

Attempts to demonstrate the reversal of reaction (6) with the purified pancreatic tryptophan activating enzyme have led to the

TABLE III

ACYL ADENYLATES EXAMINED FOR ACTIVITY IN ATP SYNTHESIS
WITH CATALYTIC QUANTITIES OF TRYPTOPHAN-ACTIVATING ENZYME[a]

Active	Inactive
L-Tryptophanyl-AMP	Carbobenzoxy-L-tryptophanyl-AMP
D-Tryptophanyl-AMP	AMP-2'(3')-tryptophanate (and other esters)
L-Alanyl-AMP	L-Tryptophanyl inosinate
L-Asparaginyl-AMP	Acetyl-AMP
L-Glutaminyl-AMP	Benzoyl-AMP
Glycyl-AMP	Phenylacetyl-AMP
L-Isoleucyl-AMP	β-Alanyl adenylate
L-Leucyl-AMP	
L-Methionyl-AMP	
L-Phenylalanyl-AMP	
D-Phenylalanyl-AMP	
L-Prolyl-AMP	
L-Seryl-AMP	
L-Threonyl-AMP	
L-Tyrosinyl-AMP	
L-Valyl-AMP	
α-Aminoisobutyryl-AMP	

[a] The reaction mixtures consisted of 2-amino-2-(hydroxymethyl)-1, 3-propanediol-HCl buffer (100 μmoles; pH 7.3), magnesium chloride (10 μmoles), P^{32}-sodium pyrophosphate (2 μmoles), enzyme (0.4 mg.), and acyl adenylate (2 μmoles) in a final volume of 2 ml.; incubated for 5 minutes at 37°.

interesting finding that a wide variety of amino acyl adenylates was active in the synthesis of ATP (Karasek *et al.*, 1958a, b; Novelli, 1958). Similar findings were observed with purified yeast methionine-activating enzyme (Berg, 1958); however, L-methionyl adenylate was more active than the other amino acyl adenylates examined. The methionine and tryptophan-activating enzymes are highly specific for the respective L-amino acids in the hydroxamate-forming reaction, and also in the pyrophosphate-ATP exchange reaction. Our studies showed that the tryptophan-activating enzyme catalyzed ATP synthesis from pyrophosphate and any one of 17 amino acyl adenylates, including D-tryptophanyl adenylate and D-phenylalanyl adenylate (Table III; Krishnaswamy and Meister, 1960). Although all of the α-amino acyl adenylates tested were active, compounds lacking a free α-amino group (acetyl adenylate, benzoyl adenylate, phenylacetyl adenylate, carbobenzoxy L-tryptophanyl adenylate), adenosine 5′-monophosphate-2′(3′)-amino acid esters, β-alanyl adenylate and L-tryptophanyl inosinate were inactive. Surprisingly, D-tryptophanyl adenylate was more active than was L-tryptophanyl adenylate (Table IV). This interesting finding, as well as the remarkably low specificity of the enzyme in catalyzing the reaction in the direction of ATP synthesis, led us to carry out further studies on ATP synthesis by the tryptophan-activating enzyme. Study of the effect of amino acyl adenylate concentration

TABLE IV

SYNTHESIS OF ATP FROM PYROPHOSPHATE AND D- AND L-TRYPTOPHANYL ADENYLATES CATALYZED BY TRYPTOPHAN-ACTIVATING ENZYME[a]

	ATP formed	
Concentration of acyl adenylate	L-Tryptophanyl adenylate (μmole)	D-Tryptophanyl adenylate (μmole)
$0.33 \times 10^{-3}\ M$	0.098	0.153
$0.67 \times 10^{-3}\ M$	0.147	0.463
$1.33 \times 10^{-3}\ M$	0.161	0.706
$2.67 \times 10^{-3}\ M$	0.168	0.885

[a] The reaction mixtures consisted of magnesium chloride (10 μmoles), 2-amino-2-(hydroxymethyl)-1, 3-propanediol-HCl buffer (pH 7.3; 100 μmoles), P^{32}-sodium pyrophosphate (2 μmoles; 100,000 c.p.m.), enzyme (0.4 mg.), and amino acyl adenylate in a final volume of 1.5 ml. The reaction was started by addition of amino acyl adenylate; incubated at 20° for 2 minutes.

on ATP synthesis revealed that synthesis of ATP was approximately 5 times greater with D-tryptophanyl adenylate than with L-tryptophanyl adenylate at initial adenylate concentrations of 2.7×10^{-3} M. It should be emphasized that these findings were obtained with a number of different preparations of D-tryptophanyl adenylate and L-tryptophanyl adenylate; these preparations were found to contain less than 5% of the isomeric adenosine 5'-monophosphate-2'(3') amino acid esters, and the amino acyl moieties of such anhydrides were not less than 99.5% optically pure.

We now believe that the greater activity of D-tryptophanyl adenylate as compared to L-tryptophanyl adenylate is due to the fact that L-tryptophan, at remarkably low concentrations, inhibits the enzyme in the direction of ATP synthesis. Thus, 50% inhibition of ATP synthesis from pyrophosphate and L-alanyl adenylate was observed with 1.18×10^{-6} M L-tryptophan. On the other hand, the concentration of D-tryptophan required for 50% inhibition was 3.3×10^{-4} M. The degree of inhibition was influenced by the order in which the components of the reaction mixture were mixed (Table V). When the enzyme was incubated with L-tryptophan prior to addition of pyrophosphate and L-alanyl adenylate, greater inhibition was observed than when the anhydride was added prior to L-trypto-

TABLE V

INHIBITION OF ATP SYNTHESIS BY L-TRYPTOPHAN AND PREVENTION
OF INHIBITION BY PRIOR INCUBATION OF ENZYME
WITH L-ALANYL ADENYLATE[a]

Reaction mixtures	Per cent inhibition
Enzyme + H₂O	0
Enzyme + L-TRY (3 min.)	42
Enzyme + Ala-AMP (20 min.); then L-TRY (3 min.)	10
Enzyme + Ala-AMP (20 min.); then H₂O (3 min.)	0

[a] The reaction mixtures consisted of 2-amino-2-(hydroxymethyl)-1, 3-propanediol-HCl buffer (pH 7.3; 100 μmoles), magnesium chloride 10 μmoles), sodium P^{32}-pyrophosphate (1 μmole), enzyme (100 μg.), L-tryptophan (0.001 μmole); and amino acyl adenylate (1 μmole) in a final volume of 2 ml. The periods of preincubation are indicated in parenthesis. The complete reaction mixtures were incubated for 3 minutes at 20°. The reactions were started by adding L-alanyl adenylate + PP at the end of preincubations indicated above. No ATP was formed when only PP was added.

phan. These observations suggest that L-tryptophan and the amino acyl adenylate combine with the same enzymatic sites. It would appear that the substrates are relatively tightly bound to the enzyme, and that combination of the enzyme with amino acyl adenylates stabilizes the anhydride. The high affinity of the enzyme for L-tryptophan as compared with D-tryptophan appears to explain the observations on ATP synthesis made with L- and D-tryptophanyl adenylates. Synthesis of ATP from L-tryptophanyl adenylate and pyrophosphate reached a plateau with relatively low concentrations of amino acyl adenylate. L-Tryptophan would be expected to form rapidly in this system, not only as a product of the reaction, but also by spontaneous breakdown of L-tryptophanyl adenylate. The formation of free L-tryptophan in this system therefore appears to be a limiting factor in ATP synthesis. In contrast, although synthesis of ATP from pyrophosphate and D-tryptophanyl adenylate is undoubtedly accompanied by some D-tryptophan formation, ATP synthesis is not markedly inhibited presumably because the affinity of the enzyme for D-tryptophan is relatively low.

Other studies also indicate that the enzyme has considerably greater affinity for L-tryptophanyl adenylate than for D-tryptophanyl adenylate and other amino acyl adenylates. Thus, it was found that incubation of enzyme with very low concentrations of L-tryptophanyl adenylate for 30 minutes, followed by addition of pyrophosphate, led to ATP synthesis, even though no free amino acyl adenylate was present at the time pyrophosphate was added (Fig. 2). Incubation of 1 mg. of purified tryptophan-activating enzyme with 4×10^{-9} mole of L-tryptophanyl adenylate, gave 1.3×10^{-9} mole of ATP on subsequent addition of pyrophosphate. With lower initial concentrations of amino acyl adenylate, a larger proportion of the AMP moiety of added amino acyl adenylate was converted to ATP. For example, 0.6×10^{-9} mole of ATP was formed when 10^{-9} mole of L-tryptophanyl adenylate was incubated with the enzyme. In view of the great tendency of amino acyl adenylates to hydrolyze spontaneously, the conversion of added amino acyl adenylate to ATP is remarkably large; this indicates that the affinity of the enzyme for L-tryptophanyl adenylate is extraordinarily high. Incubation of other amino acyl adenylates (including D-tryptophanyl adenylate) under these conditions gave no ATP; only when concentrations of D-tryptophanyl adenylate and L-alanyl adenylate of the order of 10^{-3} M were incubated with the enzyme, was ATP formed on subsequent addition of pyrophosphate.

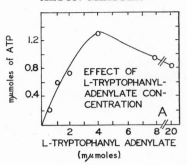

FIG. 2. Synthesis of ATP upon addition of pyrophosphate to enzyme previously incubated with L-tryptophanyl adenylate for 30 minutes. The enzyme preparation (1 mg.) was incubated with the indicated quantities of L-tryptophan adenylate, $MgCl_2$ (10 μmoles), and 2-amino-2-(hydroxymethyl)-1, 3-propanediol-HCl buffer (pH 7.3; 100 μmoles) in a final volume of 0.9 ml. at 37°. After 30 minutes, 0.1 ml. containing 100 μmoles of sodium P^{32}-pyrophosphate was added, and after 15 minutes the formation of ATP was determined. Controls in which enzyme was omitted or in which enzyme was added with the pyrophosphate gave no ATP.

These findings clarify to some extent the question of the specificity of the enzyme when the reaction is studied in the direction of ATP synthesis. They indicate that amino acyl adenylates other than L-tryptophanyl adenylate can combine with the enzyme if they are present in concentrations that are relatively large compared to that of the enzyme. The ability of the enzyme to combine with a number of amino acyl adenylates suggests that the catalytically active sites react not only with the amino acid portion of the amino acyl adenylate molecule but also with the AMP moiety. All of the amino acyl adenylates possess a common group, and it is probable that the affinity of the enzyme for the AMP moiety is partly responsible for the binding of the other amino acyl adenylates.

We may think of the active site of the enzyme as having a relationship to L-tryptophanyl adenylate as shown in Diagram A of the schematic figure (Fig. 3). In Diagram B, the binding of leucyl adenylate to the enzyme may be explained by the affinity of the enzyme for the AMP moiety, and perhaps also for the anhydride and α-amino group portions of the molecule. However, the enzyme would be expected to have relatively little affinity for the isopropyl group of leucine, and indeed L-leucine itself is not active in either the hydroxamic acid-forming reaction or the pyrophos-

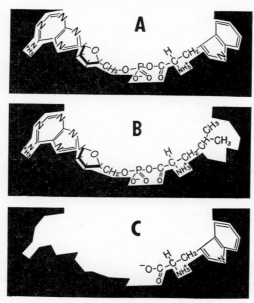

Fɪɢ. 3. Diagrammatic representation of enzyme-amino acyl adenylate relationships.

phate-ATP exchange reactions catalyzed by the tryptophan-activating enzyme. These reactions are highly specific for ʟ-tryptophan, which has a very high affinity for the enzyme as was shown in the studies on inhibition of ATP synthesis by this amino acid. It is therefore reasonable to assume that a portion of the active site is specifically designed to receive this amino acid (Diagram C, Fig. 1). We therefore postulate an active site which can combine with an externally supplied intermediate (ʟ-tryptophanyl adenylate), analogs of this intermediate (e.g., ᴅ-tryptophanyl adenylate, ʟ-leucyl adenylate), or the specific amino acid substrate (ʟ-tryptophan). This interpretation appears to be consistent with the experimental data, which initially were surprising and difficult to explain.

The data also indicate that the combination of externally supplied amino acyl adenylate (prepared by organic synthesis) results in stabilization of the anhydride, which exhibits a half life of approximately 8 minutes in the absence of enzyme. Thus, ʟ-tryptophanyl adenylate can replace ʟ-tryptophan and ATP in the formation of the enzyme-bound product:

(7)   enzyme + L-tryptophan + ATP $\xrightarrow{Mg^{++}}$

enzyme-L-tryptophanyl adenylate + PP

(8)   enzyme + L-tryptophanyl adenylate $\longrightarrow$

enzyme-L-tryptophanyl adenylate

Pyrophosphate is not required for the second reaction. Magnesium ions are required for ATP synthesis with catalytic amounts of enzyme; a requirement for magnesium ions could not be demonstrated for reaction (8); however, it is possible that the enzyme preparation contains magnesium.

Earlier work in our laboratory (Castelfranco *et al.*, 1958a, b; Moldave *et al.*, 1959) showed that amino acyl adenylates were highly reactive anhydrides capable of reacting nonenzymatically with hydroxylamine, ammonia, amino acids, nucleotides, and proteins. Similar results have been reported with mitochondrial proteins (Zioudrou *et al.*, 1958). Thus, incubation of C^{14}-labeled amino acyl adenylates with liver preparations led to appreciable labeling of the proteins subsequently isolated by precipitation with trichloroacetic acid. Much greater incorporation of isotope into such proteins occurred after they were denatured by heating, and it was concluded that the labeling was due mainly to nonenzymatic acylation of the available reactive groups of the proteins. Nonenzymatic incorporation of the labeled amino acyl moiety of amino acyl adenylates into ribonucleic acid was also observed. In these experiments it was not possible to determine whether enzymatic reactions accounted for some of the observed labeling because nonenzymatic acylation was very extensive. The results suggest, however, that the high reactivity of the amino acyl adenylates with protein and nucleic acid may explain at least some of the *in vitro* incorporation phenomena that have been reported (see, for example, Zamecnik and Keller, 1954).

The formation of enzyme-bound amino acyl adenylates by reactions of the type given in reaction (8) makes it possible to study the transfer of the amino acyl moiety of such intermediates without utilizing the activity responsible for the synthesis of amino acyl adenylates from amino acid and ATP [reaction (7)]. Thus, the formation of tryptophan-ribonucleic acid complex was demonstrated with enzyme-bound tryptophanyl adenylate in the following manner (Wong *et al.*, 1959): Tryptophan-activating enzyme was incubated with C^{14}-tryptophanyl adenylate for 20 minutes at 37°, and then pancreatic ribonucleic acid was added. Incubation was continued for an additional 20 minutes, following which the ribonucleic acid was isolated and its radioactivity was determined. Control experiments in which enzyme was omitted gave ribonucleic acid containing negligible radioactivity. However, appreciable radioactivity was found in ribonucleic acid isolated after incubation with enzyme-bound C^{14}-tryptophanyl adenylate. A similar experiment with C^{14}-glycyl adenylate indicated definite transfer of the radioactivity to ribonucleic acid; however, this was of a much lower order of magnitude than that observed with tryptophan. It therefore appears that the amino acyl moiety of synthetic tryptophanyl adenylate is transferred to ribonucleic acid in a manner analogous to that observed in experiments in which enzyme was incubated with tryptophan, ATP, and ribonucleic acid. Therefore, enzyme-bound tryptophanyl adenylate appears to be capable of replacing tryptophan, ATP, and enzyme in this system as well as in the ATP-synthesizing reaction. Whether the transfer of the amino acid to ribonucleic acid is catalyzed by the same enzyme that catalyzes synthesis of the enzyme-bound amino acyl adenylate remains to be determined unequivocally.

The observations of ATP synthesis from enzyme-bound amino acyl adenylate prepared by reaction (8), and of transfer of the tryptophanyl moiety of enzyme-bound tryptophanyl adenylate to RNA indicate that externally supplied amino acyl adenylate can be utilized by enzymatic systems. The chemical nature of the ribonucleic acid-amino acid complex remains to be fully determined, and proof is still needed for the postulated role of amino acyl adenylates and ribonucleic acid-amino acid complexes in the synthesis of the peptide bonds of proteins. However, the evidence indicates that these highly reactive anhydrides are stabilized by combination with enzyme and that they can be transferred specifically. The studies described below on the enzymatic synthesis of carnosine, anserine, and related β-alanyl and γ-aminobutyryl peptides appear to offer more direct support for the belief that amino acyl adenylates can serve as intermediates in biological peptide bond synthesis.

Synthesis of Carnosine and Related β-Alanyl and γ-Aminobutyryl Peptides

Carnosine and anserine were recognized as constituents of muscle many years ago; yet until relatively recently no information concerning the enzymatic synthesis of these β-alanyl peptides has been available, although it has been generally believed that they are synthesized from their constituent amino acids. Studies in our laboratory carried out with an enzyme preparation obtained from chick pectoral muscle showed that carnosine synthesis occurred when the enzyme preparation was incubated with β-alanine, L-histidine, ATP, and magnesium ions (Table VI; Kalyankar and Meister,

TABLE VI

CARNOSINE SYNTHESIS SYSTEM

Composition of reaction mixtures	Peptide synthesized (mμmoles)
Complete system[a]	48.4
Complete system minus enzyme	0.18
Complete system minus Mg^{++}	0.54
Complete system minus L-histidine	6.23
Complete system minus ATP	0.55

[a] The complete system consisted of L-histidine (3 μmoles), ATP (3 μmoles), MgCl$_2$ (3 μmoles), enzyme preparation (8.5 mg.), β-alanine-1-C^{14} (0.24 μmole; 260,000 c.p.m.), and 2-amino-2-(hydroxymethyl)-1, 3-propanediol-HCl buffer (pH 7.3; 50 μmoles) in a final volume of 1 ml.; incubated at 37° for 1 hour. A similar experiment was carried out with C^{14}-histidine. No peptide was formed when β-alanine was omitted.

1959a). When histidine was replaced by 1-methylhistidine, anserine synthesis was observed. Similar findings have been reported independently by Winnick and Winnick (1959). Our studies on carnosine biosynthesis, which are described in detail elsewhere (Kalyankar and Meister, 1959b), indicated that the enzyme exhibits a very high affinity for L-histidine and that D-histidine was not active in the reaction. However, when L-histidine was replaced by certain histidine analogs, histidine derivatives, and other amino acids, formation of new products occurred (Table VII). Thus, we obtained evidence for the synthesis of the β-alanyl peptides of the following amino acids: 1-methylhistidine, 2-methylhistidine, 3-methylhistidine, lysine, hydroxylysine, ornithine, arginine, and several others. When β-alanine was replaced by β-aminobutyric acid, β-aminoisobutyric acid, γ-aminobutyric acid, δ-aminovaleric acid, ϵ-aminocaproic acid, α,γ-diaminobutyric acid, or α,β-diaminopropionic acid, products were formed which appear to be the corresponding peptides of histidine (Table VIII). Evidence for synthesis of the γ-aminobutyryl peptides of lysine, ornithine, histidine, 1-methylhistidine,

TABLE VII

SYNTHESIS OF β-ALANYL PEPTIDES[a]

Amino acid	Product (mμmoles)
L-Histidine	26.5
D-Histidine	0
1-Methyl-DL-histidine	15.8
2-Methyl-L-histidine	21.5
3-Methyl-L-histidine	14.4
2-Imidazole-3-DL-alanine	18.4
1,2,4-Triazole-3-DL-alanine	7.8
L-Lysine	15.2
5-Hydroxy-L-lysine	12.4
L-Ornithine	13.7
L-Arginine	13.6
L-Canavanine	11.8

[a] The reaction mixtures contained enzyme preparation (8.5 mg.), ATP (3 μmoles), MgCl$_2$ (3 μmoles), β-alanine-1-C^{14} (0.18 μmole; 260,000 c.p.m.), amino acid as indicated in the table (2 μmoles; DL-forms, 4 μmoles), and 2-amino-2-(hydroxymethyl)-1, 3-propanediol-HCl buffer (pH 7.3; 50 μmoles) in a final volume of 1 ml.; incubated at 37° for 60 minutes. No products were formed when either ATP or MgCl$_2$ was omitted.

Inactive: Glycine, aspartic acid, agmatine, citrulline, D-arginine, 2-thiolhistidine, nitroarginine.

3-methylhistidine, and arginine was also obtained (Table IX). In each case, synthesis was dependent upon the presence of ATP and magnesium ions. Most of the enzymatically synthesized peptides were identified by paper chromatography in several solvent systems, and by paper ionophoresis. Several of the enzymatically formed products were hydrolyzed with acid or with carnosinase to the corresponding C^{14}-starting materials. In addition to carnosine and anserine, carnosinase also hydrolyzed β-alanyl lysine, γ-aminobutyryl histidine, and β-alanyl arginine. In a number of instances, the enzymatically synthesized peptides were treated with 1-fluoro-2,4-dinitrobenzene followed by hydrolysis, and the expected 2,4-dinitrophenyl amino acids were isolated by chromatography. The evidence lends strong support to the conclusion that peptides such as β-alanyl-3-methylhistidine, β-alanyl arginine, β-alanyl lysine, β-alanyl-1,2,4-triazole-3-alanine, β-alanyl-2-imidazole-3-alanine, γ-aminobutyryl histidine, and other γ-aminobutyryl peptides are enzymatically synthesized. Three of these peptides are now known

TABLE VIII

SYNTHESIS OF PEPTIDES OF HISTIDINE[a]

Amino acid	Product (mμmoles)
β-Alanine	60.3
DL-β-Aminobutyric acid	35.0
β-Aminoisobutyric acid	22.2
γ-Aminobutyric acid	41.3
δ-Aminovaleric acid	15.0
ε-Aminocaproic acid	17.9
L-α-Aminobutyric acid	0
L-α,γ-Diaminobutyric acid	20.6
DL-α,β-Diaminopropionic acid	7.85

[a] The reaction mixtures contained enzyme preparation (8.5 mg.), ATP (3 μmoles), MgCl₂ (3 μmoles), DL-histidine-2-C¹⁴ (0.8 μmole; 420,000 c.p.m.), amino acid as indicated (3 μmoles; DL-forms, 6 μmoles) and 2-amino-2-(hydroxymethyl)-1, 3-propanediol-HCl buffer (pH 7.3; 50 μmoles) in a final volume of 1 ml.; incubated at 37° for 60 minutes. No products were formed when either ATP or MgCl₂ were omitted.

Inactive: L-α-Aminobutyric acid, L-alanine, glycine, L-aspartic acid.

to occur in nature; carnosine and anserine are widely distributed in the skeletal muscles of various species (du Vigneaud and Behrens, 1939), and ophidine (β-alanyl-2-methylhistidine) has been isolated from snake muscle (Imamura, 1939; Kendo, 1944; Ono and Hirohata, 1956). The observation of the synthesis of β-alanyl peptides of lysine, arginine, and ornithine and various γ-aminobutyryl peptides suggests that these peptides may occur in nature. Attempts to investigate this possibility are now being made. It is also possible that certain histidine analogs (e.g., 1,2,4-triazole-3-alanine, 2-imidazole-alanine) may be incorporated into β-alanyl peptides *in vivo*.

In addition to these rather interesting findings concerning the specificity of the peptide-synthesizing system, we have also sought information concerning the mechanism of peptide bond formation. The observation that pyrophosphatase increased the rate of carnosine synthesis suggested that the reaction might involve formation of pyrophosphate and β-alanyl adenylate. Experiments with added synthetic β-alanyl adenylate appear to support this view. Thus, we observed formation of C¹⁴-carnosine when β-alanyl adenylate and DL-histidine-C¹⁴ were incubated with the enzyme (Fig. 4). The formation of carnosine in this system did not require ATP or mag-

TABLE IX

Synthesis of γ-Aminobutyryl Peptides[a]

Amino acid	Product (mμmoles)
L-Lysine	16.4
L-Ornithine	8.80
L-Histidine	24.3
D-Histidine	0
1-Methyl-DL-histidine	11.3
3-Methyl-L-histidine	6.60
L-Arginine	4.34

[a] The reaction mixtures contained enzyme preparation (8.5 mg.), ATP (3 μmoles), $MgCl_2$ (3 μmoles), amino acid (3 μmoles; DL form, 6 μmoles), γ-aminobutyric acid-1-C^{14} (0.3 μmole; 80,000 c.p.m.), and 2-amino-2-(hydroxymethyl)-1, 3-propanediol-HCl buffer (pH 7.3; 50 μmoles) in a final volume of 1 ml.; incubated at 37° for 60 minutes. No products were formed when either ATP or $MgCl_2$ was omitted.

nesium ions. Although there was some formation of carnosine in the absence of enzyme or when the enzyme was inactivated by heating, the rate was only about one-third of that observed in the presence of active enzyme. Furthermore, the carnosine formed nonenzymatically was shown to be racemic, while carnosine synthesized from β-alanyl adenylate and DL-histidine in the presence of enzyme was predominantly of the L-configuration. The use of racemic histidine in these studies appears advantageous in that it provides a means of distinguishing between enzymatic and nonenzymatic formation of carnosine.

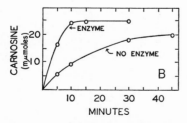

Fig. 4. Carnosine synthesis from β-alanyl adenylate and DL-histidine. The reaction mixtures consisted of enzyme preparation (8.5 mg.), β-alanyl adenylate (5.2 μmoles), DL-histidine-2-C^{14} (0.8 μmole; 420,000 c.p.m.), and 2-amino-2-(hydroxymethyl)-1, 3-propanediol-HCl buffer (pH 7.4; 150 μmoles) in a final volume of 1 ml. Incubated at 37°.

The enzyme also catalyzed ATP synthesis from β-alanyl adenylate and pyrophosphate (Table X). Initial attempts to show ATP

TABLE X

ENZYMATIC SYNTHESIS OF ATP FROM β-ALANYL
ADENYLATE AND PYROPHOSPHATE

Reaction mixtures	ATP formed (mμmoles)
Complete system[a]	114
Enzyme omitted	0.3
MgCl$_2$ omitted	1.3
NaF omitted	2.0
L-Alanyl-adenylate	2.0

[a] The reaction mixtures contained enzyme (8.5 mg.), MgCl$_2$ (2 μmoles), NaF (3 μmoles), amino acyl adenylate (4 μmoles), P^{32}-sodium pyrophosphate (1 μmole; 61,000 c.p.m.), and 2-amino-2-(hydroxymethyl)-1, 3-propanediol-HCl buffer (pH 7.3; 100 μmoles) in a final volume of 1 ml.; incubated for 15 minutes at 37°.

synthesis failed, probably because of the presence of enzyme systems capable of destroying ATP. However, when sodium fluoride was added to the reaction mixture, appreciable ATP synthesis could be demonstrated. No ATP was formed when enzyme, fluoride, or magnesium ions were separately omitted. ATP synthesis was also observed in this system with several other acyl adenylates including γ-aminobutyryl adenylate and glycyl adenylate. The synthesis of ATP observed with glycyl adenylate and certain other acyl adenylates may be catalyzed by other enzymes present in the enzyme preparation. Alternatively, such synthesis of ATP might be related to low specificity of the β-alanine-activating enzyme in the direction of ATP synthesis, as was observed with the tryptophan-activating enzyme. It is of interest, however, that β-alanyl adenylate was not active in ATP synthesis with the pancreatic tryptophan-activating enzyme. Thus far, attempts to show β-alanyl hydroxamate synthesis from β-alanine, ATP, and hydroxylamine, and to demonstrate β-alanine-dependent ATP-pyrophosphate exchange have not been successful, but further work with more purified enzyme preparations is in progress.

The results obtained with synthetic β-alanyl adenylate are consistent with the following sequence of reactions leading to carnosine synthesis:

(9) β-alanine $+$ ATP $+$ enzyme $\underset{\phantom{Mg^{++}}}{\overset{Mg^{++}}{\rightleftharpoons}}$ enzyme-β-alanyl adenylate $+$ PP

(10)   enzyme-β-alanyl adenylate $+$ L-histidine $\rightleftharpoons$ AMP $+$ enzyme $+$

β-alanyl-L-histidine.

The evidence indicates that β-alanyl adenylate can replace β-alanine, ATP, and magnesium ions in reaction (9). Presumably, the participation of β-alanyl adenylate in the enzymatic reaction is due to the formation of the enzyme-bound anhydride:

(11) β-alanyl adenylate $+$ enzyme $\rightleftharpoons$ enzyme-β-alanyl adenylate

This reaction is then similar to that of L-tryptophanyl adenylate with enzyme discussed above [reaction (8)]. Apparently neither reaction (10) nor reaction (11) requires added magnesium ions. Further purification of this peptide-synthesizing enzyme system is needed in order to demonstrate directly the formation of enzyme-bound β-alanyl adenylate, and to study other points such as pyrophosphate formation and binding of the anhydride to the enzyme. Reaction (10) requires further examination; although added ribonuclease did not inhibit carnosine formation, an intermediate acceptor (ribonucleic acid or perhaps another acceptor) may exist, and the participation of an additional enzyme cannot be excluded.

Concluding Remarks

There are many facets of the activation of amino acids that require additional exploration. Further purification of the enzymes that catalyze these reactions is of particular importance. Studies with relatively large quantities of the glutamine synthesis enzyme and of the enzymes that catalyze amino acyl adenylate formation might provide important data about the nature of the intermediates and of their binding to the enzyme. The present approach in which enzyme (as enzyme-anhydride complex), was used as a reactant rather than as a catalyst may lead to more definite information concerning enzyme-intermediate structure and function. Such investigations may also be helpful in understanding the role of the enzyme sulfhydryl groups, which appear to be necessary for activity.

The participation of acyl adenylates in the metabolism of acetate, other fatty acids, the synthesis of benzoyl glycine and phenylacetyl glutamine, and in the synthesis of carnosine and related peptides, is strongly indicated by the available information. However, in only one instance (carnosine synthesis), has it been shown that an amino acyl adenylate can participate in the enzymatic synthesis of a naturally occurring peptide bond. Acyl adenylate formation has not yet been demonstrated with all of the protein amino acids, although there are indications that many amino acids are active in pyrophosphate-ATP exchange reactions. Demonstration of the general nature of acyl adenylate formation with amino acids would be consistent with the belief that amino acyl adenylates are intermediates in protein synthesis; however, proof of such a hypothesis must necessarily rest upon more extensive data than are now available.

REFERENCES

Berg, P. (1955). *J. Am. Chem. Soc.* **77**, 3163.

Berg, P. (1956). *J. Biol. Chem.* **222**, 1025.

Berg, P. (1958). *J. Biol. Chem.* **233**, 601.

Berg, P., and Ofengand, E. J. (1958). *Proc. Natl. Acad. Sci. U.S.* **44**, 78.

Bloch, K. (1949). *J. Biol. Chem.* **179**, 1245.

Borsook, H., and Dubnoff, J. W. (1940). *J. Biol. Chem.* **132**, 307.

Borsook, H., and Dubnoff, J. W. (1947). *J. Biol. Chem.* **168**, 397.

Boyer, P. D., Koeppe, O. J., and Luchsinger, W. W. (1956). *J. Am. Chem. Soc.* **78**, 356.

Castelfranco, P., Moldave, K., and Meister, A. (1958a). *J. Am. Chem. Soc.* **80**, 2335.

Castelfranco, P., Meister, A., and Moldave, K. (1958b). *Symposium on Microsomal Particles and Protein Synthesis* p. 115.

Chantrenne, H. (1951). *J. Biol. Chem.* **189**, 227.

Chantrenne, H. (1958). *Ann. Rev. Biochem.* **27**, 35.

Cohen, P. P., and McGilvery, R. W. (1947). *J. Biol. Chem.* **171**, 121.

Davie, E. W., Königsberger, V. V., and Lipmann, F. (1956). *Arch. Biochem. Biophys.* **65**, 21.

DeMoss, J. A., and Novelli, G. D. (1956). *Biochim. et Biophys. Acta* **22**, 49.

du Vigneaud, V., and Behrens, O. K. (1939). *Ergeb. Physiol. biol. Chem. u. exptl. Pharmakol.* **41**, 917.

Elliott, W. H. (1948). *Nature* **161**, 128

Elliott, W. H. (1951). *Biochem. J.* **49**, 106.

Elliott, W. H. (1953). *J. Biol. Chem.* **201**, 661.

Hoagland, M. B. (1955). *Biochim. et Biophys. Acta* **16**, 288.

Hoagland, M. B., Keller, E. B., and Zamecnik, P. C. (1956). *J. Biol. Chem.* **218**, 345.

Hoagland, M. B., Zamecnik, P. C., Sharon, N., Lipmann, S., Stulberg, M. P., and Boyer, P. D. (1957). *Biochim. et Biophys. Acta* **26**, 215.

Hoagland, M. B., Stephenson, M. L., Scott, J. F., Hecht, L. I., and Zamecnik, P. C. (1958). *J. Biol. Chem.* **231**, 241.

Holley, R. W. (1957). *J. Am. Chem. Soc.* **79**, 658.

Imamura, H. (1939), *J. Biochem. (Tokyo)* **30**, 479.

Jencks, W. P., and Lipmann, F. (1957). *J. Biol. Chem.* **225**, 207.

Kalyankar, G. D., and Meister, A. (1959a). *J. Am. Chem. Soc.* **81**, 1515.

Kalyankar, G. D., and Meister, A. (1959b), *Federation Proc.* **18,** 256; *J. Biol. Chem.* **234,** 3210.

Karasek, M., Castelfranco, P., Krishnaswamy, P. R., and Meister, A. (1958a). *J. Am. Chem. Soc.* **80,** 2335.

Karasek, M., Castelfranco, P., Krishnaswamy, P. R., and Meister, A. (1958b). *Symposium on Microsomal Particles and Protein Synthesis* p. 109.

Kendo, K. (1944). *J. Biochem. (Tokyo).* **36,** 265.

Kingdon, H. S., Webster, L. D., Jr., and Davie, E. W. (1958). *Proc. Natl. Acad. Sci., U.S.* **44,** 757.

Kowalsky, A., Wyttenbach, C., Langer, L., and Koshland, D. E., Jr. (1956). *J. Biol. Chem.* **219,** 719.

Krebs, H. A. (1935). *Biochem. J.* **29,** 1951.

Krishnaswamy, P. R., and Meister, A. (1960). *J. Biol. Chem.* **235,** 408.

Levintow, L., and Meister, A. (1953). *J. Am. Chem. Soc.* **75,** 3039.

Levintow, L., and Meister, A. (1954). *J. Biol. Chem.* **209,** 265.

Levintow, L., and Meister, A. (1956). *Federation Proc.* **15,** 299.

Levintow, L., Meister, A., Kuff, E. L., and Hogeboom, G. H. (1955). *J. Am. Chem. Soc.* **77,** 5304.

Loftfield, R. B. (1957). *Progr. Biophys. and Biophys. Chem.* **8,** 347.

Maas, W. K., and Novelli, G. D. (1953). *Arch. Biochem. Biophys.* **43,** 336.

Mandeles, S., and Bloch, K. (1955). *J. Biol. Chem.* **214,** 639.

Meister, A. (1959). *Revs. Modern Phys.* **31,** 210.

Moldave, K., and Meister, A. (1957). *J. Biol. Chem.* **229,** 463.

Moldave, K., Castelfranco, P., and Meister, A. (1959). *J. Biol. Chem.* **234,** 841.

Moyed, H. S., and Lipmann, F. (1957). *J. Bacteriol.* **73,** 117.

Novelli, G. D. (1958). *Proc. Natl. Acad. Sci. U.S.* **44,** 86.

Ogata, K., and Nohara, H. (1957). *Biochim. et Biophys. Acta* **25,** 659.

Ono, T., and Hirohata, R. (1956). *Z. physiol. Chem.* **304,** 77.

Schachter, D., and Taggart, J. V. (1954). *J. Biol. Chem.* **211,** 271.

Schweet, R. S., Bovard, F. C., Allen, E., and Glassman, E. (1958). *Proc. Natl. Acad. Sci. U.S.* **44,** 173.

Snoke, J. E., and Bloch, K. (1955). *J. Biol. Chem.* **213,** 825.

Speck, J. F. (1947). *J. Biol. Chem.* **168,** 403.

Speck, J. F. (1949). *J. Biol. Chem.* **179,** 1387, 1405.

Weiss, S. B., Acs, G., and Lipmann, F. (1958a). *Federation Proc.* **17,** 333.

Weiss, S. B., Acs, G., and Lipmann, F. (1958b). *Proc. Natl. Acad. Sci. U.S.* **44,** 189.

Winnick, R. E., and Winnick, T. (1959). *Biochim. et Biophys. Acta* **31,** 47.

Wong, G. K., Meister, A., and Moldave, K. (1959). *Biochim. et Biophys. Acta* **36,** 531.

Zachau, H. G., Acs, G., and Lipmann, F. (1958). *Proc. Natl. Acad. Sci. U.S.* **44,** 885.

Zamecnik, P. C., and Keller, E. B. (1954). *J. Biol. Chem.* **209,** 337.

Zamecnik, P. C., Stephenson, M. L., and Hecht, L. I. (1958). *Proc. Natl. Acad. Sci. U.S.* **44,** 73.

Zioudrou, C., Fujii, S., and Fruton, J. S. (1958). *Proc. Natl. Acad. Sci. U.S.* **44,** 439.

Enzyme Activities and Tumor Progression

SIDNEY WEINHOUSE

The Institute for Cancer Research, Philadelphia, Pennsylvania

JUST A LITTLE OVER 18 MONTHS AGO, I had the privilege of participating in a program honoring Jesse Greenstein on the occasion of his award of the Hildebrand Prize of the Washington Section of the American Chemical Society. Little did those of us who witnessed this well-deserved tribute to him realize that less than one year later, we would receive the shocking news of his untimely death. Although he did not live his allotted span of years, he packed several lifetimes of scientific contributions into those he had, and he died at the height of his productivity in the midst of an active program of research and editorial work. A particularly unfortunate aspect of his untimely death is that it came at a time when I believe the results of his prodigious early program on cancer enzymology were just beginning to be appreciated in their full significance. From this work there arose an important generalization concerning cancer enzymology, and it is this generalization, together with several corollary generalizations, which will be the basis of my remarks today.

As a result of a systematic study of enzyme activities of a variety of normal and neoplastic tissues, Greenstein (1954, 1956) concluded that as a class, tumors of the most diverse origins tend to converge to a common cell type; that is to say, tumors, in their biochemical characteristics, resemble one another more closely than they resemble their tissues of origin. This generalization is best exemplified in the first chart (Fig. 1) in which there appear data on the activities of ten enzymes in a variety of normal and neoplastic tissues of the mouse (Greenstein, 1956). If we examine the behavior of cytochrome oxidase in the first column, as well as that of esterase, thymonuclease, ribonuclease, alkaline phosphatase, xanthine dehydrogenase, and arginase, we see that the activities of each of these enzymes fall within a relatively narrow range, this

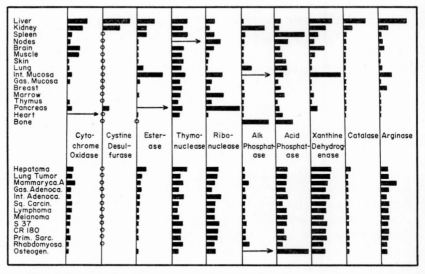

FIG. 1. Levels of various enzymes in normal and cancer tissues of mice. Relative activities are denoted by the length of the horizontal bars.

range being intermediate with respect to a much wider range of variation displayed by the normal tissues. Many other examples of the Greenstein generalization are available for a host of additional tissues and enzymes. In general, one can state, as a corollary of Greenstein's generalization, that there are no enzymes or other cell components found specifically in tumor tissues. In the past, many claims have been made with respect to unique components in cancer tissues but none of these has withstood the test of time. Enzyme differences between cancerous and noncancerous tissues are quantitative, not qualitative.

Another corollary of the Greenstein generalization, which emerges from a host of biochemical studies on tumors, is that some enzymes, in particular those involved in specific functional activities of the normal tissue, are nearly or completely lost in neoplasms. Such deletions of enzyme activity are most striking in liver tumors where the unique metabolic role of the liver endows this tissue with a highly characteristic enzyme makeup. Greenstein (1954) reported the loss or great reduction in mice and rats in the activities of arginase, catalase, cytochrome c, cytochrome oxidase, and esterase in hepatomas compared with liver. More recently, investigators have reported the loss or reduction in the Novikoff hepatoma of a large number of enzymes normally present in rat liver; for example, of 5'-nucleotidase, nucleoside phosphorylase, guanase, adenase, uricase, and xanthine dehydrogenase (de Lamirande et al., 1958), of glutamic dehydrogenase (Allard et al., 1957), of esterase and uricase (Allard and de Lamirande, 1959), of glutamic-oxalacetic and glutamic-pyruvic transaminases (Birns et al., 1959), of glycerophosphate dehydrogenase (Boxer and Shonk, 1959), of DPN-TPN transhydrogenase and TPN-cytochrome c reductase (Reynafarge and Potter, 1957), and of tryptophan peroxidase-oxidase, tyrosine transaminase, phenylalanine hydroxylase, serine and threonine dehydrase, histidase, and p-hydroxyphenylpyruvic oxidase (Auerbach and Waisman, 1958). Weber and his colleagues (Ashmore et al., 1958) have reported the absence in both primary and transplanted Novikoff hepatoma, of glucose 6-phosphatase, and of fructose-1,6-diphosphatase, enzymes involved in the important hepatic function of gluconeogenesis, a function which is also lost in the liver tumor.

In our own laboratory (Medes et al., 1956) we have compared certain metabolic characteristics of liver with those of the primary liver tumor which arises in liver on azo dye feeding and have found an almost complete loss in the ability to synthesize ketone bodies, to store glycogen on feeding of a high carbohydrate diet, and to synthesize fatty acids from acetate. Even the same tumor cultured in different laboratories may differ enzymatically; for example, Birns et al. (1959) recently reported that glutamic dehydrogenase and TPN-cytochrome c reductase are present in their strain of the Novikoff hepatoma. Again recently it was reported (Pitot et al., 1959) that the Dunning rat hepatoma, also transplanted many generations, contained high activity of DPN-cytochrome c reductase as well as lesser levels of other enzymes previously reported to be absent in the Novikoff tumor. (These discrepancies should alert us to the possibility that reported differences may sometimes reflect differences in experimental procedures rather than in neoplasms.)

One could cite many other examples of the loss of specific metabolic pathways and enzymes when a normal tissue becomes cancerous. Some of these are lost in the primary tumor, which arises directly in the tissue of origin; others may be retained in the primary tumor, but may subsequently be lost during the course of successive transplantation (Greenstein, 1954). Novikoff (1957) has pointed out that in the course of many transplant generations, the Novikoff hepatoma has undergone such great change that it no longer bears any resemblance to its tissue of origin.

As Johnson (1958) has recently pointed out, essentially the same situation exists when cells, either malignant or nonmalignant, are grown in tissue culture. Even without a neoplastic change, the artificial cultivation of cells results in profound metabolic changes accompanied by changes in enzyme activities. The work of Paul and Pearson (1957), Perske *et al.* (1957), and Eagle *et al.* (1958) on liver cells grown in tissue culture provides ample grounds for the assumption that very early in the cultivation of liver cells *in vitro*, hepatic characteristics disappear, and few, if any, biochemical features of the intact organ survive.

These examples from the literature point out to us an all-important fact; namely, that a tumor is not a fixed biochemical entity, with a characteristic invariant pattern of enzyme activities, but is continually undergoing enzyme changes with successive cell divisions and with successive transplantations. The nature of these transformations, though still not entirely clear, is becoming more explicable in the light of recent biological studies. It has been known from clinical observations over many years that tumors change during their growth in the host. In a comprehensive review of such changes, Foulds (1951) points out that apparently benign tumors of long standing suddenly take on the characteristics of malignancy. Early studies in experimental skin cancer induced by carcinogenic hydrocarbons showed that the malignant stage is usually preceded by an early neoplastic stage, during which the withdrawal of the carcinogen may result in regression. Many spontaneous tumors originating in endocrine organs of mice start as benign neoplasms which go through a stage of hormonal dependence for acceleration or inhibition of growth. At this stage these tumors are neither invasive nor transplantable. Later they may lose their responsiveness to hormones, they may stop secreting hormones, and they may become transplantable. These alterations are successive and independent, showing any combination and number of such progressive changes. Other biological transformations which have been considered as examples of this phenomenon of tumor progression and which are undergoing investigation at present are changes in chromosome number, in development of resistance to certain drugs, in cell morphology, and in the ability to grow in the ascites form (Klein, 1959). There is increasing evidence that at least in certain instances these changes are due to mutations, followed by selection, in much the same way that such changes occur in populations of bacteria; perhaps the best documented evidence is in the development of drug resistance (Law, 1956). Indeed, recent studies of Skipper and his colleagues (Brockman *et al.*, 1959) have shown that the change of a tumor from sensitivity to resistance to the toxic action of 8-azaguanine and 6-mercaptopurine can be localized biochemically as the loss of a specific enzyme, namely, the transphosphorylase responsible for converting the purine analog to the corresponding ribonucleotide.

The biochemical transformations embraced by the Greenstein generalization, namely the convergence of enzyme pattern and the deletion of specialized biochemical functions, are so obviously similar to the successive biological changes now encompassed under the term tumor progression, that both phenomena can probably be regarded as reflections of the same underlying process of successive mutations and selection undergone by rapidly dividing tumor cells.

I should now like to discuss two biochemical theories of cancer induction in the light of this interpretation of Greenstein's generalization. In 1942 and 1943 the suggestions came from the University of Wisconsin (Lavik *et al.*, 1942; Potter, 1943, 1944) that a carcinogen may act by combining with a key protein, one which is involved in the mechanism of cell replication. The presence of such an altered protein was conceived to be the initiating factor in the carcinogenic process, with continued proliferation being due to resultant lack of control of cell division. The subsequent experimental studies of the Millers (1953) resulted in a modification and expansion to an hypothesis of protein deletion. These investigators found that the carcinogenic dye, 4-dimethylaminoazobenzene, and related dyes, combined with liver proteins, presumably in a covalent link, and further observed that the dye was not bound to protein in the tumor. It was subsequently found, through studies of Sorof and Cohen and Sorof *et al.* (1951) that soluble dye-bound proteins occurred in a small fraction called "h," which could be characterized by its migration in electrophoresis, and the further significant observation was made that this class of soluble liver proteins was nearly absent from the liver tumors which subsequently developed. Work of the Millers, Heidelberger, and the Weissburgers indicate that binding of carcinogens is not confined to liver but occurs in target tissues with all carcinogens thus far tested (Weissburger and Weissburger, 1958).

The salient features of the deletion hypothesis, as now envisioned by Miller (1958) and Haddow (1958), are given in Fig. 2. Briefly summarized, this theory presupposes an attachment of the carcinogen to a key protein (or proteins) involved in control of growth, thus resulting in their inactivation or removal from their functional locus of action. Under these circumstances, control of growth is lost, and since the new cells are formed in the absence of these controlling proteins, cell division continues unchecked.

As our knowledge of cell replication has expanded, the deletion hypothesis has grown increasingly plausible. It is now generally recognized that hereditary information is coded in DNA, and this is transmitted to RNA which provides the template for protein synthesis. Both DNA and RNA probably function in nucleoproteins. Any alteration in the structure of these nucleoproteins would be expected to result in aberrations of the replication mechanisms

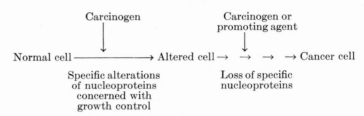

Fig. 2. Deletion hypothesis of carcinogenesis according to Miller (1958).

and thus lead to mutation. Since the cancer cell fulfills all the requirements of a mutated cell (Furth, 1959), it is plausible to assume that the conversion of a normal to a neoplastic cell represents the result of mutation [or a series of mutations (Burnet, 1957)] in which control of cell division is lost.

Despite its plausibility, as well as the compelling evidence of relationships between carcinogen-binding and deletion of "h" proteins, no specific deletion has been discovered which can be associated mechanistically with cancer initiation. Attempts have been made to "explain" hepatocarcinogenesis in terms of specific enzyme deletions (Ashmore *et al.*, 1958; Potter, 1958). An example is the suggestion by Potter (1958) that the deletion of a catabolic enzyme (or enzymes) stimulates the occurrence of alternate anabolic pathways of metabolism. The main point of evidence cited in favor of this interpretation of the deletion hypothesis is the relative weakness of purine and pyrimidine breakdown mechanisms in the hepatoma as compared with liver (de Lamirande *et al.*, 1958) and the low levels of other "catabolic" enzymes in the Novikoff hepatoma. According to this view, cell division is held in check by a deficiency of building blocks for nucleic acid synthesis. The deletion of catabolic enzymes results in the accumulation of such precursors of cell components, thus stimulating alternate metabolic pathways leading to synthesis of nucleic acids required for cell division. However, the very diversity of enzyme deletion, as embodied in the Greenstein generalization, compels one to assume in the absence of contrary data, that any specific deletion is simply a characteristic of rapidly dividing cells and not necessarily an initiating factor in carcinogenesis.

I would now like to consider what may be regarded as a special case of the deletion theory, namely, the theory of impaired respiration propounded and vigorously supported by Warburg during the past 35 years (Warburg, 1930, 1956). According to Warburg, all carcinogenic agents (and as carcinogenic agents Warburg included not only chemicals, but radiation and viruses as well) initiate the cancer process by deletion of a crucial stage in respiration. This hypothesis regards the cancer cell in terms of a reversion to a primitive mode of metabolism, like that of the lactic acid bacteria in which fermentation rather than oxidation of glucose supplies the energy required for growth. Foremost in the development of this theory was the important discovery that the tumor cell has an extraordinary capability for converting glucose to lactic acid.

Several respiratory characteristics of tumors have emerged from modern biochemical studies, against which the Warburg theory can be measured.

1. If we examine a wide variety of normal and neoplastic tissues with respect to their respiration, we find that here, as in other metabolic activities, the Greenstein generalization holds, namely, tumors by and large consume oxygen at rates which are within the wide ranges displayed by a variety of normal tissues (Weinhouse, 1955).

2. Very good evidence is now available to indicate that whatever may be the reason for the high glycolysis, tumor cells possess the same electron transport systems, and insofar as this matter has been studied, these operate in the same sequence as they do in normal tissues (Chance and Hess, 1959).

3. Warburg (1956), in a recent vigorous defense of his theory, proposed that the impairment in respiration which he regards as the *sine qua non* of cancer, may not be evident as a diminished oxygen consumption, but may be due to uncoupling of phosphorylation from respiration. In his view the cancer cell, unable to maintain an adequate supply of ATP by respiration, resorts to glycolysis for its energy needs. This interesting hypothesis is difficult to test directly, for oxidative phosphorylation in an intact cell cannot easily be measured. However, the presence of enzymatic mechanisms for coupling of phosphorylation with oxygen uptake have certainly been demonstrated in tumor mitochondria (Williams-Ashman and Kennedy, 1952; Kielley, 1952; Andrejew *et al.*, 1956).

4. For many years a critical examination of the Warburg hypothesis was difficult, owing to the uncertainty concerning the respiratory substrates of tumors. The availability of isotopic glucose and fatty acids has made possible a direct appraisal of the question whether tumor cells lack the ability to oxidize glucose, simply by following the incorporation of isotopic carbon in the respiratory CO_2. Without exception, such studies have shown that tumors can carry out the combustion of glucose and fatty acids to CO_2, again at rates within ranges displayed by normal tissues, and have also demonstrated the participation of the citric acid cycle in their oxidative metabolism (Weinhouse, 1955).

Thus, by every reasonable criterion one may use to measure respiratory activity, one cannot find a deficiency in tumors. Indeed, the persistence of high respiratory activity in tumors transplanted for many generations, when considered in the light of the numerous deletions of other functional activities of normal tissues, attests to the fundamental necessity of oxidative mechanisms for survival of the cell. It is conceivable that the high glycolysis may also have a special survival value to the cancer cell, but evidently not because aerobic energy conversion systems are lacking.

In concluding my remarks on the Greenstein generalization, I would like to point out that it has a two-fold importance to cancer biochemistry. First, it should serve as a warning to biochemists that the cancer cell cannot be precisely defined. An awareness that the cancer cell is continually changing its biochemical makeup should be a restraining influence on all of us to refrain from an all-too-prevalent tendency to regard each newly discovered enzyme deletion as the explanation for the neoplastic process. Since deletions of enzyme activity can doubtless occur after a cell becomes malignant, a deletion theory must ultimately rest on evidence linking a specific deletion to cancer initiation.

In pointing the way to research on biochemical aspects of mutation and selection, processes undergone by neoplastic no less than by nonneoplastic cells, it can serve also in a positive way as a fruitful guiding principle. For example, we may ask whether specific deletions offer selective advantages for survival? Can mutation rates be minimized? Is there a pattern of enzyme deletion or is this a random process? Can specific enzyme deletions be correlated with functional or morphologic changes? The highly neoplastic cell which has been transplanted many generations is like a stripped down racing car in which other metabolic activities have apparently been subordinated to the overwhelming compulsion to divide. Studies of the enzymes retained in such cells, no less than those which have been deleted should tell us what is the minimum enzyme machinery necessary for cellular multiplication.

Despite the spectacular advances in biochemistry, our knowledge of the cell is still primitive. Greenstein was above all a realist who had no illusions about the inadequacy of the equipment with which the biochemist has to battle against one of mankind's great scourges. In his concluding paragraph of Chapter 1 of his book on biochemistry of cancer, published in 1953, Greenstein quoted a statement, made by Woglom in 1913, which I believe deserves repetition as a viewpoint appropriate to the thoughtful cancer researchers of today. "It must be frankly confessed that so far, at least, the study of cancer, instead of affording an understanding of the nature of the disease, has but opened up new problems which were formerly not even conceived. Hence, earnest students have had to content themselves with slowly and laboriously collecting data, in the hope that at some future time these may be combined into a coherent whole. Slow at least, this is nevertheless the only way in which the goal can be surely attained. . . ."

This chapter did not end on such a pessimistic note, however, because he continued, with this hope, in which I am sure all of us join. "There is still much ground to be covered before the end is in sight, but science admits of no insuperable barricades. With confidence in the scientific method, and with tools of ever-increasing power and subtlety, it is certain that the combined efforts of the oncological sciences will ultimately yield the comprehension and mastery of the neoplastic transformation."

REFERENCES

Allard, C. and de Lamirande, G. (1959). *Proc. Am. Assoc. Cancer Research* **3,** 1.

Allard, C., de Lamirande, G., and Cantero, A. (1957). *Cancer Research* **17,** 862.

Andrejew, A., Rosenberg, A. J., Zajdela, F. (1956). *Compt. rend. soc. biol.* **150,** 1855.

Ashmore, J., Weber, G., and Landau, B. R. (1958). *Cancer Research* **18,** 974.

Auerbach, V. H., and Waisman, H. A. (1958). *Cancer Research* **18,** 543.

Birns, M., Essner, E., and Novikoff, A. B. (1959). *Proc. Am. Assoc. Cancer Research* **3, 7.**

Boxer, G. E., and Shonk, C. E. (1959). *Proc. Am. Assoc. Cancer Research* **3,** 8.

Brockman, R. W., Bennett, L. L., and Skipper, H. E. (1959). *Proc. Am. Assoc. Cancer Research* **3,** 10.

Burnet, M. (1957). *Brit. Med. J.* **I,** 779.

Chance, B., and Hess, B. (1959). *Science* **129,** 700.

de Lamirande, G., Allard, C., and Cantero, A. (1958). *Cancer Research* **18,** 952.

Eagle, H., Barban, S., Levy, M., and Schulze, H. O. (1958). *J. Biol. Chem.* **233,** 551.

Foulds, L. (1951). *Cancer Research* **14,** 327.

Furth, J. (1959). *Cancer Research* **19,** 241.

Greenstein, J. P. (1954). "Biochemistry of Cancer," 2nd ed. Academic Press, New York.

Greenstein, J. P. (1956). *Cancer Research* **16,** 641.

Haddow, A. (1958). *Brit. Med. Bull.* **14,** 79.

Johnson, I. S. (1958). *Cancer Research* **18,** 367.

Kielley, R. K. (1952). *Cancer Research* **12,** 124.

Klein, G. (1959). *Cancer Research* **19,** 343.

Law, L. W. (1956). *Cancer Research* **16,** 698.

Lavik, P. S., Moore, P. R., Rusch, H. P., and Baumann, C. A. (1942). *Cancer Research* **2,** 189.

Medes, G., Friedmann, B. F., and Weinhouse, S. (1956). *Cancer Research* **16,** 57.

Miller, J. A. (1958). *In* "Amino Acid and Protein Metabolism," Report of the 30th Ross Conference on Pediatric Research. (S. J. Fomon, ed.), p. 47. Ross Laboratories, Columbus, Ohio.

Miller, J. A., and Miller, E. C. (1953). *Advances in Cancer Research* **1,** 340.

Novikoff, A. B. (1957). *Cancer Research* **17,** 1010.

Paul, J., and Pearson, E. S. (1957). *Exptl. Cell Research* **12,** 233.

Perske, W. F., Parks, R. E., Jr., and Walker, D. L. (1957). *Science* **125,** 1290.

Pitot, H. C., Fohn, C. H., Clark, W. H., Jr., and Farber, E. (1959). *Proc. Am. Assoc. Cancer Research* **3,** 52.

Potter, V. R. (1943). *Cancer Research* **3,** 358.

Potter, V. R. (1944). *Advances in Enzymol.* **4,** 201.

Potter, V. R. (1958). *Federation Proc.* **17,** 691.

Reynafarge, B., and Potter, V. R. (1957). *Cancer Research* **17,** 1112.

Sorof, S., and Cohen, P. P. (1951). *Cancer Research* **11,** 376.

Sorof, S., Cohen, P. P., Miller, E. C., and Miller, J. A. (1951). *Cancer Research* **11,** 383.

Warburg, O. (1930). "Metabolism of Tumors" (Trans. by F. Dickens). Arnold Constable, London.

Warburg, O. (1956). *Science* **123**, 309.

Weinhouse, S. (1955). *Advances in Cancer Research* **3**, 270.

Weissburger, E. K., and Weissburger, J. H. (1958). *Advances in Cancer Research* **5**, 333.

Williams-Ashman, H. G., and Kennedy, E. P. (1952). *Cancer Research* **12**, 415.

Free Amino Acids and Related Substances in Normal and Neoplastic Tissues*

EUGENE ROBERTS and DAISY G. SIMONSEN

Department of Biochemistry, City of Hope Medical Center, Duarte, California

Introduction

THE BASIC GOAL of the research program under-taken by the writers, the pattern for which was set by Dr. Green-stein's pioneering studies, has been to attempt to delineate the roles of various metabolic systems in normal and neoplastic tissues, to study the distribution of these systems at various stages of de-velopment in a particular species, and to compare various species at different levels of the evolutionary scale. The ultimate aim of such studies is to identify those biochemical differences which dis-tinguish normal growing and nongrowing cells from cancer cells and which may underlie the neoplastic process. This constitutes, in its broadest sense, the elucidation of the distribution of various en-zyme systems and a determination of the concentrations and turn-over rates of their substrates and the products of their reactions. A necessary first step in elucidating metabolic balances in living cells is a determination of the types and amounts of various im-portant cellular constituents. The point of departure in our labora-tory was made in the study of nitrogen metabolism, fully realizing that ultimately connections would have to be established with the results obtained in similar studies on glycolysis and cellular oxida-tions, nucleic acid and lipid metabolism, distributions of inorganic ions, coenzymes, etc.

Initial experiments in 1946-1949 dealt with urea and ammonia contents (Roberts and Frankel, 1949a), arginase activity (Roberts and Frankel, 1949b), and the distribution of amino acids in hydrol-yzates of whole tissue (Roberts *et al.*, 1949) in normal epidermis

* This work was supported in part by research grant No. 2568 from the National Cancer Institute, United States Public Health Service.

of mice, in epidermis treated with methylcholanthrene in benzene or benzene alone, and in a transplantable squamous cell carcinoma originally derived from a primary carcinoma produced on the back of a mouse by the application of methylcholanthrene. Although interesting differences were observed between normal and treated epidermis and the carcinomata, it could not be concluded from these studies that the tumor tissue showed a distinctive metabolic pattern which would set it completely apart from all of the nonmalignant normal or hyperplastic epidermal samples studied. It also was apparent that in the state of our knowledge of protein metabolism at that time such studies would have only descriptive value and could only become meaningful when the basic mechanisms of protein metabolism would be elucidated. On the other hand, even then the knowledge of amino acid metabolism was substantial and the newly developed paper chromatographic procedures (Consden *et al.*, 1944; Dent, 1947; Dent *et al.*, 1947; Dent, 1948) furnished tools which were ideally suited for giving simultaneous information about the maximal number of ninhydrin-reactive constituents, and, although semiquantitative at best, could give valuable hints about which substances should be studied further.

General Comments Regarding Free Amino Acids of Tissues

The first application of the two-dimensional paper chromatographic technique to protein-free extracts prepared from mammalian tissues immediately after removal from the animal showed that the free amino acid pattern of the squamous cell carcinoma was completely different from that found in epidermis of normal adult and newborn mice, in epidermis made hyperplastic by application of carcinogen, or in nonmalignant papillomata (Roberts and Tishkoff, 1949). Extension of these observations to other tissues and types of tumors led to the finding that each tissue of the healthy adult mouse of a particular strain had a characteristic distribution of free amino acids, while quite similar patterns of free amino acids were found in many different types of transplanted and spontaneous tumors (Roberts and Frankel, 1949c). Examples typifying these results are contained in Figs. 1-4, which show a comparison of chromatograms of extracts of normal mouse liver and epidermis with those obtained from equal fresh weights of a transplanted hepatoma and squamous cell carcinoma, respectively. The findings on free amino acids were in striking agreement with

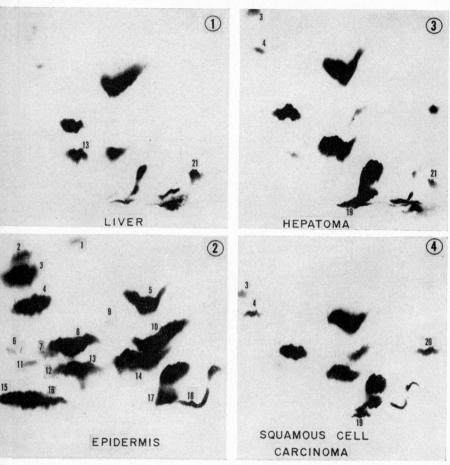

FIGS. 1–4. Comparison of free amino acid patterns of mouse-liver (Fig. 1) and epidermis (Fig. 2) with those found in a transplantable hepatoma (Fig. 3) and squamous cell carcinoma (Fig. 4). Extracts obtained from 75 mg. of fresh weight of tissue were employed for descending two-dimensional chromatography (phenol, right to left; lutidine, bottom to top). Constituents on chromatograms: tyrosine, 1; phenylalanine, 2; leucine and isoleucine, 3; valine, 4; taurine, 5; proline, 6; hydroxyproline, 7; alanine, 8; threonine, 9; serine, 10; histidine, 11; glyceryl-phosphorylethanolamine and/or β-alanine, 12; glutamine, 13; glycine, 14; arginine, 15; lysine, 16; glutamic acid, 17; aspartic acid, 18; ethanolamine phosphate, 19; cystine (cysteic acid), 20; glutathione, 21.

the generalization set forth by Greenstein on the basis of enzyme assays (Greenstein, 1954): "No matter how or from which tissues tumors arise, they more nearly resemble each other chemically than they do normal tissues or than normal tissues resemble each other."

From surveys of extracts of tissues from human, monkey, dog, cat, guinea pig, rabbit, rat, mouse, opossum, chicken, alligator, snake, turtle, frog, salamander and a wide variety of marine organisms in our laboratory it has been concluded that in a given species at a particular stage of development each normal tissue (cell type), including every type of blood cell (Rouser, 1957), has a distribution of ninhydrin-reactive constituents which is characteristic for that tissue. In healthy organisms the patterns are highly specific and reproducible from one animal to another, so that with some experience it is possible to determine the tissue from which the extract had been prepared upon inspection of the chromatogram. Analyses of various tissues from the chick embryo, frog, salamander, and mouse at different stages of development revealed that changes in distribution of free amino acids may take place at all stages of development until the final adult functional and structural patterns are laid down (Roberts et al., 1957, 1958).

Tissues generally contain much greater concentrations of a number of the ninhydrin-reactive substances than are found in whole blood or plasma, and the relative amounts of the various constituents are not the same as those in plasma. It is not known whether the easily extractable amino acids are truly in free solution in cells or whether they are retained by some as yet undetermined mechanism. Relatively gentle procedures such as homogenization in cold 80% alcohol, heat coagulation and dialysis, or deproteinization with cold trichloroacetic or perchloric acids yield extracts which give identical chromatograms. Similar patterns of amino acids were found in extracts of whole cells, ground cytoplasm, and isolated cell nuclei prepared from livers of fed Wistar rats by the Behrens technique, which utilizes organic solvents (Dounce et al., 1950). Chromatographic studies in our laboratory of extracts of particulate fractions of liver and tumor cells prepared in a variety of aqueous media ordinarily considered suitable for subsequent metabolic studies of the fractions invariably have shown a virtually complete liberation of the easily extractable amino acids to have taken place into the suspending media. However, it cannot yet be assumed that the amino acids exist in the free form in the cytoplasm or nucleoplasm in animal cells. The amino acids may be held by adsorptive forces at interfaces and surfaces. Loose bonds may exist between these constituents and proteins, nucleic acids, or phospholipids, or sequestration may take place in intracellular structures. It is even conceivable that the amino acids may exist in the cell in the form of extremely labile derivatives or complexes which are dissociated by every extraction procedure which has been employed to date.

In general, the physiological significance of the presence of relatively large quantities of some of the amino acids in the free or easily extractable form in tissues is not known. There are a number of possible alternate pathways of metabolism in the case of most of the detectable constituents. The concentration of a particular constituent must be considered to be a function of the metabolic activities of the tissue, reflecting the complex interactions involved in the formation, utilization, and concentrative assimilation.

Constancy of Free Amino Acid Patterns of Tissues: Experimental Alterations of Patterns

Free amino acids of the tissues of rats have been found to be remarkably resistant to a variety of physiological changes (Simonsen and Roberts, in preparation; see also Kit and Griffin, 1958, for relevant references). It was shown that complete inanition and dehydration in rats until death produced no marked changes in free amino acid distribution in liver, kidney, muscle, or brain. An extensive series of experiments was performed in which the free amino acid patterns were determined in liver, kidney, muscle, and brain of young Sprague-Dawley rats which had been hypophysectomized, adrenalectomized, or thyroidectomized for various periods of time. Comparisons were made in each instance with litter-mate controls of the same sex. Results showed clearly that only minor changes could be observed in any of the tissues at any of the times studied as a result of the procedures employed. It would, therefore, appear that the endocrine controls exerted by the thyroid, adrenals, or the pituitary are not essential for the maintenance of the characteristic steady state concentrations of the free amino acids of the tissues studied, although the turnover rates and relative flow of nitrogen and carbon through pathways involving these amino acids may be altered greatly (Hoberman, 1949). No significant changes in content of amino acids were noted in brains of Swiss mice when a variety of drugs were injected in pharmacologically effective doses (Roberts *et al.*, 1958).

The characteristic amino acid patterns of tissue have been altered in a variety of experiments. Concentrations of free amino acids were found to decrease profoundly in the prostate after castration and atrophy, and normal levels of these constituents were restored by administration of testosterone propionate (Marvin and Awapara, 1949). Injection of lethal doses of ammonium acetate into rats produced large increases in free aspartic acid levels in the liver and increases in glutamine levels of brain, testes, and muscle (du Ruisseau *et al.*, 1957). Remarkable increases in the content of glutamine over control levels were found in the brains of hepatectomized dogs (Flock *et al.*, 1953) and in dogs during the spontaneous coma associated with Eck fistula (Bollman *et al.*, 1957) or after the bilateral intracarotid infusion of lactate-Ringer's solution containing 1% of ammonium hydroxide (Eiseman *et al.*, 1959). Hypoglycemia produced by insulin caused a decrease in brain glutamic acid, an approximately isomolar increase in aspartic acid content, and a small decrease in γ-aminobutyric acid (Dawson, 1953), while fluoroacetate produced a reduction in the content of both glutamic and aspartic acids in the brains of rats (Dawson, 1953). Lysine and arginine contents were found to be increased and glutamic and aspartic acid levels decreased in skeletal muscle, kidney, and diaphragm of potassium-deficient rats (Iacobellis *et al.*, 1956). After the production of experimental myocardial infraction by ligation of the anterior descending coronary artery of the dog heart, progressive and marked losses of taurine, alanine, glutamine, glutamic and aspartic acids, and glutathione were noted in the infarcted area of the left ventricle, while essentially normal levels of these constituents were found in the noninfarcted areas (Chanin *et al.*, 1956).

Free Amino Acids of Tumor Cells and Host Tissues During Progressive Growth of Tumors (Simonsen and Roberts, in preparation)

It was of considerable interest to determine whether there would be progressive changes in amino acid patterns of tumors grown in animals at various times after implantation and whether if such changes were observed they could be correlated with any changes in the amino acid patterns of the host tissues. The free amino acids were studied in the Ehrlich tumor grown in C57 black mice at from 48 hours after transplantation of 5×10^6 cells until 11 days, the average life span of the tumor-bearing animals. The free amino acids of both the cells and the ascitic fluid were remarkably constant throughout this period of observation. Free glutamine was not detected either in the cells or fluid at any time. On the 8th and 11th days there were increases in the alanine content of the fluid. No changes from the controls were observed in the amino acid levels of the liver and muscle of the tumor-bearing host up to one week after transplantation of the tumor. However, at 8 and 11 days there appeared to be decreases in the glutamine levels of both muscle and liver. In the case of the kidney and brain, no consistent changes were found as a result of the growth of the tumor. Thus, growth and development of the Ehrlich ascites tumor produced only little observable change in the amino acid levels of the tissues studied, and the tumor free amino acid patterns were remarkably constant.

A study similar in all respects to that above was performed in rats bearing the ascites form of the Murphy lymphosarcoma (Figs. 5-12). Small amounts of glutamine were detectable at 48 hours after transplantation of the tumor, possibly because of the presence of a small number of leucocytes at this time, but this amino acid was not detectable at subsequent time intervals. During the progressive growth of the tumor there was a decrease in the content of glutamic and aspartic acids and glutathione with little or no change in the other observable constituents in the tumor cells. The pattern of amino acids in the fluid was unchanged throughout the period of observation (8 days). The amino acid patterns of the liver were constant in all constituents with the exception of taurine, which appeared to vary from one sample to another. The level of glutamine in the liver decreased at 8 days after transplantation of the tumor. The only change found in the kidney was a decrease in free glutamine level at 8 days. The amino acid patterns in samples of leg muscle of tumor-bearing rats were normal for 5 days after transplantation, but at 8 days decreases in alanine, glycine, serine, glutamine, and glutamic acid were observed by comparison with the controls (Figs. 13-20). No alterations, whatsoever, were found at any time in the patterns of the amino acids of the brains of the tumor-bearing animals (Figs. 21-28). A similar study giving similar results also was conducted with the solid Walker 256 tumor in rats.

It can be concluded from the above observations that the pat-

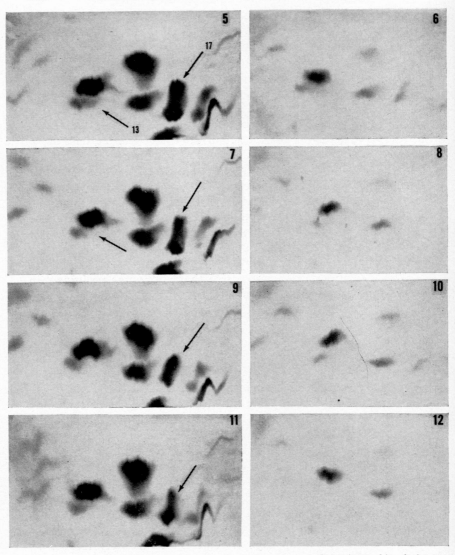

Figs. 5–12. Free amino acids of cells (75 mg.) and fluid (150 μl.) of the ascites form of the Murphy lymphosarcoma at different times after implantation into rats. Figures 5, 7, 9, and 11 are chromatograms of extracts of cells, and Figs. 6, 8, 10, and 12 are corresponding chromatograms of extracts of ascites fluid obtained at 2, 3, 4, and 8 days, respectively, after transplantation. Specific attention is directed to glutamine, 13, and glutamic acid, 17.

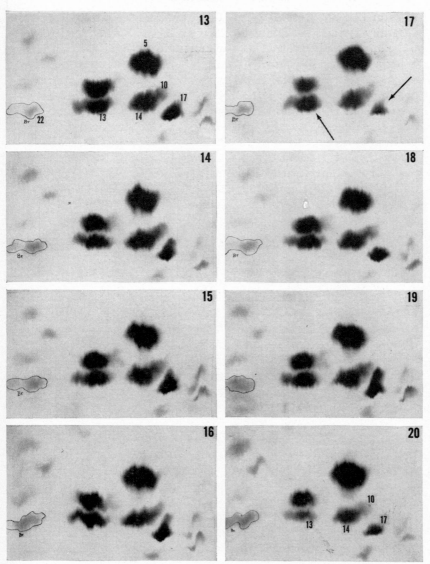

Figs. 13–20. Free amino acids of leg muscle (75 mg.) of rats bearing the Murphy lymphosarcoma (ascites) at different times after transplantation of the tumor. Figure 13 was from a control animal and Figs. 14–20 were from animals at 6 hours and 1, 2, 3, 4, 5, and 8 days, respectively, after transplantation. Taurine, 5; serine, 10; glutamine, 13; glycine, 14; glutamic acid, 17; carnosine and anserine, 22.

terns of free amino acids of the tissues of tumor-bearing hosts are generally quite constant and that only in the terminal stages do there appear to be alterations, the most frequently observed change being a decrease in content of free glutamine. It is interesting that plasma glutamine levels generally were lower and in some instances glutamic and aspartic acid and alanine concentrations were higher than normal in patients with acute myeloblastic and lymphoblastic and chronic lymphocytic leukemias and in the body fluids of patients with carcinoma of the breast, Hodgkin's disease, lymphosarcoma, and reticulum cell sarcoma (Rouser, 1957). In some patients treatment with chemotherapeutic agents tended to cause an increase in plasma glutamine toward normal levels. Decreases in glutamine and increases in glutamic acid content in plasma also were observed in tumor-bearing rats (White *et al.*, 1954).

Free Amino Acids in Growing and Regressing Tumors: Effects of Host Resistance, Chemical Agents, and X-Irradiation

Determinations were made by two-dimensional paper chromatography of free amino acid patterns in tumor C1498 in both solid and ascites forms at various times after transplantation into C57BL/10-H-2^b mice, a strain in which the tumor grows progressively and kills the animals, and into C57BL/10-H-2^d mice, a subline which differs from the former by a single histocompatability gene and in which the tumor grows initially and then regresses (Roberts and Borges, 1955). The amino acid patterns of the solid form of the tumor were virtually identical in both sublines for the first 8 days after transplantation. Subsequently the patterns diverged. The tumors in the resistant strain showed appearance of free glutamine while this amino acid was not detected at any time on the chromatograms of extracts from tumors grown in the susceptible subline. Also, there were relative increases in the content of free glutamic acid in the tumor in the resistant subline. Similar observations were made with an ascites form of tumor C1498 grown in the above two sublines of mice. The results showed that glutamine eventually appeared in the cells and ascitic fluid in the resistant strain but was not detectable in either the cells or the fluid of the susceptible mice at any time.

A detailed study was then made of the cytological characteristics of the Yoshida ascites tumor cells and of the content of the ninhydrin-reactive constituents detected on two-dimensional paper chro-

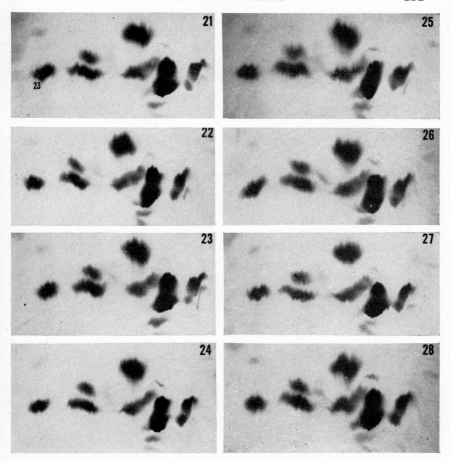

Figs. 21–28. Free amino acids of brain (75 mg.) of rats bearing the Murphy lymphosarcoma (ascites) at different times after transplantation of the tumor. Figure 21 was from a control animal and Figs. 22–28 were from animals at 6 hours and 1, 2, 3, 4, 5, and 8 days, respectively, after transplantation. γ-Amino-butyric acid, 23.

matograms prepared from extracts of cells and ascitic fluid at various times after transplantation into susceptible rats (J strain), in which the tumor grows progressively and kills the animal in approximately 14 days, and into a resistant rat strain (Wistar) in which the tumor grows initially but regresses completely within 8 days (Roberts *et al.*, 1956). At all times after transplantation the content of the free or easily extractable glutamine was higher in the cells grown in the resistant rats. The chemical findings, generally, were similar to those observed in the experiments with the mice bearing the C1498 leukemia. A detailed analysis was then made of the sequential changes in the amino acid patterns of the extracts of the cells and fluid of the Yoshida sarcoma in rats after the administration of sarkomycin, nitromin, or crude podophyllin, and of the Ehrlich ascites tumor in mice after the injection of sarkomycin and E-39 (2,5 di-n-propoxy-3,6-bis ethylenimino benzoquinone). All of the above substances produced increases in the content of free glutamine in the tumor cells and ascitic fluid, the sarkomycin showing the most marked increase most rapidly. Other changes in ninhydrin-reactive constituents also were noted. A consideration of both the cytological and chemical changes produced by sarkomycin suggested that the glutamine which appears rapidly after treatment might be intracellular in origin. When determinations were made of the free amino acid patterns of the Yoshida sarcoma following X-irradiation (Kaplan and Tanaka, unpublished observations) it was found that the free glutamine in the extracts of cells and fluid was always elevated above the nonirradiated control level. The glutamine appeared earlier and reached a higher level in the cells than in the fluid.

Some Aspects of Metabolism of Glutamine and Other Free Amino Acids in Tumors

When glutamine was injected intraperitoneally into rats bearing the Yoshida sarcoma there was a general increase in most of the detectable ninhydrin-reactive constituents in the ascitic fluid and a simultaneous decrease in the cells, notable changes occurring in alanine, glycine, glutamic acid, serine, threonine, and lysine (Roberts and Tanaka, 1956). The levels of most of these amino acids in both cells and fluid returned toward the control levels as the glutamine content fell. With the exception of glutamic acid, the changes observed may possibly be attributed to the displacement of the amino acids from the cells into the fluid with a consequent reentry into the cells when the content of glutamine fell. There was complete disappearance of the injected glutamine from the cells and the fluid in 1½ to 2 hours after the administration of glutamine. Experiments with radioactive DL-glutamine-2-C^{14} (Roberts *et al.*, 1956) confirmed that the glutamine enters the cells readily and is converted rapidly to glutamic acid, and, in addition, showed that glutamine carbon also appears rapidly in succinate, aspartate, and glutathione. An experiment with DL-glutamine-2-C^{14} showed that prior treatment with sarkomycin *in vivo* did not destroy the ability of the Yoshida tumor cells to take up labeled glutamine *in vitro* rapidly and to convert it to glutamic acid. In contrast to the findings with glutamine, the injection of L-glutamic acid did not result in notable increase in the glutamic acid content of the tumor cells or in marked changes in the content of other detectable constituents in the cells and fluid. Experiments with DL-glutamic acid-2-C^{14} showed that the tumor cells possess, at most, only a very limited permeability to this amino acid. This is in keeping with the finding of a ready permeability to glutamine and a relative impermeability to glutamic acid of animal tissues in general (Schwerin *et al.*, 1950). It has been reported that the carbon of L-glutamate-U-C^{14} which had been administered intravenously to rats bearing the Walker 256 carcinosarcoma appeared rapidly in protein, lactate, aspartate, glutamine, succinate, and in carbon dioxide (Nyhan and Busch, 1958). However, in the latter work the possibility had not been ruled out that the isotope may have found its way into the tumor via glutamine synthesized by tissues of the host and subsequently taken up by the tumor cells, where rapid breakdown of glutamine to glutamate and utilization of glutamate occurs (Roberts *et al.*, 1956). It is more likely that definitive information about the intracellular constituents and permeability of tumors to substances can be obtained employing ascites cell tumors, in which problems created by the presence of nontumor cells (blood vessels, blood cells, connective tissue) and the almost invariable presence of some central necrosis can be circumvented. The above experiments (Roberts *et al.*, 1956; Nyhan and Busch, 1958) and the finding that glucose carbon is at best a poor precursor of glutamic and aspartic acids in tumor cells (Kit and Graham, 1956) suggests that one of the important functions of glutamine in the metabolism of tumors may be as a direct precursor of glutamic acid, which can then furnish the carbon for the partial operation of the tricarboxylic acid cycle from α-ketoglutarate to oxalacetate, which can give rise to aspartic acid by transamination, and to pyruvate, which is converted rapidly to lactate. Experiments with labeled acetate (Busch and Potter, 1953) and pyruvate (Busch, 1955) in tumors *in vivo* showed that their carbon failed to equilibrate with the tricarboxylic acid cycle and little, if any, formation of glutamic and aspartic acids or alanine from pyruvate occurs in tumors. However, some carboxylation and decarboxylation of pyruvate apparently can take place in tumors (Freedman and Graff, 1958).

The combination of a slow rate of synthesis of glutamine (Levintow, 1954) with a rapid uptake and degradation or utilization (Roberts et al., 1956; Roberts and Tanaka, 1956) could account for the low levels of this amino acid in tumor cells and fluid. A number of lines of evidence suggest that glutamine is truly essential for intracellular processes in all cells. Free glutamine is a direct precursor of glutamine in proteins in the intact animal (Barry, 1954) and in tissue culture (Levintow et al., 1957) and is known to participate in transaminations (Meister, 1956), amide exchanges (Waelsch, 1952), and in purine (Goldthwait et al., 1955; Levenberg and Buchanan, 1956; Hartman et al., 1955; Lagerkvist, 1955), glucosamine (Leloir and Cardini, 1956), diphosphopyridine nucleotide biosyntheses (Preiss and Handler, 1958), and other reactions (Meister, 1956). There appears to be some relationship between glutamine and glycolysis (Keynan et al., 1954), but the connection is not clear. Glutamine is an essential constituent of media employed for supporting growth of normal and malignant cells in tissue culture and is required to be present in larger amounts than any other amino acid (Eagle, 1955), and free intracellular glutamine is required for the synthesis of poliovirus by the HeLa cell (Darnell and Eagle, 1958). It appears that tumor cells are operating at a marginal level of glutamine availability by comparison with other tissues.

The question arises about the sources of the glutamine which are used by the tumor cells for their multiple metabolic needs and the nature of the disturbances causing the appearance of free glutamine in tumors, whether tumor growth is affected by host resistance, chemicals having differing cytological effects such as sarkomycin, nitromin, E-39, and podophyllin, or by physical means such as X-rays. It is unlikely that most tumor cells are synthesizing glutamine at a sufficiently rapid rate to meet the needs for rapid growth and cell division. Tumors may obtain additional glutamine from the blood or from proteins or other substances in which glutamine is in peptide linkage. Recent experiments show that proteins can enter Ehrlich ascites cells and be used for synthesis of cellular protein without prior breakdown to free amino acids (Chin et al., 1959), and it has been shown that α-L-glutamyl-L-glutamic acid is taken up and hydrolyzed by cells of the Ehrlich ascites carcinoma

(Christensen and Rafn, 1952). It would seem unlikely at the present time that glutamine is being synthesized in the tumors or that free glutamine is being absorbed from a fluid containing no detectable free glutamine at rates which are rapid enough to account for the extremely rapid accumulation which occurs very shortly after treatment with sarkomycin in both the Ehrlich and Yoshida tumors, even if major pathways of utilization were blocked (Roberts et al., 1956). The glutamine might possibly come from sites to which it is bound by strong adsorptive forces or by liberation from some chemically bound form which either has not been detected in the extracts or which is not extracted by the methods employed. It is possible that a decrease in the relatively high levels of phosphate-activated glutaminase activity found in tumor cells also may be involved in the appearance of free glutamine after treatment. Increases in the concentrations of valine, leucine plus isoleucine, and tyrosine have been noted frequently in affected tumor cells following the rise in glutamine level. It is possible that transpeptidation reactions involving glutamine (Hanes et al., 1950) or the activation of intracellular peptidases or proteinases may account for the increase in these amino acids.

Changes in Free or Easily Extractable Amino Acids in Normal and Neoplastic Tissues Undergoing Sterile Autolysis (Simonsen and Roberts, in preparation)

Brain, muscle, liver, and kidney were removed from normal Sprague-Dawley rats or those which had been hypophysectomized or adrenalectomized, as well as from tumor-bearing hosts. The Walker carcinoma also was studied under the conditions to be described. In order to insure that all changes observed would be attributable to enzymes found in the tissues care was taken to exclude microorganisms. In an effort to avoid mixing substrates and enzymes not ordinarily in contact with each other, pieces of intact tissue were used rather than homogenates, minces, or slices. The tissues were removed observing sterile precautions and samples were placed in individual sterile weighing bottles of known weight. After weighing, samples were placed in an incubator at 38° for varying periods of time. Upon removal from the incubator cultures were made in thioglycolate broth from a small particle of each sample and the remainder of the sample was then worked up for chromatography in the usual manner. Results were used only for samples showing no microbial contamination. Virtually identical results were obtained for 'tissues of normal rats as were found for their hypophysectomized or adrenalectomized litter mates. The results for various intervals up to 96 hours after removal of the samples from the animals showed that the pattern of proteolytic breakdown is characteristic for each tissue and that the amino acid patterns observed in the freshly fixed tissues are in no way related to those found after autolytic changes have been allowed to take place. In the case of liver, extensive over-all proteolysis had taken place rapidly, while the brain showed relatively little liberation of ninhydrin-reactive constituents. Amino acids were not liberated in the same relative amounts during autolysis as during hydrolysis of the tissue proteins. The changes which were observed in the free amino acid content were the result of the processes by which the amino acids were formed or liberated and used during the period of observation. An interesting finding in the case of liver was that free arginine was not detected at any time, but only ornithine, reflecting the tremendously high arginase activity in liver. In the case of brain, relatively large increases in γ-aminobutyric acid were observed during autolysis. Since significant amounts of γ-aminobutyric acid are not found in a bound form in brain, the progressively increasing content of this amino acid, which attained the maximal level by the 24th hour, probably can be attributed to the continued activity of the glutamic acid decarboxylase, the enzyme which forms γ-aminobutyric acid from glutamic acid and which can function anaerobically (Roberts, 1956). There is probably a cessation of activity of the tricarboxylic acid cycle which must furnish α-ketoglutarate, one of the substrates of the γ-aminobutyric acid-transaminase system, probably the major reaction by which γ-aminobutyric acid is utilized in brain.

One of the chief points of interest in this study was to ascertain whether the liberation of free glutamine, which has been found to occur during the treatment of a variety of animal tumors with agents which produce regression, also would take place under the conditions of sterile autolysis. The results (Figs. 29-36) showed that only a small amount of glutamine appeared during the first 24 hours of autolysis in the samples of tumor studied, while valine, leucine and isoleucine, tyrosine, and some of the other amino acids were liberated from the protein at a more rapid rate. At later time intervals more glutamine appeared. The changes produced by chemical agents or during regression resulting from genetically conditioned

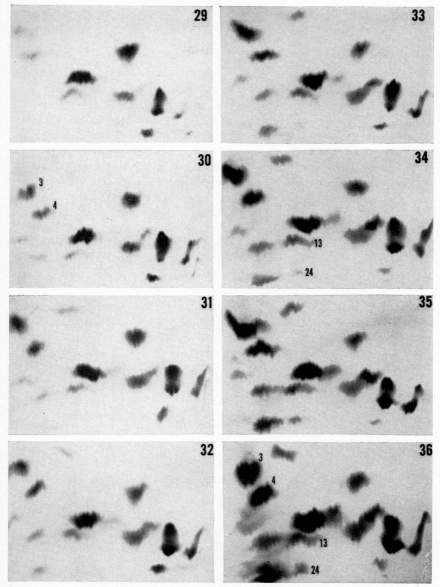

FIGS. 29–36. Changes in free amino acids of samples (37.5 mg.) of Walker carcinoma undergoing sterile autolysis. Figure 29, immediately after removal. Figures 30–36, samples extracted after 4, 8, 12, 24, 48, 72, and 96 hours, respectively, of sterile autolysis. Leucine and isoleucine, 3; valine, 4; glutamine, 13; ornithine, 24.

resistance of the host do not appear to be the same as those which occur when a tumor is allowed to autolyze under sterile conditions.

Some Chemotherapeutic Implications

The initial finding of characteristically low levels of glutamine in tumors (Roberts and Tishkoff, 1949; Roberts and Frankel, 1949c) focused interest on the role of glutamine in tumor metabolism and led to the suggestion that it might be feasible to disturb metabolic mechanisms in tumors by interference with glutamine metabolism (Ayengar and Roberts, 1952), a possibility which became even more attractive as evidence increased showing glutamine to play an important role in many metabolic reactions (see above). It was reasoned that normal tissues, which have relatively large amounts of free glutamine, presumably would be more resistant to such an interference. Since these studies were done prior to the development of suitable tissue culture techniques, microbiological systems employing *Lactobacillus arabinosus* were standardized for showing the enhancing effects of small amounts of glutamine on the utilization of D- and L-glutamic and α-ketoglutaric acids for growth (Ayengar *et al.*, 1951). Of a large number tested, some substances were found which are competitive inhibitors of the utilization of glutamine in these systems (γ-L-glutamylhydrazide, acetone-γ-L-glutamylhydrazone, β-hydroxy-DL-glutamic acid, α-DL-methylglutamic acid, and DL-methionine sulfoximine) (Ayengar and Roberts, 1953). However, none of the compounds was remarkably inhibitory, as little as 5 μg. of glutamine being capable of reversing the effects of 10 μmoles of these substances. It is not surprising, therefore, that these substances have not proven to be particularly effective in the chemotherapy of transplantable animal tumors. A careful cytological study has been made of the effect of these substances on the Yoshida ascites cells after intraperitoneal injection into rats bearing this tumor (Tanaka and Roberts, unpublished observations). γ-L-Glutamylhydrazide proved to be the substance producing maximal cytological damage in the cells and also produced changes in the pattern of free amino acids, among other changes causing the appearance of glutamine both in cells and in fluid. It is not certain that the action of γ-L-glutamylhydrazide in this particular system can be attributed to its function as a glutamine inhibitor, since attempts to prevent the effects by the simultaneous administration of glutamine gave equivocal results and it was found that β-DL-aspartylhydrazide and pyrrolidonecarbohydrazide, substances which were not glutamine inhibitors in the bacterial system, also produced effects which were similar to those found with γ-L-glutamylhydrazide. γ-L-Glutamylhydrazide has been found to be destroyed with great rapidity in the tumor cells after intraperitoneal administration. The appearance of two new ninhydrin-reactive constituents in the tumor cells after the administration of γ-L-glutamylhydrazide suggests that the hydrazide may react directly with naturally occurring materials possessing aldehyde or ketone groups. In contrast to its effect on Yoshida tumor, γ-L-glutamylhydrazide had little effect on Ehrlich ascites tumor. No changes of any significance were noted in the amino acids of the cells. There was a slight increase of alanine and glycine in the fluid. Cytological effects were negligible. Experiments with glycine-1,2-C^{14} have shown that the simultaneous administration of γ-L-glutamylhydrazide with the isotopically labeled amino acid did not decrease the extent of concentrative assimilation of this amino acid by the tumor cells *in vivo*. γ-Glutamylhydrazide actually has been shown to accelerate incorporation of amino acids into protein in mouse ascites lymphomas in *in vitro* experiments (Rabinovitz *et al.*, 1959). Methionine sulfoximine (Rabinovitz *et al.*, 1954) and δ-hydroxylysine (Rabinovitz *et al.*, 1957) were found to inhibit the incorporation of amino acids *in vitro* into the proteins of Ehrlich ascites cells. The inhibitions were noncompetitive with the specific amino acids studied but were prevented by small amounts of glutamine. The inhibitory action of these compounds apparently was exerted by blocking the synthesis of glutamine by the Ehrlich ascites cells and thus making glutamine become the limiting amino acid in protein synthesis. Neither of the above compounds exerted inhibitory effects on tumor growth in intact animals. O-diazoacetyl-L-serine (azaserine), a more effective chemotherapeutic agent, competes with glutamine in the enzymatic conversion of formylglycinamide ribonucleotide to formylglycinamidine ribonucleotide (Levenberg and Buchanan, 1957).

It would be difficult to destroy the tumors in a host even with an extremely effective glutamine antagonist of the structural-analog type, because glutamine is generally found in relatively high concentrations in blood in man (and in experimental animals), furnishing approximately 25% of the total plasma amino nitrogen (Meister, 1956). The oral administration to fasted human subjects of an amount of glutamine (50 gm.) that was in great excess of that expected to be made available per unit time by absorption from the intestine during digestion of protein, produced elevations of glutamine in plasma from a fasting level of approximately 4×10^{-4} moles/liter to maximal concentrations of approximately 18×10^{-4} moles/liter in one hour, with a return to normal values occurring within four hours (Rouser et al., in preparation). It was estimated that at most 3% of the administered dose of glutamine was present in the circulation at any time. There was no increase in urinary glutamine, but a substantial increase in urea excretion occurred. Experiments with perfused rat livers have shown that one-half of the glutamine nitrogen in the perfusate was converted to urea (Burke and Miller, 1957). The formation of radioactive glutamate, α-ketoglutarate, and pyrrolidone carboxylate from L-glutamine-U-C^{14} took place on incubation with homogenates of human liver (Moldave and Meister, 1957). It is likely that a relatively large proportion of intestinally absorbed glutamine is metabolized by the liver and that the remainder is taken up rapidly by the other tissues (Schwerin et al., 1950). From the above results and from the finding that relatively large amounts of glutamine are present in the plasma of fasted individuals it seems unlikely that dietary sources could contribute importantly to the supply of circulating glutamine. It is of interest that even though glutamine feeding does not increase the glutamine excretion, the administration of ACTH produces marked increases in urinary excretion of both glutamine and asparagine (Ronzoni et al., 1953). In order to be able to employ glutamine antagonists in a maximally effective manner it will be necessary to direct attention to methods of decreasing formation and liberation of glutamine into the circulation by the normal tissues, as well as to disturbing its uptake and utilization in the tumor cells themselves. The exploration of glutamine antagonism in tumor growth is interesting even if a virus should be the causative agent, since glutamine appears to play an important role in intracellular virus biosynthesis (Darnell and Eagle, 1958).

Will It Be Possible to Devise Better Inhibitors of Glutamine Utilization?

Although experiments with bacterial or animal cells under defined conditions of culture may help in determining the general metabolic areas in which growth-inhibitory substances may act, there are many difficulties in ascertaining the exact enzymatic locale of the action of a metabolic inhibitor from experiments dealing with the growth of intact cells (Kihara and Snell, 1952). None of the potential glutamine antimetabolites which has been designed according to structural analogy with glutamine has proven to be an effective anti-tumor agent or to be a really potent antagonist to glutamine on a molar basis in any system tested. It was felt that the study of the characteristics of specific enzymes of glutamine metabolism might prove more fruitful in suggesting new approaches. It was indicated in the previous discussion that the glutaminase activity of tumors might be important in converting glutamine coming from extracellular sources to glutamic acid, which among various functions could furnish carbon for the partial operation of the tricarboxylic acid cycle. Since the phosphate-activated glutaminase of

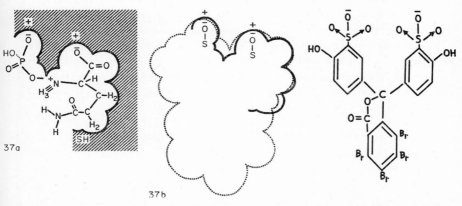

Figs. 37a and 37b. (a) Two-dimensional projection of scale models (Catalin) showing postulated attachment of glutamine to active site of glutaminase. (b) Superposition of two-dimensional projection of bromosulfalein model on projection of the postulated active site. The three rings are not coplanar.

tumors resembles renal glutaminase in most respects, initial study was made of the enzyme from dog kidney, a rich source of the enzyme. Studies of the properties and inhibition of the purified enzyme (Sayre and Roberts, 1958) led to the suggestion that the active site includes both phosphate and glutamine as shown in Fig. 37a. One of the best inhibitors of the enzyme is bromosulfalein (disodium phenoltetrabromophthalein disulfonate), a substance competitive with phosphate and not with glutamine, the action of which could best be explained by assuming that it covers the whole postulated active site (Fig. 37b). Substances related in structure to glutamine were, at best, poor inhibitors of renal glutaminase. These results suggest that the first step in obtaining suitably potent inhibitors of other glutamine enzymes, especially those involving amide transfer, might be to delineate the essential features of the active site. Tests for inhibition could then be made with substances that would have the required structure and distribution of charges that would fit closely the *whole* postulated active site without necessarily having any formal structural resemblance to glutamine itself. One system which might be of particular value to study in this manner would be the first step in purine biosynthesis, the synthesis of glycinamide ribonucleotide from glutamine and 5-phosphoribosylpyrophosphate (Goldthwait *et al.*, 1955; Hartman *et al.*, 1955). Only substances having very high affinities for the active sites of glutamine-utilizing enzymes are likely to be effective in inhibiting tumor growth, since in many instances an initial inhibition of tumor growth might lead to an eventual increase in intracellular glutamine content sufficient to overcome the inhibition of relatively small intracellular concentrations of weak competitive inhibitors. Many extensions of these ideas are possible, some of which are being pursued in our laboratory.

Some Comparative Studies of Free Amino Acids

The tissues of a large variety of marine organisms are now in the process of being examined for their content of free or easily extractable amino acids. These studies completely confirm those previously performed on various other organisms in that each tissue of each species shows a characteristic distribution of the constituents studied. The patterns appear to be highly constant. For instance, patterns found in the livers of a number of octopi caught in San Diego Bay were found to be remarkably similar. The same general finding was made in a variety of other species from a number of different phyla. To date, representative specimens have been studied from among the sponges, coelenterates, worms, brachiopods, fishes, arthropods, and echinoderms. In general, no aspects of the patterns have been found to be directly correlated with position of the species or class on the phylogenetic scale. Remarkably high levels of taurine have been found in many of the organisms examined. In the chick embryo, inorganic sulfate is fixed into organic linkage in taurine without going through cysteine, methionine, or glutathione (Lowe and Roberts, 1955), while in hatched chick and in mammalian organisms most of the taurine sulfur is derived from cysteine. Attempts will be made to elucidate the mechanisms involved in taurine biosynthesis both in the marine organisms and in the chick embryo. Particularly large amounts of carnosine and anserine have been found in the muscle of the tuna fish. The tuna muscle thus appears to be a particularly favorable source for the study of the biosynthesis and utilization of these substances. The O-phosphodiester of serine and ethanolamine has been found to date only in reptilian tissues (Roberts and Lowe, 1954), where it is synthesized slowly.

It has been observed that the patterns of free amino acids in sea anemones bear a resemblance to those found in the Ehrlich and Yoshida ascites cell tumors. It will, therefore, be of great interest to study the metabolism of the sea anemone, which possesses remarkable properties of regeneration and the ability to form complete new organisms from fragments, and to compare other biochemical characteristics of the anemones with tumors to see if resemblances exist at other metabolic levels.

A cooperative study was performed with Dr. Philip R. White of the Roscoe B. Jackson Memorial Laboratory, Bar Harbor, Maine, in which the free amino acids were studied in a variety of plant tumors grown in synthetic medium which included normal and malignant tissues of Virginia creeper, periwinkle, carrot, tobacco, raspberry, Boston ivy, fern, salsify, and cactus. There was, as in the case of animal tissues, a remarkable uniformity of the patterns in different samples of the same type of tissue. However, the plant tumors did not resemble each other as closely as did the animal tumors, and a number of the plant tumor samples showed significant quantities of free glutamine, a finding which had not been made in the case of animal tumors. It would thus appear that, at least with regard to amino acid metabolism, there are considerable differences in various plant tumors and no generalizations will be possible which will hold for both animal and plant material.

Final Comment

Dr. Greenstein had given one of us (E. R.) friendly encouragement virtually at every point of this work. His assistance ranged from advice on the preparation of grant requests to directions for performing organic syntheses and enzyme assays. He had taken time from his busy schedule to visit our laboratory and to share his wisdom and enthusiasm with our whole staff, especially with graduate students and young postdoctoral fellows. Many experiments were performed in our laboratory in which were employed the highly pure materials prepared in Dr. Greenstein's laboratory, and we received from him a complete set of pure D- and L-amino acids before they became commercially available. It would, indeed, be a fitting tribute to his memory if our work would eventually be of value in the basic understanding of some aspects of the biochemistry of amino acids in normal and neoplastic tissues, a subject in which he, himself, took such an active interest.

REFERENCES

Ayengar, P., and Roberts, E. (1952). *Proc. Soc. Exptl. Biol. Med.* **79,** 476.

Ayengar, P., and Roberts, E. (1953). *Growth* **17,** 201.

Ayengar, P., Roberts, E., and Ramasarma, G. B. (1951). *J. Biol. Chem.* **193,** 781.

Barry, J. M. (1954). *Nature* **174,** 315.

Bollman, J. L., Flock, E. V., Grindlay, J. H., Bickford, R. C., and Lichtenheld, F. R. (1957). A.M.A. *Arch. Surg.* **75,** 405.

Burke, W. T., and Miller, L. L. (1957). *Federation Proc.* **16,** 161.

Busch, H. (1955). *Cancer Research* **15,** 365.

Busch, H., and Potter, V. R. (1953). *Cancer Research* **13,** 168.

Chanin, M., Roberts, E., and Goldman, A. (1956). *Circulation Research* **4,** 713.

Chin, L. E., Tannenberg, W. J., and Moldave, K. (1959). *Proc. Soc. Exptl. Biol. Med.* **101,** 140.

Christensen, H. N., and Rafn, M. L. (1952). *Cancer Research* **12,** 495.

Consden, R., Gordon, A. H., and Martin, A. J. P. (1944). *Biochem. J.* **38,** 224.

Darnell, J. E., Jr., and Eagle, H. (1958). *Virology* **6,** 556.

Dawson, R. M. C. (1953). *Biochim. et Biophys. Acta* **11,** 548.

Dent, C. E. (1947). *Biochem, J.* **41,** 240.

Dent, C. E. (1948). *Biochem. J.* **43,** 169.

Dent, C. E., Stepka, W., and Steward, F. C. (1947). *Nature* **160,** 682.

Dounce, A. L., Tishkoff, G. H., Barnett, S. R., and Freer, R. M. (1950). *J. Gen. Physiol.* **33,** 629.

du Ruisseau J., Greenstein, J. P., Winitz, M., and Birnbaum, S. M. (1957). *Arch. Biochem. Biophys.* **68,** 161.

Eagle, H. (1955). *Science* **122,** 501.

Eiseman, B., Osofsky, H., Roberts, E., and Jelinek, B. (1959). *J. Appl. Physiol.* **14,** 251.

Flock, E. V., Block, M. A., Grindlay, J. H., Mann, F. C., and Bollman, J. L. (1953). *J. Biol. Chem.* **200,** 529.

Freedman, A. D., and Graff, S. (1958). *J. Biol. Chem.* **233,** 292.

Goldthwait, D. A., Greenberg, G. R., and Peabody, R. A. (1955). *Biochim. et Biophys. Acta* **18,** 148.

Greenstein, J. P. (1954). "Biochemistry of Cancer," 2nd ed. Academic Press, New York.

Hanes, C. S., Hird, F. J. R., and Isherwood, F. A. (1950). *Nature* **166,** 288.

Hartman, S. C., Levenberg, B., and Buchanan, J. M. (1955). *J. Am. Chem. Soc.* **77,** 501.

Hoberman, H. D. (1949). *Yale J. Biol. Med.* **22,** 341.

Iacobellis, M., Muntwyler, E., and Dodgen, C. L. (1956). *Am. J. Physiol.* **195,** 275.

Keynan, A., Strecker, H. J., and Waelsch, H. (1954). *J. Biol. Chem.* **211**, 883.
Kihara, H., and Snell, E. E. (1952). *J. Biol. Chem.* **197**, 791.
Kit, S., and Graham, O. L. (1956). *Cancer Research* **16**, 117.
Kit, S., and Griffin, A. C. (1958). *Cancer Research* **18**, 621.
Lagerkvist, U. (1955). *Acta Chem. Scand.* **9**, 1028.
Leloir, L. F., and Cardini, C. E. (1956). *Biochim. et Biophys. Acta* **20**, 33.
Levenberg, B., and Buchanan, J. M. (1956). *J. Am. Chem. Soc.* **78**, 504.
Levenberg, B., and Buchanan, J. M. (1957). *J. Biol. Chem.* **224**, 1005.
Levintow, L. (1954). *J. Natl. Cancer Inst.* **15**, 347.
Levintow, L., Eagle, H., and Piez, K. A. (1957). *J. Biol. Chem.* **227**, 929.
Lowe, I. P., and Roberts, E. (1955). *J. Biol. Chem.* **212**, 477.
Marvin, H. N., and Awapara, J. (1949). *Proc. Soc. Exptl. Biol. Med.* **72**, 93.
Meister, A. (1956). *Physiol. Revs.* **36**, 103.
Moldave, K., and Meister, A. (1957). *Federation Proc.* **16**, 222.
Nyhan, W. L., and Busch, H. (1958). *Cancer Research* **18**, 385.
Preiss, J., and Handler, P. (1958). *J. Biol. Chem.* **233**, 493.
Rabinovitz, M., Olson, M. E., and Greenberg, D. M. (1954). *J. Biol. Chem.* **210**, 837.
Rabinovitz, M., Olson, M. E., and Greenberg, D. M. (1957). *Cancer Research* **17**, 885.
Rabinovitz, M., Olson, M. E., and Greenberg, D. M. (1959). *Cancer Research* **19**, 388.
Roberts, E. (1956). *Progr. in Neurobiol.* **1**, 11.
Roberts, E., and Borges, P. R. F. (1955). *Cancer Research* **15**, 697.
Roberts, E., and Frankel, S. (1949a). *Arch. Biochem.* **20**, 386.
Roberts, E., and Frankel, S. (1949b). *Cancer Research* **9**, 231.
Roberts, E., and Frankel, S. (1949c). *Cancer Research* **9**, 645.
Roberts, E., and Lowe, I. P. (1954). *J. Biol. Chem.* **211**, 1.
Roberts, E., and Tanaka, T. (1956). *Cancer Research* **16**, 204.
Roberts, E., and Tishkoff, G. H. (1949). *Science* **109**, 14.
Roberts, E., Caldwell, A. L., Clowes, G. H. A., Suntzeff, V., Carruthers, C., and Cowdry, E. V. (1949). *Cancer Research* **9**, 350.
Roberts, E., Tanaka, K. K., Tanaka, T., and Simonsen, D. G. (1956). *Cancer Research* **16**, 970.
Roberts, E., Lowe, I. P., Chanin, M., and Jelinek, B. (1957). *J. Exptl. Zool.* **135**, 239.
Roberts, E., Lowe, I. P., Guth, L., Jelinek, B. (1958). *J. Exptl. Zool.* **138**, 313.
Ronzoni, E., Roberts, E., Frankel, S., and Ramasarma, G. B. (1953). *Proc. Soc. Exptl. Biol. Med.* **82**, 496.
Rouser, G. (1957). *In* "The Leukemias," pp. 361-378. Academic Press, New York.
Rouser, G., Roberts, E., and Jelinek, B. In preparation.
Sayre, F. W., and Roberts, E. (1958). *J. Biol. Chem.* **233**, 1128.
Schwerin, P., Bessman, S. P., and Waelsch, H. (1950). *J. Biol. Chem.* **184**, 37.
Simonsen, D. G., and Roberts, E. In preparation.
Waelsch, H. (1952). *Advances in Enzymol.* **13**, 238.
White, J. M., Ozawa, G., Ross, G. A. L., and McHenry, E. W. (1954). *Cancer Research* **14**, 508.

The Nucleic Acids of Normal Tissues and Tumors

SAUL KIT*

Department of Biochemistry, The University of Texas M. D. Anderson Hospital and Tumor Institute, Texas Medical Center, Houston, Texas

Enzymes, Genes, and Cancer

TWO ATTRIBUTES OF CANCER CELLS are particularly noteworthy: (1) The enzymatic and metabolic patterns are abnormal; and (2) the chromosome number and structure are abnormal. In the present paper, an effort will be made to relate the biochemical and cytological observations. This necessitates a discussion of the relationships between genes, enzyme-forming-systems (EFS), and enzymes; and of the structure and function of the presumed active components of the genes and EFS, the deoxyribonucleic acids (DNA) and the ribonucleic acids (RNA). And, since any theory of cancer must answer the question of whether the EFS originate exclusively in the nucleus or are independently synthesized in the cell cytoplasm, the evidence concerning the sites of RNA synthesis will also be reviewed.

We are indebted to Jesse P. Greenstein for much of our knowledge concerning the abnormal enzymatic patterns of neoplastic cells. Greenstein's studies (1956) of a number of enzyme systems in a wide variety of normal and tumor tissues demonstrated the high degree of biochemical differentiation among normal tissues and the relative uniformity among tumors. The uniformity among the tumors may in part be ascribed to: (1) the loss or diminution of specialized functions which had been characteristic of the normal tissues of origin; and (2) the development of a new balance between specific anabolic and catabolic enzyme systems such as to facilitate tumor growth. The loss during hepatic neoplasia of enzymes associated with urea synthesis, ketone body synthesis, glu-

* Aided in part by grants from the American Cancer Society (P35-A), the Leukemia Society Inc. and the National Cancer Institute (C-4238).

coneogenesis, glycogen storage, and catabolism of purines, pyrimidine, and amino acids has already been reviewed by Weinhouse (1959). As for the balance between anabolic and catabolic enzymes, a general outline of the direction of change has been suggested (Kit and Griffin, 1958) but much remains to be done.[1]

Abnormalities of the chromatin complex were proposed many years ago by Boveri as a possible cause of cancer. Although chromosomal irregularities should be considered as but one aspect of the genetic theory of cancer (Strong, 1958), a series of remarkable cytological observations by Hsu, Yerganian, Hauschka, Levan, Biesele, Ford, and others have focused attention upon such changes. The following three points are particularly noteworthy:

a. Many *transplanted* tumors have chromosome *numbers* and *types* differing from the diploid idiogram of the host species. These alterations include minor anaphase disturbances, multipolarity, endomitosis, and endoreduplication, and cryptostructural changes attributable to translocations. Genetic change produced by karyotypic drift is a *sine qua non* in tumor progression and autonomy, regardless of its disputed role in the genesis of tumors (Hauschka, 1958).

b. The great majority of *primary* reticular neoplasms of mice, whether spontaneous or radiation induced, show a real variation in chromosome number, which is usually confined to an over-all range of five or less, and the appearance of new marker chromosomes indicative of cytogenetic individuality (Ford et al., 1958).

c. Normal embryonic cells mutate immediately on their explantation *in vitro*. In one case, after 22 or more passages of em-

---

[1] The following observations may serve as models for some of the specific rate limiting enzymatic alterations in neoplasia: (*1*) In *Escherichia coli*, infection with T₂ phage signals an abrupt change in the metabolic pattern and leads within minutes to the synthesis of new enzymes essential for phage replication: (a) enzymes which hydroxymethylate deoxycytidine-5′-phosphate; (b) enzymes which transfer glucose from uridine diphosphoglucose to the hydroxymethyl-cytosine of DNA; (c) those which phosphorylate the hydroxymethyl cytosine deoxyribonucleotide to the triphosphate; and (d) enzymes which remove the terminal pyrophosphate from deoxycytidine triphosphate (Kornberg et al., 1959; Flaks and Cohen, 1958; Somerville and Greenberg, 1959). Increases in thymine and guanine deoxyribonucleotide phosphorylating enzymes also occur. (*2*) The capacity of slices of the regenerating liver to degrade uracil and thymine is reduced, while extracts of regenerating liver have an appreciably greater ability to phosphorylate thymidine to the mono-, di-, and triphosphates and to incorporate the thymidine into DNA (Canellakis et al., 1959; Potter et al., 1958; Bollum and Potter, 1959).

bryonic skin cells, the cultured cells could be transferred back to mice where they produced spindle cell sarcomas. Here, the chromosomal irregularities preceded the malignancy; and there was strong evidence for a causal relation between the two phenomena (Levan and Biesele, 1958).

The numerical aberrations in the karyotypes of cancer cells have important biochemical implications. In populations in which aneuploid or heteroploid cells preponderate, some cells have three or four representations of a given chromosome, but only two, one, or no representations of other chromosomes. The *chromosomal imbalance* can be observed by cytological methods. However, analogous aberrations in gene dosage, or mutations leading to *hypermorphic, hypomorphic,* or *amorphic* genes, might also take place, even though the latter changes might be undetectable by present methods. Boveri recognized that cells with a heteroploid chromosome number would produce some substances in excess and others in reduced amounts or not at all. Experimental evidence strongly supporting the latter concept has recently been obtained (Kit *et al.*, 1959, and in press; Kit and Gross, 1959a).

The enzyme content and metabolism of a series of near diploid and near tetraploid ascites lymphomas and carcinomas of mice have been investigated. It was observed, (Klein, 1951; Freed and Hungerford, 1957; Kit and Griffin, 1958; Richards *et al.*, 1956) that the DNA content per cell was approximately proportional to the chromosome number, that of near tetraploid cells being twice that of near diploid cells. The metabolic activity and enzyme content per cell of tetraploid cells was twice that of the histologically related diploid cells. Thus, the enzyme content and metabolic activity per microgram of DNA of histologically related diploid and tetraploid tumors were approximately constant (Table I).

The following parameters have so far been studied: (1) respiration, (2) glycolysis, (3) succinoxidase activity, (4) transaminase, (5) histones, (6) free amino acids, (7) dry weight and cell volume (Kit *et al.*, 1959; Kit and Gross, 1959a), (8) nitrogen content, and (9) peptidase activity (Patterson and Podber, 1956). In each case the ploidy dependence was observed. Significantly, the total RNA content of tetraploid cells was also twice that of histologically related diploid cells (Table I). This relationship was by no means fortuitous. In asynchronously dividing ascites tumor cells, the relative constancy of the metabolism per microgram DNA was not greatly modified by: (a) the sex of the tumor bearing animals,

TABLE I

DNA Content and Metabolism of Diploid
and Tetraploid Ascites Tumors

Tissue	Chromosome[a] number	μg. DNA[a] per 10^6 cells	μg. RNA-ribose per μg. DNA	μg. Histones per μg. DNA	Glycolysis[b]
Ehrlich hypotetraploid carcinoma	78	18.0	0.47	3.46	1.31
Lettré-Ehrlich hyperdiploid carcinoma	46	11.1	0.46	2.86	1.27
6C3HED-DBA-2 Hypotetraploid lymphoma	76-78	15.3	0.35	0.98	1.02
6C3HED Diploid lymphoma	40	9.8	0.33	0.83	1.09
E9514A Diploid lymphoma	40	7.9	—	0.84	0.94

[a] The modal chromosome number and the DNA content of normal mouse spleen cells are 40 and 8.3 μg. DNA per 10^6 cells, respectively.

[b] μl CO_2 per hour per μg. DNA.

(b) the temperature at which the tumor bearing animals were maintained, (c) the age of the "in vivo culture" of tumor cells, or (d) the mouse strain in which the tumor cells had multiplied.

The metabolic activities of histologically unrelated tumor cells were, however, not the same. For example, the ratios of glycolysis or histones to DNA were approximately 30 and 300% greater, respectively, for the carcinoma cells than for the lymphoma cells. The qualitative effect of the genome in determining the metabolism of the cells may be illustrated by the following observations: The dry weight and cell volume of the Lettré-Ehrlich *hyperdiploid carcinoma* cells were not very different from those of the 6C3HED-DBA-2 *hypotetraploid lymphoma* cells. Yet, the DNA content, and the ratios of DNA to respiration, glycolysis, or histones were very different. Likewise, the *hypotetraploid* Ehrlich *carcinoma* cells were very dissimilar from the *hypotetraploid lymphoma* cells as were the respective diploid carcinoma and lymphoma cells.

These experiments represent one aspect of gene-enzyme relationships. They demonstrate that a quantitative relationship exists between the chromosome number, the DNA content, the RNA content, and the protein and enzyme content of histologically related cells. One may infer as a first approximation that homologous chromosomes (or allelic genes) act independently and additively, provided that comparisons are made under conditions where the genotypic milieu and the cytoplasmic milieu are held constant. Adaptive changes within limits prescribed by the genome may take place when the environment of the cell is modified. Changes of the age of the growth medium (Wagner *et al.*, 1958), temperature (Horowitz and Fling, 1956), inducing or repressing agents (Cohn, 1957; Yates and Pardee, 1957), or endocrine factors (Greenbaum and Slater, 1957a, b; Knox *et al.*, 1956) all will modify the enzyme content and metabolism of cells. Such changes are, however, reversible. As such, they are to be distinguished from irreversible enzyme changes (Lederberg, 1956; Bonner, 1951; Horowitz and Leupold, 1951; Yanofsky, 1956; Ingram, 1957) which are based upon genetic alterations and which probably play an important role in neoplasia (Kit *et al.*, in press; Kit and Griffin, 1958). Of great interest are the as yet unexplained enzyme and metabolic patterns of cells which seem irreversible, but do not seem to be based upon gene mutations. These include the enzymatic differences between adult and fetal tissues (Kenney *et al.*, 1958) and those between the various adult tissues of the same organisms (Grollman and Lehninger, 1957). The clarification of the latter phenomena will almost certainly affect our ideas concerning irreversible enzyme changes which are genetically determined and reversible enzyme changes which depend on the environment.

DNA and the Genetic Concept of Cancer

On the basis of the genetic concept of cancer, one might expect that there would be differences in the DNA of normal tissues and tumors. Such differences have not been observed, however, with respect to the purine and pyrimidine base composition (Chargaff, 1955; Kit, in press; Uzman and Desoer, 1954) (Table II). Physical chemical differences between the DNA of normal and leukemic human tissues have been reported by Polli (1958). It was found that the effect of urea and of alkali on the viscosity of solutions of DNA prepared from myeloid leukemic leucocytes was different from that of solutions of DNA from normal or lymphatic leukemic leucocytes. Differences between the electrometric-titration curves

TABLE II

DNA Base Ratios of Normal Mouse Tissues and Tumors

Tissue	Molar base ratios[a]					
	G	C	T	$\dfrac{A + T}{G + C}$	$\dfrac{pu}{pyr}$	$\dfrac{6\text{-am}}{6\text{-keto}}$
Spleen (C3H)	0.76	0.78	0.95	1.27	1.02	1.04
Spleen (Akr)	0.79	0.79	0.96	1.24	1.02	1.02
Thymus (Akr)	0.85	0.81	0.94	1.17	1.06	1.01
Leukemia (Akr), (spontaneous)	0.82	0.81	1.02	1.24	0.99	0.99
6C3HED (diploid lymphoma)	0.81	0.80	1.00	1.24	1.01	0.99
6C3HED-DBA-2 to C3H (hypotetraploid lymphoma)	0.79	0.87	0.98	1.19	0.97	1.06
S91 (tetraploid melanoma)	0.80	0.86	0.98	1.19	0.98	1.04
Ehrlich (hypotetraploid carcinoma)	0.77	0.85	0.96	1.21	0.98	1.07

[a] The molar base ratios are expressed relative to adenine = 1.00. Abbreviations are: A = adenine, G = guanine, C = cytosine, T = thymine, pu = purines, pyr = pyrimidines, 6-am = adenine plus cytosine, 6-keto = guanine plus thymine.

of these preparations were also found (Polli, 1958). The sedimentation constant distribution curves demonstrated a difference among normal, myeloid, and lymphatic leukemic DNA's while chromatographic fractionation of DNA's showed a higher degree of heterogeneity between normal and leukemic DNA (Polli and Shooter, 1958; Polli, 1958).

The chromatographic fractionation of the DNA of various tumors and normal tissues has been investigated in this laboratory. A typical chromatographic profile on ECTEOLA-cellulose of mouse spleen DNA is shown in Fig. 1. One DNA peak is eluted by 0.6 M NaCl at pH 7 (Peak I) and about 5 others by 2 M NaCl and NH_3 solutions of increasing alkalinity. Some of our early experiments suggested that spleen DNA-Peak I might be significantly increased as compared with that of transplanted lymphoma DNA (Kit and Gross, 1959b; Kit, in press). However, it has since been shown that the amount of DNA eluted in Peak I may be rather variable unless certain precautions are taken in connection with the preparation of the DNA samples and the chromatographic methods. Thus, in contrast to the results of Polli (1958) but in agreement with the experiments of Smith and Kaplan (1959) we have found that the DNA chromatographic profiles of normal

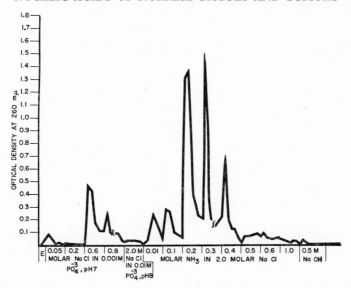

FIG. 1. DNA chromatographic profiles of C3H mouse spleen on ECTEOLA-cellulose; exchange capacity 0.39 meq. per gram; nitrogen content, 0.55%; 5 cc. aliquots were collected. DNA recovery, 97%.

mouse spleen and either spontaneous or transplanted lymphomas are very similar (Figs. 2, 3). The DNA chromatographic profiles of tetraploid as well as diploid lymphomas, diploid or tetraploid carcinomas, and melanotic or amelanotic melanomas have also been compared. These include tissues in which the chromosome number and the karyotype are known to differ from the normal diploid idiogram and from each other. As such, they seemed particularly favorable for testing the capacity of the chromatographic system to resolve small differences. Nevertheless, significant differences in DNA were not observed.

The DNA chromatographic profiles of the normal tissues of the mouse were also very similar as were those of the rat (Kit and Gross, 1959b). To date, the DNA chromatographic profiles of rat spleen, kidney, and brain and of mouse spleen, thymus, kidney, lung, and liver have been compared and no marked differences have been found. These results are in agreement with those of Kondo and Osawa (1959) but are at variance with the findings of Bendich et al. (1956; see also Polli and Shooter, 1958).

It is, therefore, appropriate that some of the problems incidental

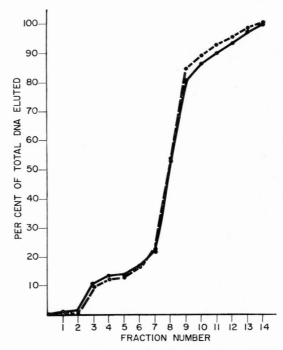

Fig. 2. DNA-chromatographic elution profiles of Akr mouse spleen (broken line) and Akr spontaneous leukemia (solid line). 500 mg. ECTEOLA-cellulose (Brown Co., Berlin, New Hampshire; exchange capacity, 0.39 meq./gram; nitrogen content, 0.55%). Approximately 2.5-3.5 mg. of DNA were applied to each column. The recoveries for 2 analyses on the Akr spleen DNA and 3 analyses on the Akr spontaneous leukemia were 94 and 99% respectively. Optical density was recorded at 258-260 mμ. Elution rate: 5-10 cc. per hour. Five cc. aliquots were collected, and 30 or 60 cc. per elution fraction. The fraction numbers shown on the abscissa are: Fraction 1, 0.05 M NaCl; Fraction 2, 0.2 M NaCl; Fraction 3, 0.6 M NaCl, Fraction 4, 0.8 M NaCl; Fractions 1-4 were dissolved in 0.001 M phosphate buffer, pH 7; Fraction 5, 2.0 M NaCl, 0.01 M phosphate buffer, pH 8; Fraction 6, 0.01 M NH$_3$; Fraction 7, 0.1 M NH$_3$; Fraction 8, 0.2 M NH$_3$; Fraction 9, 0.3 M NH$_3$; Fraction 10, 0.4 M NH$_3$; Fraction 11, 0.5 M NH$_3$; Fraction 12, 0.6 M NH$_3$; Fraction 13, 1.0 M NH$_3$. Fractions 6-13 contained 2.0 M NaCl, Fraction 14, 0.5 M NaOH.

to the fractionation of such complex macromolecules as nucleic acids be critically reviewed. Among the variables which we have investigated are: (1) the properties of the anion exchanger and (2) the method used to isolate the DNA from the tissues. The application of perfectly uniform isolation methods to diverse tissues

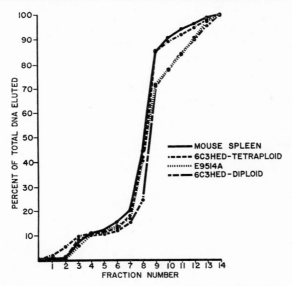

FIG. 3. DNA chromatographic elution profiles on ECTEOLA-cellulose of C3H and DBA mouse spleen, diploid lymphomas E9514A, and 6C3HED, and tetraploid lymphoma 6C3HED-DBA-2. The average recoveries from the columns of four determinations with the spleen DNA, two determinations with the diploid E9514A or 6C3HED DNA, and three determinations with tetraploid 6C3HED DNA were 103%, 85%, 93%, and 93% respectively. (For further details, see the legend to Fig. 2.)

need not necessarily lead to products of comparable purity and integrity (Geiduschek and Holtzer, 1958). Moreover, it is well known that DNA prepared by different methods from the same tissue may vary considerably in molecular size and physical chemical properties (Geiduschek and Holtzer, 1958; Bendich *et al.*, 1958; Polli and Shooter, 1958; Kit, in press).

With respect to the properties of the anion exchanger, most of our experiments were carried out with an ECTEOLA-Solka Floc anion exchanger (Brown Co., Berlin, New Hampshire, type 20) having a rather high nitrogen content, 0.55%; exchange capacity, 0.39 meq. per gram. However, comparisons were also made with a weaker anion exchanger (nitrogen content, 0.42%; exchange capacity, 0.30 meq./gram) and with an anion exchanger having intermediate properties to the above two exchangers and obtained through the kindness of Dr. Aaron Bendich. The detailed features of the chromatographic profiles depended upon the exchanger used but the DNA profiles obtained with a given exchanger were similar for each of the normal tissues or tumors. The effect on the profiles of performing the chromatography under conditions where the exchanger was saturated with DNA, three-fourths saturated, or about half saturated was investigated. The elution profiles were similar in each case.

The problem of the method used in preparing DNA resolves itself into: (1) the removal of contaminating proteins or ribonucleic acids, and (2) the avoidance of procedures which tend to denature or partially degrade the DNA. It is obvious that although the chromatographic profiles obtained with a given DNA sample might be extraordinarily reproducible on replicate columns run on the same or different days, the results would be of questionable biological significance if the samples happened to be degraded or denatured.

The DNA samples which are described in the present paper were prepared by the p-aminosalicylate-phenol procedure of Kirby (1957). This method has three important advantages: (1) DNA can be extracted from tissues by this method in better than 90% yield. (2) The DNA is relatively pure and contains less than 5% RNA, and about 1% or less of contaminating protein. (The chromatographic profiles were not greatly modified in samples in which the protein concentration exceeded 3% or in samples in which the DNA was further treated with chymotrypsin). (3) The tissues are very quickly exposed to 50% phenol so that the action of nucleases is arrested. We have shown that the DNA elution profiles are markedly shifted to the left if partially autolyzed tissue samples or DNA samples deliberately exposed to crystalline DNase are chromatographed (Fig. 4). However, if DNase was added to the tissues after the extraction with phenol and p-aminosalicylate had begun, the elution profiles were not changed (Fig. 5).

The use of an Omnimixer rather than an all glass homogenizer in dispersing the tissue prior to the extraction of the DNA with phenol and p-aminosalicylate was also investigated. The amount of DNA eluted in Peak I was increased from about 10% to about 30% when the Omnimixer was used.

These results suggest that large differences in the DNA molecular size distribution, or differences in the purine and pyrimidine base composition do not distinguish the DNA of the normal tissues of the same animal or normal tissues and tumors. The results do not, of course, preclude the possibility that the DNA of tumors and

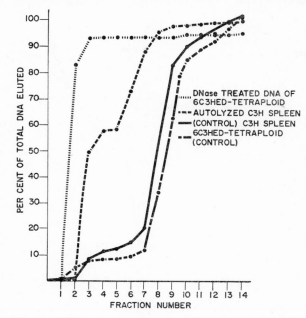

FIG. 4. Effect of DNase treatment and of tissue autolysis on DNA elution pattern from ECTEOLA-cellulose columns. Control DNA samples: C3H spleen and tetraploid lymphoma, 6C3HED. Recovery of DNA from column, 102% and 90%, respectively. Experimental samples: C3H spleen tissues homogenized in 0.075 M NaCl and incubated at 37° for 4 hours. DNA was then extracted from the autolyzed tissue with p-aminosalicylate and phenol. Recovery of DNA from the column: 91%. DNase treated sample: The DNA of tetraploid tumor 6C3HED was dissolved in 5 cc. of 0.05 M NaCl and 0.5 cc. of 19.1% MgSO₄. Two mg. of deoxyribonuclease-I (Worthington, Lot #D687-4, one time recrystallized) was added. After 30 seconds, 5 cc. of 90% phenol was added and the solution was shaken. The aqueous phase was withdrawn, extracted several times with ethyl ether and applied to the column.

normal tissues might differ: (1) in the sequence of purine and pyrimidines along the polynucleotide chains, (2) in the relative proportions of different DNA molecules within a given cell, and (3) in the arrangement of the DNA molecules within the chromosomes.

RNA and Enzyme Forming Systems (EFS)

There is reason to believe that RNA functions as a component of EFS and that genetic information which defines the specific sequence of the amino acids in the protein chain is transmitted from DNA through the nucleotide sequence of RNA (Brachet,

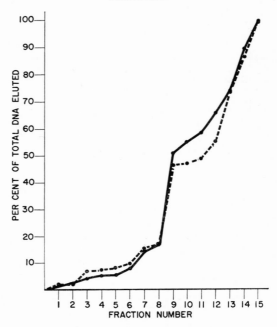

Fig. 5. Comparison of chromatographic profiles on 500 mg. of ECTEOLA-cellulose of the DNA of tetraploid lymphoma 6C3HED prepared in the presence or absence of deoxyribonuclease. [Solid line-DNase added after PAS-phenol; broken line = 6C3HED-tetraploid (control).] The control DNA was prepared as previously described. To the experimental tissue homogenate, 1.7 mg. of deoxyribonuclease (Worthington Biochemical Corporation, Free-hold, New Jersey; 1 time recrystallized; lot #654) was added 5 minutes after the DNA extraction with p-aminosalicylate and phenol had begun. The optical density between 258-260 mμ of each fraction was recorded; 58,300 optical density units of DNA were applied to the control column and 67,200 of the DNA sample prepared in the presence of deoxyribonuclease.

1957; Crick, 1958). Nucleic acid-protein codes and codes linking DNA with RNA have been discussed by Crick (1958) and by Zubay (1958) and Stent (1958) and need not detain us here.

There are two ways in which RNA may function in EFS: (1) as transfer-RNA, and (2) as ribosomal-template RNA (Hecht *et al.*, 1959).[2]

---

[2] Aside from the functions of RNA in EFS, the suggestion has been made that RNA functions in developmental processes (Brachet, 1957; Yamada, 1958; Benitez *et al.*, 1959). A genetic function for certain kinds of RNA has been demonstrated. The RNA of many animal or plant viruses is infectious

In order to function in the transfer of genetic information, RNA must interact in some way with the DNA of the chromosomes. An understanding of the configurational properties of RNA is essential for the formulation of hypotheses concerning such interaction. The Watson-Crick model of DNA as a double stranded helical structure, in which complementary polynucleotide chains of opposite polarity are held together by hydrogen bonds between specific base pairs, has proven adequate to explain the chemical, hydrodynamic, and X-ray diffraction data of the DNA (Crick, 1958) in all but one or two instances (Sinsheimer, 1959; Tessman, 1959). The DNA of the bacteriophages, ϕX174 and S13, are composed of single stranded molecules.

All ribonucleic acids which have so far been examined are also single stranded polynucleotide chains. These include the RNA of various tumors, cytoplasmic RNA of tumors (Kit, 1959), microsomal RNA of liver (Doty et al., 1959), the RNA of tobacco mosaic virus (Hart, 1958; Ginoza, 1959; Gierer, 1958; Commoner et al., 1958; Wildman, 1959; Fraenkel-Conrat, 1959; Franklin and Klug, 1959), and that of Escherichia coli (Littauer and Eisenberg, 1959). The conclusion that RNA is a single stranded molecule is based upon many of the same kinds of experiments which led to the suggestion that most DNA's are double stranded structures: (1) electron microscope and X-ray diffraction studies, (2) measurements of sedimentation and viscosity, and the kinetics of RNase degradation, (3) the kinetics of heat inactivation, (4) the effect of heat on ultraviolet absorption and the chromatographic profiles of RNA, (5) the reaction of formaldehyde with the amino groups of RNA cytosine, adenine, and guanine, and particularly, (6) the ratios of purine and pyrimidine bases in RNA. Unlike DNA, there is frequently observed in RNA preparations a lack of equivalence of adenine to uracil, of guanine to cytosine, and of purines to pyrimidines (Elson and Chargaff, 1955).

The RNA-purine and pyrimidine base composition of several normal tissues of the mouse and of spontaneous leukemias, transplanted lymphomas, carcinomas, and melanomas were recently measured in this laboratory. In contrast to the composition of DNA, guanine and cytosine were found to preponderate in RNA

(Fraenkel-Conrat et al., 1957; Gierer and Schramm, 1956; Kaper and Steere, 1959; Colter et al., 1957; Alexander et al., 1958; Franklin et al., 1959; Wecker, 1959; Huppert and Sanders, 1958; Brown et al., 1958; Ada and Anderson, 1959; Sanders et al., 1958).

TABLE III

RNA BASE RATIOS OF NORMAL MOUSE TISSUES AND TUMORS

Tissue	Molar base ratios[a]					
	G	CRP	URP	$\dfrac{G + CRP}{A + URP}$	$\dfrac{pu}{pyr}$	$\dfrac{6\text{-am}}{6\text{-keto}}$
Spleen	2.19	2.05	1.16	1.96	0.99	0.91
Lung	2.07	1.93	1.06	1.94	1.03	0.94
Liver	2.01	1.97	1.05	1.94	1.00	0.97
Kidney	2.06	1.94	1.24	1.78	0.99	0.89
Liver (newborn)	2.09	2.01	1.08	1.97	1.00	0.95
Kidney (newborn)	2.15	2.09	1.10	2.02	0.99	0.95
Leukemia (spontaneous)	1.99	1.95	1.09	1.89	0.99	0.96
6C3HED-DBA-2 (hypotetraploid lymphoma)	2.06	1.93	1.19	1.82	0.98	0.90
6C3HED (diploid lymphoma)	1.89	1.92	1.06	1.85	0.97	0.99
S91 (tetraploid melanoma)	2.06	1.95	1.10	1.91	1.00	0.93
Ehrlich (hypotetraploid carcinoma)	2.17	1.98	1.12	1.96	1.02	0.91

[a] The molar base ratios are expressed relative to adenine = 1.00. Abbreviations are: A = adenine, G = guanine, CRP = cytidylate, URP = uridylate, pu = purines, pyr = pyrimidines, 6-am = adenine plus cytidylate, 6-keto = guanine plus uridylate.

(Table III). The ratios of guanine plus cytosine to adenine plus uracil were about 1.90 in RNA whereas the ratios of guanine plus cytosine to adenine plus thymine of DNA were approximately 0.80.[3] The ratios of the purines to pyrimidines and of 6-amino bases to 6-keto-bases $(A + C)/(G + U)$ of RNA were fairly close to one, although the uracil content slightly exceeded that of adenine and the guanine content that of cytosine. No significant differences in the base ratios were observed between the normal tissues and the

[3] The ratios of $(G + C)/(A + U)$ and $(G + C)/(A + T)$ in RNA and DNA, respectively, suggest further possible enzymatic switchpoints for the control of DNA synthesis. Since the synthesis of DNA requires a rather marked decrease in the preceding ratios, one might predict that at the time of DNA synthesis, the dehydrogenase and aminase enzymes which convert inosinic acid to guanylic acid will decrease relative to the enzymes which convert inosinic to adenylic acid and that the enzyme which aminates uridylic acid to cytidylic acid will be decreased relative to enzyme systems which convert uridylic to deoxyuridylic, thymidylic and thymidine triphosphate.

tumors or between the different adult normal tissues of the mouse. The diploid and the tetraploid tumors, the carcinomas and the lymphomas, the melanotic and amelanotic melanomas all had approximately the same base ratios.

The kidney and the liver RNA of newborn mice were also examined. The base ratios of these RNA's were also similar to those of the adult tissues. Thus, rapidly growing tissues and non-growing tissues and tissues having widely differing functions and enzymatic patterns all contained RNA of very similar base composition. Minagawa *et al.* (1959) have reported that in *Neurospora,* the base ratios of RNA and DNA of conidia, germinated conidia, and mycelium were the same. Here, also, the base ratios were not changed at different growth stages although the enzyme content was demonstrably different.

Heterogeneity of RNA

The interpretation of the molar base ratios of the total RNA requires that we take into account the profound heterogeneity of RNA. Heterogeneity exists with respect to: (1) distribution within the cell, (2) molecular size, (3) function, (4) purine and pyrimidine base composition, and (5) metabolic activity.

RNA is found in both the nucleus and the cytoplasm of the cell. Within the nucleus, the RNA of the nucleoli and of the chromatin appear to be metabolically distinct (McMaster-Kaye and Taylor, 1958; Swift, 1959). Several kinds of nuclear RNA have been distinguished by histochemical staining methods (Love, 1957; Love and Liles, 1959; Love and Bharadwaj, 1959).

In the cytoplasm, mitochondrial, microsomal, and transfer-RNA may be distinguished. The microsomal and the transfer-RNA are both heterogeneous (Reid and Stevens, 1958; Bhargava *et al.,* 1958; Smith *et al.,* 1959). A nuclear RNA fraction which resembles cytoplasmic ribosomal RNA in electrophoretic mobility and base composition has been found (Osawa *et al.,* 1958), and there is preliminary evidence that an RNA fraction which cannot be sedimented by centrifugation of the nuclear extract at 105,000 g for two hours (nuclear-transfer-RNA?) also exists. The chloroplasts of plant cells contain RNA, the base composition of which differs significantly from that of the RNA of the remainder of the cytoplasm (Leyon, 1957). Plant chloroplasts may be the site of synthesis or assembly of the protein and the nucleic acid of tobacco mosaic virus (Boardman and Zaitlin, 1958).

The distribution of the RNA within the fractions of tumor cells differs consistently from that of normal cells. Laird and Barton (1956) have observed that the concentration of RNA in each cell fraction varied considerably when the concentrations were expressed as the amount per unit of DNA in an equivalent amount of the whole tissue. On the other hand, when the quantity of RNA in each cell fraction was expressed as a percentage of the total amount present in the tissue, it became evident that all the tumors showed a consistent pattern. The nuclear fraction contained 30% or more of the RNA of the tumors; this was considerably more than the amount found in the nuclear fraction of any of the normal tissues studied.

Properties of Transfer and Ribosomal RNA

Although the molecular weight of ribosomal RNA may be as high as a million (Hall and Doty, 1958), the weight of transfer-RNA appears to be considerably lower (10,000-40,000) (Hoagland et al., 1959; Hecht et al., 1958). Different transfer-RNA molecules appear to exist, but each possesses the same terminal end groups, cytidylic-cytidylic-adenylic, to which activated amino acids may attach (Hecht et al., 1959). Specificity between a particular transfer-RNA and an activated amino acid has been deduced from three kinds of experiments: (1) The individual amino acids are incorporated into transfer-RNA additively and there seems to be no competition for sites on the transfer-RNA between natural amino acids. (2) A particular transfer-RNA may be protected against destruction by periodate by the attachment of a specific amino acid to the 2' or the 3' hydroxyl group of the terminal ribose moiety (Bergmann et al., 1959). (3) Transfer-RNA has been fractionated by ion exchange chromatography, with the partial separation of leucine-transfer-RNA from tyrosine-transfer-RNA (Leahy et al., 1959; Smith et al., 1959).

Considering the number of enzymes present in the cell for which templates must exist, it seems likely that specific Ribosomal-RNA templates for each enzyme may exist. The RNA of the microsomes has already been shown to be heterogeneous with respect to metabolic turnover (Bhargava et al., 1958). Although differences between the molar base ratios of microsomal subfractions are rather small (Siekevitz and Palade, 1959), Reid and Stevens (1958) found some changes in the ratios of cytosine to uracil.

The possibility has been considered that a precursor product relationship exists between the ribonucleoprotein particles of the cell nucleus and the ribosomes of the microsomes (Osawa *et al.*, 1958). The ribonucleoprotein particles of the nucleus can be extracted by isotonic saline solutions or 0.1 M phosphate buffer, pH 7.1 (Fraction N-I) (Zbarsky and Georgiev, 1959; Osawa *et al.*, 1958). The particles may be sedimented by centrifuging the phosphate buffer extract at 105,000 g for 1-2 hours in the Spinco-preparative centrifuge.

As in the case of the cytoplasmic ribosomes, the nuclear ribonucleoprotein particles consist of about 50% RNA and 50% protein. The electrophoretic mobilities of the nuclear and microsomal ribonucleoprotein particles are also very similar (Osawa *et al.*, 1958). The nuclear particles (Fraction N-I) comprise approximately 5% of the total RNA of tumor cells. The purine and pyrimidine base composition of the cytoplasmic and nuclear particles were found to be similar to each other in determinations made by Osawa *et al.* (1958) and in this laboratory (Table IV).

TABLE IV

MOLAR BASE RATIOS[a] OF MICROSOMAL AND NUCLEAR FRACTION I[b]
RNA OF SPLEEN AND LYMPHOMAS

Tissue	Microsomal RNA			
	G	CRP	URP	$\frac{G + CRP}{A + URP}$
Spleen	2.14	2.01	1.03	2.05
6C3HED Lymphoma	2.22	2.04	1.12	2.01
Leukemia (spontaneous)	2.14	2.10	1.09	2.03
Nuclear fraction-I[b]				
6C3HED Lymphoma	2.23	1.96	1.26	1.85
Leukemia (spontaneous)	2.06	1.81	1.08	1.86

[a] The molar base ratios are expressed relative to adenine = 1.00. Abbreviations are the same as in Table III. The molar base ratios of the residual nuclear fraction (Fraction II) of calf thymus were measured by Osawa *et al.* (1958) and were found to be: adenine, 10.0; guanylic, 15.1; cytidylic, 12.5; uridylic, 12.9.

[b] Extracted from the nuclei by 0.1 M phosphate, pH 7.1.

No significant differences have been noted by us between the base composition of the microsomal RNA of lymphomas and spleen cells. The cytoplasmic RNA fractions of maternal and fetal rabbit liver and those of regenerating and normal rat liver also have the same base compositions (Crosbie *et al.*, 1953). The

RNA of the mitochondria, microsomes, and the supernatant fraction of the kidney or liver of the rat do not differ appreciably in base composition and the same situation prevails in the frog (Davidson and Smellie, 1952; Crosbie *et al.*, 1953; Elson *et al.*, 1955).

Preliminary experiments have been carried out in this laboratory on the fractionation of the total RNA and of the microsomal RNA of tumors on anion exchangers. Smith and Kaplan (1959) have observed that the RNA chromatographic profiles of leukemic mouse cells may be distinguished from those of normal adult thymus RNA but not from the thymus RNA of newborn mice.

The Nucleus as the Primary Site of RNA Synthesis

The previous discussion of the RNA of tissue fractions serves as background to the crucial problem of whether part, if not all, of the RNA of cells originates in the nucleus. This concept, which depended first on kinetic studies of the turnover of P^{32} in tissue fractions is now supported by several lines of evidence.

a. Radioautographic studies with tritiated cytidine or uridine show that radioactivity is rapidly taken up and concentrated in the RNA of the nucleus of plant (Woods and Taylor, 1959), *Neurospora* (Zalokar, 1959), *Drosophila* (McMaster-Kaye and Taylor, 1958), and ascites lymphoma cells (Kit and Chang, unpublished). Within the nucleus, the nucleolar region appears to be the first locus of labeling (Woods and Taylor, 1959). As shown in Figs. 6 and 7, uridine was incorporated into the nuclear RNA of asynchronously dividing ascites lymphoma cells 30 minutes after the injection of the labeled precursor, although little or no radioactive RNA was found in the cytoplasm. At 60 minutes, the nucleus was still heavily labeled. By 2 and 4 hours, radioactivity appeared in the cytoplasmic RNA. By 24 hours, there were cells present in which radioactivity could be found in the cytoplasm but little radioactivity was present in the nucleus. In the case of *Neurospora* hyphae, labeled uridine appeared only in the nucleus at 1-4 minutes. After 4 minutes, some isotope was detected in the cytoplasmic RNA. By 1 hour, the ergastoplasm became labeled more heavily than the nuclei and some activity was found in the mitochondria while the supernatant remained virtually inactive. When tritiated uridine was fed for 1 minute only and then washed out and replaced with an excess of nonlabeled uridine, the label again appeared first in nuclei and then was found in the ergastoplasm. The labeling of the ergasto-

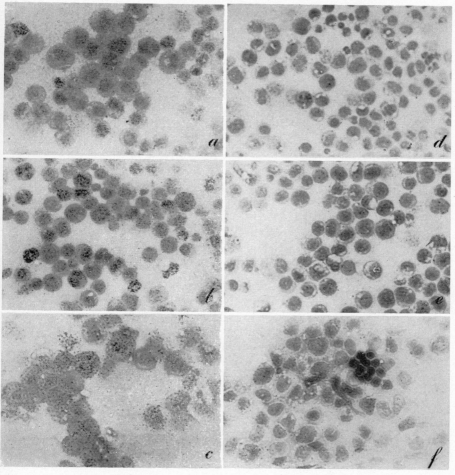

Fig. 6. Radioautograms of ascites lymphoma, "6C3HED-DBA to C3H," after: (a) and (d), 30 minutes; (b) and (e), 60 minutes; and (c) and (f), 2 hours of incorporation of uridine-H³ into RNA. The cells shown in (a), (b), and (c) were fixed with ethyl alcohol-ethyl ether (1:1) at 4° and washed with ice cold 2% perchloric acid and alcohol. The cells shown in (d), (e), and (f) were also treated with ribonuclease (Pentex Inc., 5 times recrystallized, 0.1 mg./ml.) for 3 hours at room temperature. Uridine-H³ was purchased from New England Nuclear, #L-63, specific activity, 1 millicurie per 0.36 mg. in 1 ml. H₂O. 0.15 ml. of the uridine-H³ was injected into adult female mice in which the tumor had grown for 14 days. Cells were stained with hematoxylin-eosin and exposed to Eastman-Kodak, permeable base stripping film, Spec. 764, for 5 weeks. (Magnification of cells, X400). For details, see Chang and Russell (1959).

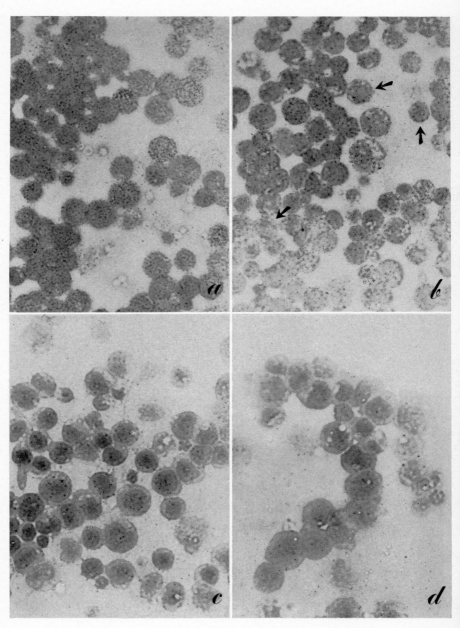

FIG. 7. Radioautograms of ascites tetraploid lymphoma, "6C3HED-DBA to C3H" after: (a) and (c), 4 hours; and (b) and (d), 24 hours of incorporation of uridine-H³ into RNA. The conditions were the same as those described in Fig. 6. The arrows in (b) point to cells in which the cytoplasm is labeled but the nucleus contains little radioactivity. (Magnification of cells, X400). The cells shown in (c) and (d) were treated with ribonuclease for 3 hours at room temperature.

plasm increased with time at the expense of the nuclear label (Zalokar, 1959).

b. The transplantation of a radioactive *Amoeba* nucleus to a nonradioactive *Amoeba* was followed by the transfer of radioactivity to the host cytoplasm (Goldstein and Plaut, 1955). In other experiments, liver nuclei were isolated from rats at various times after the injection of labeled orotic acid and the labeled nuclei were incubated *in vitro* with cytoplasmic fractions from noninjected rats. If the nuclei were isolated shortly after the injection and incubated, nearly all the labeled nuclear RNA was readily transferred to the cytoplasmic fractions; while if the nuclei were isolated several hours after the administration of the label, they retained most of their radioactivity in the subsequent *in vitro* incubation (Scholtissek *et al.*, 1958).

c. The fact that the RNA of the nuclear fraction has a higher specific activity than the cytoplasmic cell fractions after animals are injected with P^{32} and other RNA precursors was first shown by Marshak (1949) and Marshak and Vogel (1950) and has since been confirmed by many investigators (Barnum and Huseby, 1950; Tyner *et al.*, 1953; Smellie *et al.*, 1955). Shortly after the injection of the labeled precursor, the order of specific activity is as follows: (a) nucleus > soluble cytoplasm > mitochondria-microsomes. Of the microsomal subfractions, the ribonucleoprotein granules which are most active in protein synthesis appear to be least active in RNA labeling (Bhargava *et al.*, 1958; Shigeura and Chargaff, 1958; Siekevitz and Palade, 1959). Of the nuclear-RNA, Fraction I, which resembles the microsomes, has a lower specific activity than the residual-nuclear RNA (Fraction II), although both nuclear fractions are far more radioactive than any of the cytoplasmic fractions (Table V) (Osawa *et al.*, 1957; Logan, 1957). Later, the RNA of the tissue fractions approached isotopic equilibrium. Both the relative specific activity of the nuclear RNA, the position of the maximum in the nuclear RNA time curve and the inflection point of the curve relative to the microsomal RNA were consistent with the hypothesis of the nuclear RNA as a precursor of cytoplasmic RNA (Barnum and Huseby, 1950).

d. Some incorporation of isotopic precursor into RNA takes place in homogenate systems. The evaluation of the incorporation of P^{32}, adenine, or cytidine into cytoplasmic RNA is, however, complicated by the fact that there is very rapid turnover of the terminal cytidine and adenine of the transfer-RNA and probably interaction

TABLE V

HETEROGENEITY OF INCORPORATION OF URIDINE-H[3] INTO TUMOR RNA

Tumor	Total	"Cyto-plasmic soluble"	Micro-somal	Nuclear-I	Nuclear-II
	(% of total specific activity)				
6C3HED-DBA to C3H[a]	100	49	28	117	408
Ehrlich[b]	100	58	25	229	430

[a] Animals sacrificed 60 minutes after injection of 2 μc.-uridine-H[3].
[b] Animals sacrificed 30 minutes after injection of 2 μc.-uridine-H[3].

between this transfer-RNA and ribosomal-RNA during protein synthesis (Heidelberger et al., 1956; Edmonds and Abrams, 1957; Canellakis, 1957; Hecht et al., 1958). Incorporation of precursors of RNA in homogenate systems is largely due to such terminal labeling rather than to the synthesis of the polynucleotide chain (Patterson and LePage, 1957). Herbert (1958a, b) showed that in pigeon liver homogenates, incorporation of ADP-C[14] into the 2'-3'-adenylic acid moiety of RNA (interior of the chain) occurs most rapidly in the *nuclear fraction*. The cytoplasmic and soluble enzyme fractions attached ADP almost exclusively to *monoesterified* end groups of RNA as evidenced by the appearance of labeled adenosine in the alkaline hydrolysate of RNA. No incorporation took place into microsomal or mitochondrial RNA when the latter were incubated in the absence of nuclei except in terminal linkage.

The evidence contraindicating the nuclear RNA as an exclusive precursor of cytoplasmic RNA and favoring the independent synthesis of at least part of the cytoplasmic-RNA is as follows:

1. On the basis of extensive studies of the time course of labeling by P[32] of the RNA fractions of mouse liver or mammary carcinomas, Barnum and Huseby (1950), and Barnum et al. (1953) drew the conclusion that it was more likely that both the cytoplasmic and the nuclear RNA had a common P donor such as ATP.

2. Anucleate *Amoeba* (Plaut and Rustad, 1959) or *Acetabularia* (Naora et al., 1959) incorporated labeled adenine, orotic acid, or uracil into their RNA.

3. The nuclear RNA fraction (Fraction II), which shows the earliest isotopic labeling, has a purine and pyrimidine base compo-

sition differing from that of the cytoplasmic RNA (Osawa *et al.*, 1958; McIndoe and Davidson, 1952; Elson *et al.*, 1955). This is, of course, very difficult to reconcile with the concept that Fraction II is a precursor of the cytoplasmic RNA.

There is one possible escape from the latter dilemma. One might assume that the nuclear Fraction II is heterogeneous, and that it contains a minor component which turns over exceedingly rapidly and has a base composition similar to that of ribosomal and transfer-RNA while the bulk of the nuclear Fraction II-RNA performs a function involving slow turnover. An analogous situation exists in the case of *E. coli* infected with T_2 or T_7 phage. In the latter instance, the RNA of one particulate fraction, though only a small part of the total cell RNA, has the highest specific activity whereas the major portion of the cell RNA has extremely low activity. The specific activity ratios of the RNA mononucleotides bear a striking resemblance to the molar composition of the analogous deoxynucleotides in phage DNA and are quite unlike the molar composition of ribonucleotides in *E. coli* RNA (Volkin *et al.*, 1958). Certain experiments previously reported in the literature also suggest that the above concept may have some merit. The specific activities of the ribonucleotides of rat liver, mouse liver, and mouse hepatoma were measured by Volkin and Carter (1951) 20 minutes after the injection of P^{32}. At this time, one might assume that the nuclear Fraction II accounts for most of the radioactivity. It was found by Volkin and Carter (1951) that the mononucleotides were about equally labeled. One might argue that if the nuclear Fraction II-RNA were being synthesized, the specific activity (c./m./μg, nucleotide) of the guanine and cytosine nucleotides should both be reduced. This is owing to the fact that the latter are present at lower concentrations in nuclear Fraction-II than in the mixed RNA of the whole cell. On the other hand, were an RNA species whose composition resembled that of the cytoplasmic RNA being synthesized, a near equality of specific activity would be predicted, as was indeed found.

Since there are a number of complications which might invalidate the foregoing argument, this problem requires further study. One might conclude, therefore, that the evidence is quite good for the synthesis of at least part of the cytoplasmic RNA in the cell nucleus. However, there is also reasonable evidence that at least some RNA can be synthesized in the cytoplasm of cells.

Summary

Neoplastic tissues are frequently abnormal with respect to enzyme content and metabolism and with respect to the number and structure of the chromosomes. In relation to the above facts, the structure, molar purine and pyrimidine composition, metabolism, and chromatographic heterogeneity of DNA and RNA of normal tissues and tumors were investigated. It was observed that:

a. There were no significant differences between the DNA of normal tissues or tumors with respect to molar base composition or chromatographic elution profiles.

b. There were no significant differences among the molar base ratios of the total RNA of various adult tissues, tissues of newborn mice, and lymphomas, carcinomas, or melanomas. The cytoplasmic or nuclear particulate RNA were similar in base composition in the case of normal spleen, spontaneous lymphoma, and transplanted lymphoma.

c. RNA is a single stranded polynucleotide chain in contrast to the double stranded DNA of animal tissues and tumors.

d. Evidence concerning the role of the nucleus as the site of synthesis of RNA was reviewed.

e. Experiments were presented indicating that a quantitative relationship exists between chromosome number, the DNA content, the enzyme content, RNA content, and the metabolism of diploid and tetraploid ascites tumors.

REFERENCES

Ada, G. L., and Anderson, S. G. (1959). *Nature* **183**, 799.

Alexander, H. E., Koch, G., Mountain, I. M., and Van Damme, O. (1958). *J. Exptl. Med.* **108**, 493.

Barnum, C. P., and Huseby, R. A. (1950). *Arch. Biochem.* **29**, 7.

Barnum, C. P., Huseby, R. A., and Vermund, H. (1953). *Cancer Research* **13**, 880.

Bendich, A., Pahl, H. B., and Beiser, S. M. (1956). *Cold Spring Harbor Symposia Quant. Biol.* **21**, 31.

Bendich, A., Pahl, H. B., Rosenkranz, H. S., and Rosoff, M. (1958). *Symposia Soc. Exptl. Biol.* **12**, 31.

Benitez, H. B., Murray, M. R., and Chargaff, E. (1959). *J. Biophys. Biochem. Cytol.* **5**, 25.

Bergmann, F. H., Berg, P., Preiss, J., Ofengand, E. J., and Dieckmann, M. (1959). *Federation Proc.* **18**, 191.

Bhargava, P. M., Simkin, J. L., and Work, T. S. (1958). *Biochem. J.* **68**, 265.

Boardman, N. K., and Zaitlin, M. (1958). *Virology* **6**, 758.

Bollum, F. J., and Potter, V. R. (1959). *Cancer Research* **19**, 561.

Bonner, D. M. (1951). *Cold Spring Harbor Symposia Quant. Biol.* **16**, 143.

Brachet, J. (1957). "Biochemical Cytology." Academic Press, New York.

Brown, F., Sellers, R. F., and Stewart, D. L. (1958). *Nature* **182**, 535.

Canellakis, E. S. (1957). *Biochim. et Biophys. Acta* **25**, 217.

Canellakis, E. S., Jaffe, J. J., Mantsavinos, R., and Krakow, J. S. (1959). *J. Biol. Chem.* **234**, 2096.

Chang, J. P., and Russell, W. O. (1959). *Stain Technol.* **34**, 187.

Chargaff, E. (1955). *In* "The Nucleic Acids" (E. Chargaff and J. N. Davidson, eds.), Vol. I, p. 307. Academic Press, New York.

Cohn, M. (1957). *Bacteriol. Revs.* **21**, 140.

Colter, J. S., Bird, H. H., Moyer, A. W., and Brown, R. A. (1957). *Virology* **4**, 522.

Commoner, B., Shearer, G. B., and Strode, C. (1958). *Proc. Natl. Acad. Sci. U.S.* **44**, 1117.

Crick, F. H. C. (1958). *Symposia Soc. Exptl. Biol.* **12**, 138.

Crosbie, G. W., Smellie, R. M. S., Davidson, J. N. (1953). *Biochem. J.* **54**, 287.

Davidson, J. N., and Smellie, R. M. S. (1952). *Biochem. J.* **52**, 599.

Doty, P., Boedtker, H., Fresco, J. R., Haselkorn, R., and Litt, M. (1959). *Proc. Natl. Acad. Sci. U.S.* **45**, 482.

Edmonds, M., and Abrams, R. (1957). *Biochim. et Biophys. Acta* **26**, 226.

Elson, D., and Chargaff, E. (1955). *Biochim. et Biophys. Acta* **17**, 367.

Elson, D., Trent, L. W., and Chargaff, E. (1955). *Biochim. et Biophys. Acta* **17**, 362.

Flaks, J. G., and Cohen, S. S. (1958). *Federation Proc.* **18**, 220.

Ford, C. E., Hamerton, J. L., and Mole, R. H. (1958). *J. Cellular Comp. Physiol.* **52** (Suppl. 1), 235.

Fraenkel-Conrat, H. (1959). *Trans. Faraday Soc.* **55**, 494.

Fraenkel-Conrat, H., Singer, B., and Williams, R. C. (1957). *Biochim. et Biophys. Acta* **25**, 87.

Franklin, R. E., and Klug, A. (1959). *Trans. Faraday Soc.* **55**, 494.

Franklin, R. M., Wecker, E., and Henry, C. (1959). *Virology* **7**, 220.

Freed, J. J., and Hungerford, D. A. (1957). *Cancer Research* **17**, 177.

Geiduschek, E. P., and Holtzer, A. (1958). *Advances in Biol. and Med. Phys.* **6**, 431.

Gierer, A. (1958). *Z. naturforsch.* **13b**, 477.

Gierer, A., and Schramm, G. (1956). *Nature* **177**, 702.

Ginoza, W. (1959). *Trans. Faraday Soc.* **55**, 493.

Goldstein, L., and Plaut, W. (1955). *Proc. Natl. Acad. Sci. U.S.* **41**, 874.

Greenbaum, A. L., and Slater, T. F. (1957a). *Biochem. J.* **66**, 155.

Greenbaum, A. L., and Slater, T. F. (1957b). *Biochem. J.* **66**, 161.

Greenstein, J. P. (1956). *Cancer Research* **16**, 641.

Grollman, A. P., and Lehninger, A. L. (1957). *Arch. Biochem. Biophys.* **69**, 458.

Hall, B. D., and Doty, P. (1958). First Symposium, Biophysical Society (edited by R. B. Roberts), Vol. 27. Pergamon Press, New York.

Hart, R. G. F. (1958). *Biochim. et Biophys. Acta* **28**, 457.

Hauschka, T. S. (1958). *J. Cellular Comp. Physiol.* **52** (Suppl. 1), 197.

Hecht, L. I., Zamecnik, P. C., Stephenson, M. L., and Scott, J. F. (1958). *J. Biol. Chem.* **233**, 954.

Hecht, L. I., Stephenson, M. L., and Zamecnik, P. C. (1959). *Proc. Natl. Acad. Sci. U.S.* **45**, 505.

Heidelberger, C., Harbers, E., Leibman, K. C., Takagi, Y., and Potter, V. R. (1956). *Biochim. et Biophys. Acta* **20**, 445.

Herbert, E. (1958a). *J. Biol. Chem.* **231**, 975.

Herbert, E. (1958b). *Federation Proc.* **17**, 241.

Hoagland, M. B., Zamecnik, P. C., and Stephenson, M. L. (1959). *In* "A Symposium on Molecular Biology" (R. E. Zirkle, ed.), p. 105. Univ. Chicago Press, Chicago, Illinois.

Horowitz, N. H., and Fling, M. (1956). *In* "Enzymes: Units of Biological Structure and Function" (O. H. Gaebler, ed.), p. 139. Academic Press, New York.

Horowitz, N. H., and Leupold, U. (1951). *Cold Spring Harbor Symposia Quant. Biol.* **16**, 65.

Huppert, J., and Sanders, F. K. (1958). *Nature* **182**, 515.

Ingram, V. M. (1957). *Nature* **180**, 326.

Kaper, J. M., and Steere, R. L. (1959). *Virology* **7**, 127.

Kenney, F. T., Reem, G. H., and Kretchmer, N. (1958). *Science* **127**, 86.

Kirby, K. S. (1957). *Biochem. J.* **66**, 495.

Kit, S. (1959). *Nature* **184**, 36.

Kit, S. *Arch. Biochem. Biophys.* In press.

Kit, S., and Griffin, A. C. (1958). *Cancer Research* **18**, 621.

Kit, S., and Gross, A. L. (1959a). *Biochim. et Biophys. Acta* **36**, 185.

Kit, S., and Gross, A. L. (1959b). *Federation Proc.* **18**, 262.

Kit, S., Fiscus, J., Graham, O. L., and Gross, A. L. (1959). *Cancer Research* **19**, 201.

Kit, S., Graham, O. L., Gross, A. L., Ragland, R. S., and Fiscus, J. *Acta Unio Intern. contra Cancrum*, in press; Also, Abstr. *7th Intern. Cancer Congr.*, *London*, p. 40 (1958).

Klein, G. (1951). *Exptl. Cell. Research* **11**, 518.

Knox, W. R., Auerbach, V. H., and Lin, E. C. C. (1956). *Physiol. Revs.* **36**, 164.

Kondo, N., and Osawa, S. (1959). *Nature* **183**, 1602.

Kornberg, A., Zimmerman, S. B., Kornberg, S. R., and Josse, J. (1959). *Proc. Natl. Acad. Sci. U.S.* **45**, 772.

Laird, A. K., and Barton, A. D. (1956). *Science* **124**, 32.

Leahy, J., Allen, E., and Schweet, R. (1959). *Federation Proc.* **18**, 270.

Lederberg, J. (1956). *In* "Enzymes: Units of Biological Structure and Function" (O. H. Gaebler, ed.), p. 161. Academic Press, New York.

Levan, A., and Biesele, J. J. (1958). *Ann. N.Y. Acad. Sci.* **71**, 1022.

Leyon, H. (1957). *Acta Chem. Scand.* **11**, 1599.

Littauer, U. Z., and Eisenberg, H. (1959). *Biochem. et Biophys. Acta* **32**, 320.

Logan, R. (1957). *Biochim. et Biophys. Acta* **26**, 227.

Love, R. (1957). *Nature* **180**, 1338.

Love, R., and Bharadwaj, T. P. (1959). *Nature* **183**, 1453.

Love, R., and Liles, R. H. (1959). *J. Histochem. Cytochem.* **7**, 164.

McIndoe, W. M., and Davidson, J. N. (1952). *Brit. J. Cancer* **6**, 200.

McMaster-Kaye, R., and Taylor, J. H. (1958). *J. Biophys. Biochem. Cytol.* **4**, 5.

Marshak, A. (1949). *J. Cellular Comp. Physiol.* **34,** 451.

Marshak, A., and Vogel, H. J. (1950). *J. Cellular Comp. Physiol.* **36,** 97.

Minagawa, T., Wagner, B., and Strauss, B. (1959). *Arch. Biochem. Biophys.* **80,** 442.

Naora, H., Richter, G., and Naora, Hatsuko (1959). *Exptl. Cell Research* **16,** 434.

Osawa, S., Takata, K., and Hotta, Y. (1957). *Biochim. et Biophys. Acta* **25,** 656.

Osawa, S., Takata, K., and Hotta, Y. (1958). *Biochim. et Biophys. Acta* **28,** 271.

Patterson, A. R. P., and LePage, G. A. (1957). *Cancer Research* **17,** 409.

Patterson, E. K., and Podber, E. (1956). *Ann. N.Y. Acad. Sci.* **63,** 988.

Plaut, W., and Rustad, R. C. (1959). *Biochim. et Biophys. Acta* **33,** 59.

Polli, E. E. (1958). *Abstr. 7th Intern. Cancer Congr., London,* p. 38.

Polli, E. E., and Shooter, K. V. (1958). *Biochem. J.* **69,** 398.

Potter, V. R., Brumm, A. F., and Bollum, F. J. (1958). *Cancer Research* **2,** 336.

Reid, E., and Stevens, B. M. (1958). *Nature* **182,** 441.

Richards, B. M., Walker, P. M. B., and Deeley, E. M. (1956). *Ann. N.Y. Acad. Sci.* **63,** 831.

Sanders, F. K., Huppert, J., and Hoskins, J. M. (1958). *Symposia Soc. Exptl. Biol.* **12,** 123.

Scholtissek, C., Schneider, J. H., and Potter, V. R. (1958). *Federation Proc.* **17,** 306.

Shigeura, H. T., and Chargaff, E. (1958). *J. Biol. Chem.* **233,** 197.

Siekevitz, P., and Palade, G. E. (1959). *J. Biophys. Biochem. Cytol.* **5,** 1.

Sinsheimer, R. (1959). *J. Molecular Biol.* **1,** 43.

Smellie, R. M. S., Humphrey, G. F., Kay, E. R. M., and Davidson, J. N. (1955). *Biochem. J.* **60,** 177.

Smith, K. C., and Kaplan, H. S. (1959). *Nature* **183,** 1602.

Smith, K. C., Cordes, E., and Schweet, R. S. (1959). *Biochim. et Biophys. Acta* **33,** 286.

Somerville, R., and Greenberg, G. R. (1959). *Federation Proc.* **18,** 327.

Stent, G. S. (1958). *Advances in Virus Research* **5,** 95.

Strong, L. C. (1958). *Ann. N.Y. Acad. Sci.* **71,** 810.

Swift, H. (1959). *In* "A Symposium on Molecular Biology" (R. E. Zirkle, ed.), p. 266. Univ. Chicago Press, Chicago Illinois.

Tessman, I. (1959). *Virology* **7,** 263.

Tyner, E. P., Heidelberger, C., and LePage, G. A. (1953). *Cancer Research* **13,** 186.

Uzman, L. L., and Desoer, C. (1954). *Arch. Biochem. Biophys.* **48,** 63.

Volkin, E., and Carter, C. E. (1951). *J. Am. Chem. Soc.* **73,** 1519.

Volkin, E., Astrachan, L., and Countryman, J. L. (1958). *Virology* **6,** 545.

Wagner, R. P., Bergquist, A., and Karp, G. W. (1958). *Arch. Biochem. Biophys.* **74,** 182.

Wecker, E. (1959). *Virology* **7,** 241.

Weinhouse, S. (1959). *Abstr. Am. Chem. Soc. Meeting, Atlantic City, New Jersey,* Sept. 1959. See also this volume, p. 109.

Wildman, S. G. (1959). *Proc. Natl. Acad. Sci. U.S.* **45,** 300.

Woods, P. S., and Taylor, J. H. (1959). *Lab. Invest.* **8,** 309.

Yamada, T. (1958). *In* "A Symposium on the Chemical Basis of Development" (W. D. McElroy and B. Glass, eds.), p. 217. Johns Hopkins Press, Baltimore, Maryland.

Yanofsky, C. (1956). *In* "Enzymes: Units of Biological Structure and Function" (O. H. Gaebler, ed.), p. 147. Academic Press, New York.

Yates, R. A., and Pardee, A. B. (1957). *J. Biol. Chem.* **227**, 677.

Zalokar, M. (1959). *Nature* **183**, 1330.

Zbarsky, I. B., and Georgiev, G. P. (1959). *Biochim. et Biophys. Acta* **32**, 301.

Zubay, G. (1958). *Nature* **182**, 112.

Carbohydrate Metabolism in Ascites Tumor and HeLa Cells[1]

E. RACKER, R. WU, and J. B. ALPERS

Division of Nutrition and Physiology, The Public Health Research Institute of the City of New York, Inc., New York, New York

THE CLASSIC STUDIES of Warburg (1930) have established that cancer tissues produce considerable amounts of lactic acid under aerobic conditions. At the same time, Warburg proposed that tumors have an impaired respiration, a viewpoint which, as you know, has been challenged (Weinhouse, 1955). We hope that we can avoid entering into this polemic by partially agreeing with both sides. In an excellent evaluation of the problem, Greenstein (1954) has pointed out that there is considerable evidence that certain tumors, although they do not necessarily exhibit a low respiration, have a low content of certain respiratory catalysts, as manifested by their response to stimuli such as p-phenylenediamine or cytochrome c. On the other hand, some tumors have a high content of respiratory enzymes and a respiration that is well within the "normal" range (Chance and Castor, 1952). Moreover, mitochondria obtained from ascites tumor cells exhibit an active respiration with P:O ratios which are as high as in mitochondria from normal cells (Wu and Racker, 1959b).

Since a respiratory defect is not a *uniform* feature of cancer cells, one can assign to it a secondary role at best. In contrast to this, is the aerobic lactic acid production, that is generally accepted to be a *uniform* feature of cancer cells. It is not believed, however, to be a *unique* feature, since a few normal tissues such as retina, leucocytes, kidney, and others have been observed to produce lactic acid *in vitro* under aerobic conditions. During the past few years, Warburg has endeavored to demonstrate that acid production in these exceptional tissues is an artifact due to injury of the tissues during manipulation. He demonstrated that kidney and leucocytes

[1] This work was supported by Grant No. C-3463 from the National Institutes of Health, United States Public Health Service.

produce little lactic acid aerobically if certain precautions are taken (Warburg *et al.*, 1957, 1958).

It seems to us that the uniform metabolic feature of aerobic lactic acid formation in cancer cells may have a great metabolic significance even if a few normal tissues such as the retina do indeed exhibit the same phenomenon. Just as the possession of a pen (admittedly a dangerous instrument) does not make a writer, aerobic lactic acid production is not likely to make a cell malignant. On the other hand, lactic acid production may be a feature essential for the growth or the spread of tumors *in vivo*. In view of the well known effects of even small changes in pH on enzyme catalysis, one might expect profound alterations of the metabolic machinery due to the considerable increase in hydrogen ion concentration. That tumors actually produce lactic acid *in vivo* has been established (Cori and Cori, 1925). Administration of glucose to the tumor bearing animal stimulates lactic acid production and results in a drop of intracellular pH (Voegtlin *et al.*, 1935; Kahler and Robertson, 1943).

In spite of the fact that the aerobic production of lactic acid in tumor cells has been known for over 30 years, the cause of this phenomenon is still obscure. The slow progress in this field can be traced to the inadequacy of methods for the study of intracellular metabolism. Consequently, there is a lack of knowledge of what limits the rate of various metabolic pathways in normal as well as in tumor cells. Only in recent years have biochemists taken the first timid steps in a systematic approach to these complex problems. Instead of talking in generalities it may be appropriate to outline the experimental procedure that has been chosen in our laboratory in attempts to determine the rate-limiting factors of carbohydrate metabolism in intact cells. The first studies were carried out with cell populations which were as uniform as possible in cell type, e.g., ascites tumors, cells grown in tissue cultures, and leucocytes. These cells can be manipulated in such a way that the intracellular content of enzymes, coenzymes, and various ions as well as the transport of extracellular components into the cells could be analyzed with a reasonable degree of accuracy. In view of recent developments of techniques for preparation of cell suspensions from parenchymal organs such as the liver or the kidney, it is hoped to extend these studies in the future to cells which are more representative of "normal" cells than leucocytes or cells grown in tissue culture.

The enzymes of carbohydrate metabolism were assayed individually in cell-free extracts by accurate and sensitive spectrophotometric tests (Wu and Racker, 1959a). A profile of the capacity of the glycolytic enzymes, measured at optimal substrate concentrations, is not informative in respect to the activity of the individual enzymes within the metabolic sequence of a multienzyme system. However, as will be pointed out later, it does tell us something about the potential capacity of the enzymes in competitive systems. The next step in the analysis is an evaluation of the multienzyme system in a cell-free extract or homogenate. The over-all glycolysis is measured in the presence of an excess of coenzymes and necessary ions. In some instances (e.g., in brain homogenates) it may be necessary to prevent DPN destruction by protective agents such as nicotinamide or to regenerate ATP if the ATPase activity is too high. Creatine phosphate, together with creatine kinase, is particularly suitable as a regenerating system of ATP in studies of glycolysis (Racker and Krimsky, 1948). By the addition of the individual enzymes of glycolysis the rate-limiting factor in a multienzyme system can be determined, a procedure employed some years ago in a study of a metabolic defect in homogenates obtained from brains of animals infected with certain neurotropic viruses (Racker and Krimsky, 1948) and more recently in the analysis of the metabolism of tumor extracts (Wu and Racker, 1959a).

A comparison of the enzyme activities in cell-free extracts or homogenates with the over-all metabolic rate of the intact cell permits a broad evaluation of the probable role played by any one of the enzymes as a rate-limiting factor. The analysis of the intact cell itself consists of a systematic investigation of the rate of utilization of substrate and formation of products together with a parallel study of the intracellular concentration of intermediates, coenzymes, and ions under various experimental conditions. Particular emphasis has been placed on a comparison of aerobic and anaerobic conditions in the hope of obtaining clues to the mechanism of the Pasteur effect. Studies on ascites tumor cells, on the HeLa cells grown in tissue culture, on leucocytes and brain tissue were selected for the present discussion.

Carbohydrate Metabolism of Ascites Tumor Cells

Since the details of the experimental work with ascites tumor cells have recently been published (Wu and Racker, 1959a), it should suffice to summarize briefly the pertinent findings. The profile of the glycolytic enzymes showed a large excess of enzymes in comparison to the over-all glycolytic activity of the intact cells. The enzymes that form ADP from ATP, namely hexokinase and phosphofructokinase had the lowest capacities, while the enzymes that regenerate ATP from ADP, namely phosphoglycerate kinase and pyruvate kinase were among the most active ones. The activity of phosphoglycerate kinase was 50 to 100 times that of the hexose kinases. Such an excess of the ADP phosphorylating enzymes of glycolysis represents a formidable competitive force against the ADP utilizing system of oxidative phosphorylation in the mitochondria. Indeed, addition of glucose to respiring tumor cells results in an inhibition of respiration, a phenomenon referred to as the Crabtree effect. The presence of a large excess of ADP transphosphorylating glycolytic enzymes may emerge as another uniform feature of tumor cells and may in fact be essential for the high aerobic production of lactic acid.

The study of extracts from ascites tumor cells revealed that in the presence of excess essential coenzymes and ions, the rate of glycolysis was 3 times as rapid as the anaerobic glycolysis of intact cells and 6 times as rapid as the aerobic glycolysis. Addition of phosphofructokinase and glyceraldehyde 3-phosphate dehydrogenase markedly accelerated glycolysis of dilute extracts, whereas at high protein concentrations the major limiting factor was found to be hexokinase.

Extensive studies with intact ascites tumor cells pointed to inorganic phosphate as the rate-limiting factor of glycolysis. Fluctuation in the intracellular inorganic phosphate content appeared to parallel changes in glycolytic rate. Moreover, cells suspended in a very high phosphate medium ($0.08\ M$) glycolyzed at a rate approaching that of the fortified extract. Because of the very high concentration of phosphate that was required for maximal glycolysis of intact cells, an exploration of the transport of phosphate into the ascites cells was undertaken. The rate of entrance of phosphate at low concentrations was indeed slow compared to the rate of lactate production and was found to be dependent on an energy-yielding reaction. Glycolysis and oxidative phosphorylation facilitated transport of phosphate independently.

However, the first step of glucose phosphorylation requires ATP and not P_i and lack of P_i therefore does not explain the depression of glucose phosphorylation due to aerobic conditions. In fact, an ample supply of ATP should be available due to oxidative phosphorylation. A study of the intracellular ATP concentration revealed that while little or no glucose was utilized during initial phases of aerobic metabolism, the intracellular ATP concentration was quite high. On the other hand, if dinitrophenol was used to eliminate pre-existing ATP as well as regeneration of ATP by mitochondria, glucose utilization proceeded at a very high rate even at relatively low intracellular ATP concentrations. These findings pointed to a physical or functional compartmentation in ascites cells that hinders the efficient utilization of mitochondrial ATP for the phosphorylation of glucose. The following explanation for the diminished aerobic glucose utilization emerged from these studies: In the presence of oxygen, the respiring mitochondria compete with glyceraldehyde 3-phosphate dehydrogenase for inorganic phosphate with the result that the regeneration of glycolytic ATP and its utilization for hexose phosphorylation is diminished. Mitochondrial ATP is used inefficiently for this process. 2,4-Dinitrophenol, which eliminates ATP formation and P_i utilization by mitochondria, therefore abolishes the Pasteur effect. Since, as pointed out before, the rate of P_i entrance into the cells is slow compared to glycolysis, a mechanism must be operative within the cell that maintains the phosphate level by regenerating P_i from ATP. Various ATPase activities, including many biosynthetic reactions that utilize ATP and liberate P_i, fulfill this function. In fact, the liberation of P_i during biosynthetic reactions can be looked upon as an important release mechanism of the Pasteur effect permitting increased utilization of glucose. The well known phenomenon of aerobic lactate production during cell growth in tissue cultures may well be due to such a mechanism. It would be of interest in this connection to explore the mode of action by which certain viruses (e.g., the adenoviruses and the Rous sarcoma viruses) induce further increases in lactate production in growing tissue culture cells.

This leads us to the discussion of the carbohydrate metabolism of cells grown in tissue cultures. It should be emphasized that all our studies were carried out on resting cells suspended in buffered salt solutions rather than on cells growing in a complete medium.

Carbohydrate Metabolism of HeLa Cells

The profile of glycolytic enzymes in extracts of HeLa cells has a remarkable resemblance to that of ascites tumor cells (Wu, 1959). Hexokinase and phosphofructokinase were found to be relatively low and phosphoglycerate kinase about 100 times as active (Tables I and VI). The values shown in Table I in brackets represent ac-

TABLE I

GLYCOLYTIC ENZYMES IN EXTRACTS OF HeLA CELLS[a]

Enzyme	μmoles/minute/100 mg. protein	
Phosphorylase a	0.28	(0.05)[b]
Phosphoglucomutase	17	(16)
Hexokinase	3	(3)
Phosphofructokinase	6.5	(6.5)
Glyceraldehyde 3-P dehydrogenase	92	(87)
Phosphoglycerate kinase	665	(685)
Enolase	13	(16)
Pyruvate kinase	133	(127)
Lactate dehydrogenase	320	(300)

[a] Grown in a "total change" medium (Wu, 1959) with high glucose (0.005 M).
[b] Values in parentheses obtained with cells grown in a "no change" medium with low glucose (0.0017 M).

tivity measurements of glycolytic enzymes in an extract of HeLa cells grown in the presence of low concentrations of glucose. It can be seen that with the exception of phosphorylase, which will be discussed later, the enzyme activities were the same as in the cells grown at higher glucose levels.

Fortified homogenates from HeLa cells glycolyzed about twice as fast as intact cells. In contrast to ascites cells, the uptake of glucose and its breakdown to lactate was as rapid aerobically as anaerobically (Table II). In HeLa cells respiration was considerably lower than in ascites cells, while the glycolytic enzymes that compete with mitochondria for P_i and ADP were as high or higher than in ascites cells (Table VI). This might explain why glucose utilization was as rapid aerobically as anaerobically. In contrast, endogenous lactate formation, which is dependent on the phosphorolytic cleavage of glycogen, was much slower than lactate formation from glucose, and exhibited a pronounced Pasteur effect as shown in Table II. This is of considerable interest since it eliminates both glucose transport and hexokinase as essential participants in this regulatory mechanism. It is indeed in line with the proposed concept of P_i being limiting, and compartmentation being a major contributing factor to the Pasteur effect (Racker and Wu, 1959; Lynen et al., 1959) since phosphorylase action is dependent on P_i and evidence for compartmentation of phosphorylase has been presented previously (Cori, 1956). As can be seen in Table II, endogenous

TABLE II

CARBOHYDRATE METABOLISM OF HeLa CELLS[a]

			Lactate production		
μmoles P_i per ml. of medium	Gas phase	Glucose uptake	With glucose	Endo-genous	Δ
0.45	air	13	28	7	21
	N_2	15	44	20	24
4.5	air	22	41	11	30
	N_2	22	52	24	28
45	air	34	72	17	55
	N_2	36	82	29	53

[a] HeLa cells (5.4 mg. protein) were used in each experiment. The results are expressed as μmoles per 100 mg. of protein per hour at 38°.

fermentation as well as glucose utilization is markedly stimulated by raising the external phosphate concentration. As was shown in Table I phosphorylase activity in HeLa cells, which was measured in the direction of glycogenolysis[2] is very slow in comparison with phosphoglucomutase and all the other glycolytic enzymes. In view of this low activity, phosphorylase itself might be expected to limit lactate production provided P_i is present in excess ($K_m = 4 \times 10^{-3}$ M). A comparison of endogenous lactate formation at high P_i concentration (Table II) with the capacity of phosphorylase (Table I) reveals that the latter must have indeed operated almost at maximum capacity at high P_i concentrations.

It has been shown previously (Wu and Racker, 1959a) that adenosine 5-phosphate (AMP) had no effect on the glycolysis of ascites tumor cells although it seemed to penetrate the cells and raise the intracellular concentration of ADP and ATP as well as that of AMP. In HeLa cells addition of AMP (0.01 M) increased the rate of endogenous lactate production even at high phosphate concentrations (Table III). As will be shown below, phosphorylase of HeLa cells is stimulated by AMP to a degree depending on the

[2] The forward rate of phosphorylase is less than half as rapid as the rate in the direction of glycogen synthesis. Moreover, the forward rate was measured spectrophotometrically under rather favorable conditions of product removal in the presence of excess phosphoglucomutase, glucose 6-phosphate dehydrogenase and TPN.

TABLE III

Effect of AMP and P_i on HeLa Cell Carbohydrate Metabolism[a]

| | Lactate production | |
	Without glucose	With glucose
Additions		
—	28	112
P_i	48	165
AMP	53	126
P_i and AMP	68	182

[a] HeLa cells (2 mg. protein) were incubated aerobically in a final volume of 1 ml. for 40 minutes at 38°. P_i (0.06 M), AMP (0.01 M), and glucose (0.006 M) were added as indicated. The results are expressed as in Table II.

condition of growth in tissue culture. These findings of an AMP stimulation of endogenous fermentation gives additional support to the concept that the nucleotide can penetrate intact cells to some extent.

It was observed that the glycogen content and the endogenous lactate production of HeLa cells varied greatly with slight variations in the growth conditions. As shown in Table IV, total medium replacement after 4 days of growth had a much more stimulatory effect on glycogen storage than "no change" medium (Wu, 1959). The major stimulatory factor in the medium was found to be

TABLE IV

Effect of Change of Growth Medium on Endogenous Lactate Formation and on Glycogen Content[a]

| | Lactate production | | Glycogen (glucose equivalent) |
Growth condition[b]	Air	N_2	
"No change" of medium	1.5	4.3	5
"Half change" after 4 days of growth	4.5	12	—
"Total change" after 4 days of growth	20	48	38

[a] HeLa cells (10 mg. protein) after 7 days of growth were used in each experiment. Results are expressed as in Table II.

[b] Growth conditions as previously described (Wu, 1959).

glucose since the addition of the sugar alone to the "no change" medium yielded high glycogen containing cells. Parallel with the low glycogen content of cells grown at low glucose concentrations was a rather sharp drop in phosphorylase activity (Table V). In fact,

TABLE V

ACTIVITIES OF PHOSPHORYLASE AND UDPG-GLYCOGEN TRANSFERASE OF HeLa CELLS GROWN IN DIFFERENT CONCENTRATIONS OF GLUCOSE

Residual glucose in medium	Glycogen	Phosphorylase		UDPG-glycogen transferase
		a	b	
0.79	102	0.69	0.79	1.6
0.22	3.8	0.01	0.12	0.6

a Residual glucose is expressed as μmoles per ml. of medium and glycogen as μmoles of glucose equivalents per 100 mg. of cell protein. Enzyme activities are expressed as μmoles per 100 mg. of protein per minute. The data represent average values of three experiments.

phosphorylase a activity (tested without AMP) was so low that it could not be measured very accurately. Phosphorylase b activity (tested with AMP) was less than 20% that of the cells grown at higher glucose levels. UDPG-glycogen transferase (Leloir and Cardini, 1957) which was found to be quite active in HeLa cells showed a similar though smaller depression. To explain the intracellular changes resulting from glucose depletion in the medium the following sequence of events may be visualized: A diminished rate of phosphorylation of glucose by hexokinase leads to a drop in the intracellular level of glucose 6-phosphate, glucose 1-phosphate and UDPG. The lack of substrate for glycogen synthesis in turn results in a rapid depletion of the glycogen store. The lack of this polysaccharide then produces a phosphorylase deficiency in the cell due to decrease in either formation or stability of the enzyme. Actually, the latter alternative is favored at the present time since it offers a better explanation for the more pronounced loss of phosphorylase a in glucose depleted cells. Conversion of phosphorylase a to phosphorylase b is catalyzed by proteolytic enzymes (Cori and Cori, 1945) and protection of enzymes by their substrates against proteolysis is quite common.

Whatever the mechanism of this phenomenon of enzyme variation might be, it demonstrates a dependence of cellular enzyme content on the conditions of growth. It also affords a tool to explore the effect of the presence or absence of a carbohydrate store on the response of the cell to various conditions, e.g., virus infection or nutritional deficiency.

Carbohydrate Metabolism of Chicken Leucocytes

Chicken leucocytes were selected as the next cell population to be studied. A comparison of the profile of glycolytic enzymes of the leucocytes with the two types of tumor cells described above revealed that in these tumor cells there was a higher concentration of phosphoglycerate kinase and glyceraldehyde 3-phosphate dehydrogenase than in leucocytes as shown in Table VI. Isolated chicken

TABLE VI

PROFILES OF GLYCOLYTIC ENZYMES IN TISSUE HOMOGENATES[a]

	Ascites tumor	HeLa[b] cells	Chicken leucocytes	Mouse brain
Hexokinase	4.8	3.7	4.7	25
Phosphofructokinase	5.0	7.6	14.0	51
Aldolase	17	6.7	15.6	16
Glyceraldehyde 3-phosphate dehydrogenase (G-3-p DH)	121	110	19	18
Phosphoglycerate kinase	640	700	165	111
Phosphoglycerate mutase	41	41	30	43
Enolase	27	22	21	18
Pyruvate kinase	138	150	55	145
Lactic dehydrogenase	230	370	111	79
Lactate production (intact cells)[a]				
aerobic	0.58	0.5	0.13	0.14[c]
anaerobic	0.96	0.5	0.36	1.2[c]
Oxygen uptake[a]	0.16	0.05	0.17[d]	0.86
G-3-p DH/respiratory P_i esterification[e]	250	730	38	7

  [a] μmoles of substrate/min./100 mg. protein at 26°.
  [b] Grown in the presence of "human serum" (Wu, 1959).
  [c] Data taken from Warburg (1930) for rat brain slices.
  [d] Warburg et al. (1958).
  [e] Calculated from oxygen uptake, assuming a P:O of 3.

leucocytes exhibited a pronounced Pasteur effect even after being washed and suspended in salt solution. They appear to be more stable than human leucocytes which lose the Pasteur effect after centrifugation in the cold (Warburg *et al.*, 1958). It was reported (Beck, 1955) that glycolysis of human leucocytes is limited by the hexokinase content of the cells. This is not the case in chicken cells, which contain at least a five-fold excess of hexokinase in comparison to the maximal rate of anaerobic glycolysis. The discrepancy with aerobic glycolysis is, of course, even greater. A comparison of lactate production with glucose uptake by leucocytes revealed that a considerable proportion of the glucose that entered the cells could not be accounted for as lactate even when a small correction for oxidation was included. In fact, after subtraction of the lactate from the glucose there was little or no difference between aerobic utilization of glucose. In extensive studies on yeast cells (Stickland, 1956), very similar observations were reported. Although yeast cells showed a pronounced Pasteur effect in respect to glucose fermentation, the synthesis of polysaccharide from glucose was in fact increased under aerobic conditions. In terms of the concept of P_i-compartmentation these findings are readily explained. A decreased availability of P_i under aerobic conditions should shift the balance of glycogen synthesis and breakdown in favor of synthesis.

Enzymes of Carbohydrate Metabolism of Brain

The profile of glycolytic enzymes in brain homogenates shown in Table VI is rather different from the other profiles so far investigated. The activities of hexokinase and phosphofructokinase were found to be relatively high while aldolase, glyceraldehyde 3-phosphate dehydrogenase, and enolase had somewhat lower activities. Some variability was observed with different brain homogenates in the relative activity of phosphoglycerate kinase, pyruvate kinase, and lactic dehydrogenase. In all cases, however, the activity of these enzymes was high in comparison to the other enzymes of glycolysis. Brain homogenates that are fortified with cofactors, nicotinamide, and phosphate, metabolize glucose very rapidly to lactic acid (Racker and Krimsky, 1945). Slices of brain have a high anaerobic glycolysis and a pronounced Pasteur effect (Warburg, 1930).

Comparative Biochemistry of Glycolysis

A summary of the enzyme profiles and of the carbohydrate metabolism of intact cells is presented for four types of cells in Table VI. Although it is obviously unjustifiable to make generalizations from so few examples, the pattern of enzyme distribution lends itself so readily to an interpretation of the metabolic pattern that it is difficult to resist the temptation to speculate. The above described tumors, as well as two solid tumors kindly provided by Dr. A. Goldfeder, were found to contain a very high content of phosphoglycerate kinase and glyceraldehyde 3-phosphate dehydrogenase as compared with the normal cells thus far studied. Since glyceraldehyde 3-phosphate dehydrogenase competes for P_i and phosphoglycerate kinase competes for ADP with the system of oxidative phosphorylation in mitochondria, it is not surprising that glycolysis inhibits oxidative processes (Crabtree effect), and that the control mechanism exerted by oxidative phosphorylation (Pasteur effect) is insufficient in tumor cells to prevent the aerobic lactic acid production.

To obtain a numerical relationship of these two competing systems, the activity of glyceraldehyde 3-phosphate dehydrogenase which represents the potential glycolytic capacity to esterify inorganic phosphate, was divided by the rate of P_i esterification due to oxidative phosphorylation. The latter was calculated from the oxygen uptake assuming a P:O ratio of 3. As shown in Table VI, the per cent Pasteur effect increased as the ratio of the dehydrogenase: respiratory P_i esterification decreased as expected from the competition theory. A comparison of the potential rate of ADP phosphorylation by phosphoglycerate kinase with respiratory ADP phosphorylation revealed a similar correlation. The affinity constants for P_i are not too far apart in the two competing systems thus allowing for a direct comparison of the activity ratios.

A second comparative study was made on the rate of P_i transport. In leucocytes the rate of entrance was only a small fraction of the rate of lactate formation; in ascites cells it was still slow compared to glycolysis but several times more rapid than in leucocytes, while in HeLa cells the P_i transport reached 50 to 80% of the rate of glycolysis. In all cases, however, the rate of P_i entrance at physiological P_i concentration was too small to maintain glycolysis. It follows therefore that the intracellular P_i concentration must be maintained by hydrolysis of phosphate esters either directly from ATP or indirectly through biosynthetic reactions involving phosphorylated intermediates.

Some Speculation on the Significance of Lactate Formation in Tumors

According to Warburg the transformation of normal to tumor cells is the result of an injury to the respiratory machinery. As a consequence of this lesion a fermenting cell emerges with the property of autonomous growth. This hypothesis may prove untenable in view of the reported findings of tumor tissues with a very high content of respiratory enzymes. One could, however, propose instead that the primary biochemical change is an increase in the biosynthesis of glyceraldehyde 3-phosphate dehydrogenase and phosphoglycerate kinase, which are sequential in function and therefore perhaps coupled in their genetic control mechanism (Hartman, 1957). The higher activity of these two enzymes results in an aerobic glycolysis and increased intracellular hydrogen ion concentration. The lower pH may stimulate a rate-limiting biosynthetic process either directly or by releasing a control mechanism which has held it in check in normal cells.

Alternatively, a mutation resulting in the loss of control of certain rate-limiting biosynthetic processes may be the primary lesion. The increased ATPase activity due to the accelerated biosynthetic processes may result in an increased glycolysis. An increased availability of P_i and ADP may furthermore induce an increased formation of those glycolytic enzymes that utilize these "substrates." Thus the increased production of lactate would be secondary to a primary change in the biosynthetic machinery of the cell.

As a third possibility, the increased lactate production as well as the increased biosynthetic reactions may be secondary to a primary change which is a common control mechanism. For example, the loss of a cell surface component which controls the entrance of phosphate could lead to intracellular conditions favoring the increased biosynthesis of certain glycolytic as well as biosynthetic enzymes.

Conclusions and Summary

A study of the carbohydrate metabolism of HeLa cells is reported and a comparison is made with ascites tumor cells, leucocytes, and brain. The evaluation of enzyme profiles and of the intracellular concentration of intermediates, inorganic phosphate and coenzymes under a variety of experimental conditions has led to the following over-all picture of the control of carbohydrate metabolism: The glycolytic enzymes are present in large excess and in intact cells glycolysis is limited by the availability of inorganic phosphate, which in turn is required for the regeneration of glycolytic ATP. Since phosphate transport is slow compared to glycolysis the regeneration of inorganic phosphate and its availability for glyceraldehyde 3-phosphate dehydrogenase is therefore in the final analysis the rate-limiting factor of glycolysis. Rapidly growing cells that convert ATP to ADP in the course of many synthetic processes can thus be expected to express their glycolytic capacity more effectively than cells with restricted synthetic functions.

Under aerobic conditions the mitochondrial enzymes that catalyze oxidative phosphorylation compete with the glycolytic enzymes for inorganic phosphate and ADP. The very active glyceraldehyde 3-phosphate dehydrogenase and phosphoglycerate kinase found in tumor cells compete successfully with the mitochondria. Thus, the Pasteur effect is either partly or completely eliminated and a Crabtree effect often appears. The effective competition of glycolysis with oxidative phosphorylation results in the aerobic formation of lactate, a uniform feature of cancer cells.

Whether this formation of lactate and the resulting change in intracellular pH is contributory or even essential to the loss of control of biosynthetic processes, or whether the increased glycolysis is just a secondary, though uniform, feature of the tumor remains to be answered in the future.

References

Beck, W. S. (1955). *J. Biol. Chem.* **216**, 333.

Beck, W. S. (1958). *J. Biol. Chem.* **232**, 251.

Chance, B., and Castor, L. N. (1952). *Science* **116**, 200.

Cori, C. F., and Cori, G. T. (1925). *J. Biol. Chem.* **64**, 11.

Cori, G. T., and Cori, C. F. (1945). *J. Biol. Chem.* **158**, 321.

Cori, C. F. (1956). *In* "Currents in Biochemistry," p. 198. Interscience, New York.

Greenstein, J. P. (1954). "Biochemistry of Cancer," 2nd ed. Academic Press, New York.

Hartman, P. E. (1957). *In* "The Chemical Basis of Heredity" (W. McElroy and B. Glass, eds.), p. 408. Johns Hopkins Press, Baltimore, Maryland.

Kahler, H., and Robertson, W. van B. (1943). *J. Natl. Cancer Inst.* **3**, 495.

Leloir, L. F., and Cardini, C. E. (1957). *J. Am. Chem. Soc.* **79**, 6340.

Lynen, F., Hartmann, G., Netter, K. F., and Schuegraf, A. (1959). *In* "Regulation of Cell Metabolism." Ciba Foundation Symposium, p. 256. J. and A. Churchill, Ltd., London.

Racker, E., and Krimsky, I. (1945). *J. Biol. Chem.* **161**, 453.

Racker, E., and Krimsky, I. (1948). *J. Biol. Chem.* **173**, 519.

Racker, E., and Wu, R. (1959). *In* "Regulation of Cell Metabolism." Ciba Foundation Symposium, p. 205. J. and A. Churchill, Ltd., London.

Stickland, L. H. (1956). *Biochem. J.* **64**, 503.

Voegtlin, C., Fitch, R. H., Kahler, H., Johnson, J. M., and Thompson, J. W. (1935). *Natl. Inst. Health Bull.* **164,** 1.

Warburg, O. (1930). "The Metabolism of Tumors." Constable & Co., London.

Warburg, O., Gawehn, K., and Geissler, A. W. (1957). *Z. Naturforsch.* **12b,** 115.

Warburg, O., Gawehn, K., and Geissler, A. W. (1958). *Z. Naturforsch.* **13b,** 515.

Weinhouse, S. (1955). In *Advances in Cancer Research* **3,** 269.

Wu, R., and Racker, E. (1959a). *J. Biol. Chem.* **234,** 1029.

Wu, R., and Racker, E. (1959b). *J. Biol. Chem.* **234,** 1036.

Wu, R. (1959). *J. Biol. Chem.* **234,** 2806.

A Digital Computer Representation of Chemical and Spectroscopic Studies on Chemical Control of Ascites Tumor Cell Metabolism*

BRITTON CHANCE

Johnson Research Foundation, University of Pennsylvania, Philadelphia, Pennsylvania

Ehrlich ascites tumor cells have been found especially suitable for experimental and theoretical studies on metabolic control. These cells not only have a high lactate production as described by Dr. Racker *et al.* (1960), but also exhibit an unusual series of short term metabolic responses upon addition of glucose and uncoupling agents (Chance and Hess, 1959a-e). These responses give insight on chemical mechanisms of living cells generally, even though they are most clearly observed in the ascites cell. In considering metabolic control in general and the fermentative character of the tumor cell in particular, we may enumerate some characteristics of metabolic control systems, particularly those applicable to cancer cells. The long-postulated deficiency of some component of these cells was carefully considered by Greenstein. An enzyme deficiency is most frequently suggested, but surely substrate or coenzyme deficiencies should also be considered, as should an enzyme inhibition, either by a reaction product or by another substance.

More recently, attention has been turned from a chemical deficiency to a chemical control mechanism in which the concentration of an essential intermediate becomes rate-limiting because its rates of formation and disappearance are unbalanced so as to favor the latter. Thus a slight adjustment in its concentration may control metabolic processes over a wide range. We will now attempt to define the desirable properties of a control substance. Perhaps the first consideration is that the control substance influence a variety

* This research has been supported in part by grants from the American Cancer Society and the Office of Naval Research.

191

of systems (as would be true of ADP and ATP) or a key point in one large system, or both. For example, an increase in the concentration of ADP in a system previously limited with respect to this component would activate not only respiration, but also glycolysis. Similar considerations apply to phosphate and, if mitochondrial permeability were not a factor, to reduced pyridine nucleotide. Conversely, metabolic control by the substrate concentration would not be suitable for simultaneous activation of a number of pathways because of the high substrate specificity of enzymes. It is important to note that the ADP, ATP, and phosphate responses are common characteristics of enzyme systems located in different parts of the metabolic pathway.

A second criterion for a control intermediate is high affinity for the control substance whereby a large control response could be obtained with only a small buildup in the concentration of the rate-controlling intermediate (Chance, 1959b). In fact, it is important that the rates of formation and utilization of the control substance be finely balanced so that no great excess of the control substance accumulate and thereby prevent a rapid reversibility of the control. Reversibility is highly desirable in a control reaction and may be accomplished in two ways. First, the control chemical may be an active participant in the metabolic process and thereby be expended; for example, ADP is converted to ATP. On the other hand, if the control substance is not a direct participant in the metabolic system, then chemical processes for its decomposition or physical processes for its segregation must be available in order to reverse the control effects.

The type of control process that one considers for the complex sequence of reactions involved in cell metabolism is necessarily a continuous one wherein the rate of metabolism is proportional over a reasonable range to the concentration of the control substance. Higher concentrations of the control substance may fail to give any rate increase, as for example by the saturation of an enzyme system (cf. Fig. 1). It is obvious that the metabolism is no longer under control of the reaction in question on the horizontal portion of the control characteristic curve. Under these conditions, some other reaction is controlling. As stated above, it is undesirable to proceed too far onto the horizontal portion of the curve lest reversibility of the control be sluggish.

There has been an increasing tendency to apply to metabolic control the terms "feedback" or "negative feedback," which are

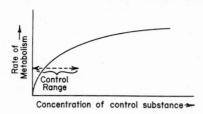

Fig. 1. A schematic illustration of the relationship between the concentration of a control substance and the metabolic rate for a hypothetical metabolic system. The interval *control range* represents that range within which a control substance exerts appropriate effects upon the metabolic rate. At higher concentrations, control efficiency is diminished.

borrowed from the electrical engineers. However, the analogy between the operation of an electrical feedback network and metabolic control processes (Chance, 1959a) is at best a poor one, and we shall attempt to avoid the use of this borrowed terminology in describing the chemical control system.

We will first cite some control characteristics of ascites tumor cells and then indicate the extent to which these properties can be simulated by means of a complete solution of the chemical reactions involved in the main pathway from glucose to oxygen. Our ability to formulate such a system of equations is a consequence not only of detailed spectroscopic and chemical analyses for various intermediates carried out in this laboratory, but also of the extensive studies of others in the field who have carried out similar analyses (Ibsen *et al.*, 1958), as well as studies on the nature and distribution of enzymes in the metabolic pathways (Racker *et al.*, 1960; Wu and Racker, 1959). The time appears to be ripe for assembling these various data in a form in which their dynamic characteristics can be evaluated and compared with those observed directly in the tumor cell.

Experimental

A 6-day growth of Lettré hyperdiploid Ehrlich ascites tumor cells was suspended either in the ascitic fluid or in a "saline phosphate" medium (Chance and Hess, 1959b), and freed from erythrocyte contamination by centrifugation or differential lysis (Chance and Hess, 1959b, d). Because of the high cytochrome content and adequate transparency of the ascites cell, both the double-beam (Chance, 1951, 1954) and the split-beam (Chance, 1954; Yang and

Legallais, 1954) techniques could be applied to the material. Chemical assays were made by methods described in detail elsewhere.[1]

For studying the spectroscopic and respiratory responses to ADP, mitochondria were prepared by high-speed mechanical disintegration and subsequent differential centrifugation, and then suspended in isotonic sucrose and taken for analysis (Chance and Hess, 1959b).

The vibrating platinum microelectrode (Harris and Lindsey, 1948; Chance, 1955a; Chance and Williams, 1955a) was used to measure the kinetics of oxygen utilization in experiments with both cells and mitochondria.

Results

Cytochromes of Ascites Tumor Cells

It is appropriate to consider, at this memorial symposium for Jesse Greenstein, a topic to which he gave much thought and attention, namely the cytochromes of various cancer cells. Recent investigations have confirmed the earlier findings (Chance and Castor, 1952) that ascites tumor cells have concentrations of cytochromes (Chance and Hess, 1959a, b) comparable to normal cells. In the difference spectra of Fig. 2, in which chemical treatments have enabled us to display the absorption bands that appear in

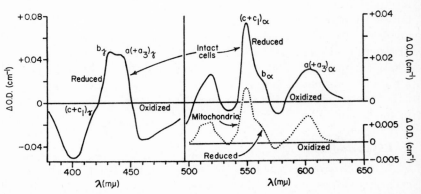

Fig. 2. Identification of the presence of recognized cytochrome components by spectra representing the difference between the fully reduced (anaerobic) and oxidized (aerobic) components of the intact ascites cell (solid traces) and of the mitochondria (dotted trace) (Expt. 675e).

[1] B. Hess and B. Chance, in preparation.

the transition from the fully oxidized to the fully reduced cytochrome (Amytal-treated aerobic cells–anaerobic cells), all the
components of the cytochrome a_3-a-c-b system of the intact cell are
seen (solid trace). Mitochondria isolated from the ascites tumor
cell also show the characteristic cytochrome pattern (dashed trace).
Of the known components of the cytochrome chain, none appears
to be deficient in the ascites tumor cell.

Additional experiments, in which suspensions of intact ascites
tumor cells are rapidly mixed with low concentrations of oxygen,
show a rapid oxidation of the cytochromes to their steady-state
values at rates comparable to those observed in isolated liver
mitochondria (Chance and Williams, 1955b) and only slightly less
than those observed earlier in yeast cells (Chance, 1955b). Apparently, therefore, no unknown inhibitor acts upon the transfer
of oxidizing equivalents along the respiratory chain. Similarly,
there appears to be reasonable dehydrogenase activity; for example, cytochrome b is largely reduced in the steady state (without
Amytal treatment, cytochrome b would have been difficult to distinguish in the difference spectrum of Fig. 2). The phosphorylative
activities of the isolated mitochondria are high and some degree of
respiratory control can be observed. In fact, the only distinction
between the respiratory chains of the intact cell and isolated
mitochondria is the rate of electron transfer, which is about one-
third as slow *in vivo* as *in vitro*. It is as if metabolic control were
impressed upon the respiratory chain, possibly in terms of a limitation on the ADP or phosphate concentration.

GLUCOSE RESPONSE

Evidence favoring the operation of a metabolic control on the
respiratory activity of ascites tumor cells metabolizing endogenous
substrate is provided by short time measurements of the response
of these cells to glucose addition. The most important feature of
this response (Fig. 3) is the acceleration of endogenous respiration.
Since the acceleration immediately follows the addition of glucose,
it is reasonable to conclude that ADP, formed in glucose phosphorylation from ATP, has stimulated respiration. This result favors
the explanation that metabolic control of respiratory activity acts
in the ascites tumor cell and suggests that the partitioning of ADP
between the respiratory and the glycolytic pathways is such that
a significant portion of ADP arrives at the mitochondria. Thus,
insofar as their responses to ADP are concerned, it is not correct to

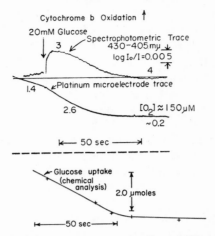

Fɪɢ. 3. A composite plot of spectroscopic effects following glucose addition to an ascites tumor cell suspension (top trace) and of the associated activation and inhibition of respiration (middle trace). Assays of glucose utilization in a separate cell suspension are recorded in the bottom trace (Expt. 498b, 0-92).

state that the high activity of the glycolytic enzymes of the ascites cell so greatly exceeds the respiratory capacity that glycolytic resynthesis of ATP operates to the exclusion of respiration.

The lower trace of Fig. 3 shows that glucose is rapidly utilized[2] upon its addition to cells in the endogenous state, suggesting that a considerable store of ATP is available for the immediate phosphorylation of glucose. The rate of glucose utilization during this phase ($\sim$1000 μmoles per hour per gram wet weight of cells) is one of the fastest observed in the ascites tumor cell. This suggests an extremely high activity of hexokinase in the intact cells; so high, in fact, that it appears greatly to exceed the capabilities of the system to resynthesize ATP by the combined efforts of the respiratory and glycolytic pathways. The relatively low hexokinase activity obtained under the assay conditions used by Dr. Racker and colleagues (Racker and Wu, 1959; Racker et al., 1960) ($<$1.0% of the value for 1,3-diphosphoglycerate kinase) must therefore be due

[2] The rapid phase of glucose utilization is not accurately recorded in other laboratories (Wu and Racker, 1959 [cf. Figs. 1 and 2]; Ibsen et al., 1958). It was this effect which initially called our attention to the unusual metabolic control phenomena in the ascites tumor cell (Chance and Hess, 1956).

either to difficulties with the extraction procedure or to an inconsistency between the substrate concentrations present in the cell and the assay procedure. It is, of course, the function of studies of the intact cell to evaluate critically the efficiency of extraction procedures and the conditions for *in vitro* assay systems to determine whether or not they give results comparable to those observed in the living cell.

The top trace of Fig. 3 identifies the response of the cytochrome chain with an effect due to ADP or phosphate and rules out an effect of substrate. The characteristic oxidation of cytochrome b indicated by the upward deflection of the top trace upon the addition of glucose could not have been due to an increased concentration of substrate, which would cause a reduction, and is the same response that was obtained upon addition of ADP to isolated mitochondria.

At the end of about a minute, all three effects recorded in Fig. 3 have subsided and respiration and glucose utilization are almost completely inhibited. This intensely inhibited state gives evidence favoring a barrier for the return of newly phosphorylated ATP to hexokinase as suggested by Lynen and Koenigsberger (1951) and, in fact, has led us to postulate that the mitochondria retain ATP (Chance and Hess, 1956). This is a much more intense inhibition than the Crabtree effect and has a considerably shorter lifetime. It is found in other experiments that the rate of glucose utilization will increase after several minutes of inhibition as has been confirmed by others (Ibsen *et al.*, 1958; Wu and Racker, 1959). The effect is scarcely a Pasteur reaction, since not only glucose utilization, but also oxygen utilization is inhibited. Thus, we are faced with a manifestation of a new type of intense metabolic control.

REVERSIBILITY OF GLUCOSE INHIBITION

It has already been mentioned that the inhibition of glucose utilization and of respiration, after reaching a maximum, spontaneously diminishes over the course of several minutes. Abrupt reversal of inhibition can readily be obtained by uncoupling agents such as dicoumarol and dinitrophenol. In Fig. 4, polarographic measurements of the respiration of an ascites tumor cell suspension show the typical activation and inhibition phenomena on adding glucose. Shortly thereafter, dicoumarol at the concentration used

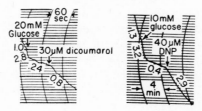

Fig. 4. Polarographic measurements of the effect of uncoupling agents in reactivating oxygen metabolism in a glucose-inhibited ascites tumor cell suspension. Left, oxygen utilization is partially restored by addition of 30 μM dicoumarol; right, oxygen utilization is almost completely reactivated by addition of 40 μM dinitrophenol. Respiratory rates are given in μmoles per liter (μM) O₂ per second (Expt. 489d, 647e).

partially relieves the inhibition of respiration (left-hand portion of the figure) and dinitrophenol almost completely relieves the inhibition.

An explanation of the mechanism of reactivation of respiratory metabolism is afforded by the chemical analyses of Fig. 5 in which

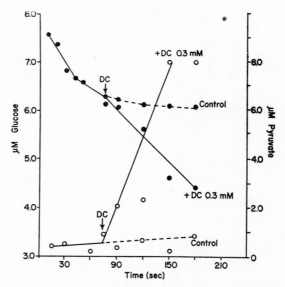

Fig. 5. Time course of the kinetics of glucose utilization (black circles) and pyruvate formation (open circles) in ascites tumor cell suspension, plotted from chemical analysis. The addition of dicoumarol (0.3 mM) at the point marked "DC" restores the rate of glucose utilization almost to its initial level, and also elicits a large production of pyruvate (H-10).

the time course of glucose utilization (top curve) is plotted in the absence of dicoumarol. A short time after the onset of the intensely inhibited phase of glucose utilization (see control trace) dicoumarol is added and glucose utilization almost immediately resumes its maximal initial rate. Thus, the reactivation of respiration can be attributed either to the direct action of the uncoupling agent upon respiratory control in the mitochondria or to the increased concentration of ADP due to glucose phosphorylation.

Evidence that an uncoupling of oxidative phosphorylation has occurred is indicated by the bottom trace, where the concentration of pyruvate is plotted. In this case, only a small change of pyruvate concentration is observed during the initial phases of glucose addition, and no further change occurs in the intensely inhibited phase. If dicoumarol is added shortly after the onset of the inhibited phase, an immediate and large production of pyruvate occurs, in evidence of the initiation of an intense aerobic glycolysis. Thus, it is apparent that oxidative phosphorylation has been disabled by the concentrations of dicoumarol used in these experiments.

The failure of pyruvate to accumulate except upon the addition of dicoumarol suggests that, for ascites cells under our conditions, the chief pathway for ADP utilization in the activated phase of glucose metabolism is in the mitochondria and not in the glycolytic enzymes. Thus, despite the high activity of 1,3-diphosphoglycerate kinase and even of glyceraldehyde 3-phosphate dehydrogenase in the presence of reasonable concentrations of intracellular phosphate, as determined by independent analysis, the studies of the intact cells differ sharply from those predicted by Racker et al. (1960) on the basis of enzymatic assays of cell extracts: namely, the respiratory activity wins over the glycolytic enzymes in the competition for ADP in this metabolic response. Since chemical measurements indicate that, under favorable conditions, up to 30% of the ADP may go into the glycolytic pathway, it is of interest to determine why the corresponding amount of ATP does not continue glucose utilization during the inhibited phase of metabolism. As a matter of fact, it is apparent that this ATP probably is recycled through the glucose phosphorylation, since the oxygen utilization in the presence of glucose alone is greater than that in the iodoacetate-treated cells.[3] The reason for the almost complete cessation of oxygen utilization and glucose metabolism, despite the partial recycling of ATP, may be that the mitochondria complete more

[3] Similar results are obtained with deoxyglucose.

effectively at lower ADP concentrations. Thus, the proportion of ADP going to glycolysis diminishes and falls to zero as the activated phase of metabolism terminates and the inhibition becomes established. This explanation is in accord with the criterion mentioned above that an effective metabolic control system should have a high affinity for the controlling substance.

In summary, we have briefly outlined a few experiments that are relevant to the problem of metabolic control in ascites tumor cells. The essential features of these regulations are:

1. An acceleration of endogenous respiration upon the addition of glucose to cells freshly withdrawn from the mouse.

2. An extremely rapid utilization of glucose in the absence of appreciable pyruvate production.

3. About a minute thereafter, both the glucose and oxygen activity become intensely inhibited by a lack of phosphate or phosphate acceptor at the mitochondria.

4. This inhibition is spontaneously reversible in the course of some minutes, after which the classical Crabtree pattern of low respiration and high glucose utilization is obtained.

5. The inhibited state of metabolism may be rapidly terminated by the addition of uncoupling agents which restore glucose and oxygen utilization very nearly to the values obtained during the activated phase. Under these conditions, however, high glycolytic activity is observed in terms of pyruvate and lactate production, and the oxidative phosphorylation system has been uncoupled.

METABOLIC CONTROL SEQUENCE

It is now appropriate to investigate the simplest sequence of metabolic control reactions that would explain the phenomena observed experimentally. The rudiments of a metabolic control sequence are indicated in Fig. 6 by a simplified control loop in which the rate of formation of ADP from glucose phosphorylation limits the rate of oxidative phosphorylation. Mitochondria provided with pyruvate and phosphate, but lacking ADP, would not utilize oxygen at an appreciable rate. However, the addition of glucose with the attendant expenditure of ATP from store 1 and the increase of concentration of ADP would accelerate respiration. Glucose and oxygen utilization would continue as long as ATP was present in store 1. Upon depletion of this store, however, the metabolic system would be inhibited and both glucose and oxygen utilization would

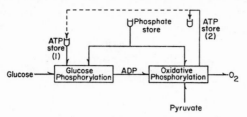

Fig. 6. A simplified schematic diagram showing the metabolic control sequence that would lead to a glucose-activated phase of respiration followed by an inhibition of both glucose and oxygen utilization.

diminish. The activity of the system might be reinitiated by a transfer of ATP from store 2 to store 1. Although oxygen utilization would be reactivated upon addition of an uncoupling agent, glucose utilization would not because no ATP would be formed. Thus, this model is too simple, since the glycolytic phosphorylations have been omitted. It also suffers from the fault that the respiratory rate in the absence of glucose is zero.

Figure 7 shows a more nearly complete metabolic loop in which the rate of respiration in the absence of glucose is set by a breakdown of ATP from store 1 by an ATP-utilizing reaction (for example, synthesis or ion transport). In this way, the level of respiration is set at a value corresponding to that observed in the intact cell under endogenous metabolism. Substrate for this function is indicated to be pyruvate, although fatty acid oxidation could surely provide a considerable fraction.[4] The activation of

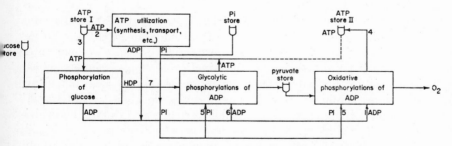

Fig. 7. A more complete schematic diagram of metabolic control pathways involved in the glucose-activated phase of respiration, followed by the inhibition of both glucose and oxygen utilization and their reactivation by the transfer of ATP from store II to store I.

[4] S. Weinhouse, personal communication.

respiration by glucose phosphorylation occurs similarly as before, as does the eventual inhibition of both glucose and oxygen utilization when ATP in store 1 is exhausted. Some ADP may be rephosphorylated in glycolytic phosphorylations and returned to store 1, but the higher affinity of the mitochondria for ADP eventually wins with the result that the system reaches the inhibited state characteristic of the living cell. The response to the uncoupling agent is now more accurately simulated, since not only is respiration reactivated by the uncoupling effect, but, it is also postulated, ATP in store 2 is transferred according to the dotted line into store 1 which allows a reactivation of glucose phosphorylation, and an increase of the ADP concentration which is sufficient to activate fully the glycolytic phosphorylations of ADP. It should be pointed out that the ADP level may or may not control the glycolytic activity under these conditions and, with a limited phosphate store, it is inevitable that phosphate itself would become limiting. Such a phosphate control of metabolism, put forward particularly by Johnson (1941), Lynen (1941), and Racker (1956) does not apply to the glucose-activated and inhibited phases of metabolism. In fact, phosphate control would be readily suggested if glucose addition (cf. Fig. 3) did *not* cause an activation of respiration and an oxidation of cytochrome b.

COMPUTER REPRESENTATION

It is apparent from physical arguments that the components of the metabolic systems so far described explain qualitatively many of the features of the metabolic regulations observed in the living cells. Since the pathways of metabolism are fairly well known, as are the types and amounts of enzymes, coenzymes, and substrates involved, it seems only reasonable to attempt to extend a qualitative discussion of the control properties of this system to a quantitative presentation of the kinetics of the system as solved in detail by a digital computer representation of the mass law equations. We have, over the past 5 years, developed a differential equation-solving program for a digital computer (Univac I)[5] which allows the handling of a multicomponent enzyme system such as that involved here.[6] Such a computer study is taken up not only

[5] Computations supported by the University of Pennsylvania Computer Center.

[6] Among the contributors to this program are: Dr. D. Garfinkel, Dr. J. J. Higgins, Messrs. J. D. Rutledge, E. M. Chance II, P. Sellers, R. Meyer, R. Ochser, and W. Polk.

for what we can learn by a comparison of the computer results with the experimental data, but also for the new aspects of metabolic control that might be revealed by the computer solutions themselves.

In considering a model for the metabolic control pattern of ascites tumor cells, it is important to distinguish between an hydraulic or electric model, which indeed might be made of the diagrams of Figs. 6 and 7, and a full-fledged mass law representation of the chemical equations involved. In the former, any relationship with the actual physicochemical system might be purely fortuitous, whereas in the latter, the chief assumption is that the law of mass action applies to both systems.

In presenting the results of the computer solution, some transposition from ordinary chemical terminology is necessary, since the computer has been set up to accept three-letter code names for chemicals. These, together with the one-letter symbols used in the graphical representation, appear in Table I (p. 204). It should be noted that there are two forms of pyridine nucleotide, extramitochondrial and intramitochondrial, and two forms of ATP, that in store 1 (cytoplasmic) and that in store 2 (mitochondrial).

The chemical equations themselves, written in the three-letter terminology, are illustrated in Fig. 8. Here, we find that the pathways of Fig. 7 can be represented by chemical equations as follows: the phosphorylations of glucose, Equations 1 to 5; the glycolytic phosphorylations, Equations 6 to 14; the oxidative phosphorylations of ADP, Equations 15 to 19; and the reactions of ATP utilization, Equations 20 to 22. It is important to note that the enzyme-substrate intermediates are not included in all equations, as they are in Equations 1-4 and 8-10, and in 21. In other cases, second- or third-order reactions are represented, the rate constant being that characteristic of an unsaturated enzyme. In addition, reverse reactions appear only in those cases where the DPN-DPNH equilibrium is involved, for example in dihydroxyacetone phosphate-α-glycerophosphate or in lactate-pyruvate equilibria. Improvements and extensions in the computer program are needed and the most important are discussed below.

The velocity constant for the particular reaction is indicated on the top of the arrow. The initial concentration of a reactant (if it has one) is indicated above and to the left of a chemical; if during the solution a new value is given the concentration, this is indicated by an arrow. The maximal concentration of the substance used in

TABLE I

ABBREVIATIONS USED IN WRITING DIFFERENTIAL EQUATIONS FOR DIGITAL
COMPUTER SOLUTIONS AND SYMBOLS USED IN GRAPHING THE CHEMICAL
CONSTITUENTS (CF. FIG. 9)

Chemical name	Symbol		
	Equations	Graphs	
Glucose	GLU	G	
Hexokinase	ENZ	—	
Hexokinase-glucose intermediate	ENG	E	
Adenosine triphosphate in store 1	1TP	C	
Adenosine diphosphate	ADP	#	
Glucose 6-phosphate	GLP	L	
Phosphofructokinase	ETZ	—	
Phosphofructokinase intermediate	ETG	T	
Hexosediphosphate	GPP	P	
Glyceraldehyde 3-phosphate	GAP	A	
Dihydroxyacetone phosphate	DHA	*	Graph 3, 5
Extramitochondrial diphosphopyridine nucleotide	DPN	N	
Extramitochondrial reduced diphosphopyridine nucleotide	DPH	H	Graph 5
Inorganic phosphate	PIΔ	$	Graph 1
1,3-Diphosphoglycerate	DGA	D	
3-Phosphoglycerate	PGA	Q	
Pyruvate	PYR	R	
Lactate	LAC	S	
Intramitochondrial diphosphopyridine nucleotide	DIN	—	
Intramitochondrial reduced diphosphopyridine nucleotide	DIH	H	Graph 1, 4
Low energy intermediate in oxidative phosphorylation	X·I	X	Graph 4
High energy intermediate in oxidative phosphorylation	XSI	I	
Oxygen	OXY	O	
Phosphorylated intermediate in oxidative phosphorylation	XSP	*	Graph 4
Adenosine triphosphate in store 2	2TP	V	
Dibromophenol	DBP	—	
Enzyme concerned in ATP utilization	PUE	—	
Enzyme intermediate concerned in ATP utilization	PPP	%	
α-Glycerophosphate	AGP	$	Graph 3, 5
Glyceraldehyde 3-phosphate dehydrogenase-DPN complex	MOD	M	
Acyl enzyme intermediate of glyceraldehyde 3-phosphate dehydrogenase	MOB	B	
Glyceraldehyde 3-phosphate dehydrogenase	MOX	X	Graph 5

plotting the graphs of Fig. 9 is indicated below the initial concentration. Thus, the scale of the graph is a percentage of the maximal value.

A plot of nine of the variables of the computer solution is shown in the graph of Fig. 9. The variables represented can be measured by chemical assays and the data are therefore comparable with the experimental data given above. The problem is begun with the cells metabolizing endogenous substrate and the initial changes are largely due to an adjustment of the initial values of concentration to steady-state values. Thus, by the time 61 time units of the

Phosphorylation of glucose

1. 3×10^{-3} GLU $+ 1.02 \times 10^{-5}$ ENZ $\xrightarrow{3 \times 10^9}$ ENG $-$ GLU $-$ ENZ
 (GLU: $0 \to 3 \times 10^{-3}$ / 3×10^{-3}; ENZ: 1×10^{-5})

2. 1.02×10^{-5} ENG $+ 1.5 \times 10^{-3}$ 1TP $\xrightarrow{1 \times 10^{10}}$ ADP $+$ GLP $+$ ENZ $-$ ENG $-$ 1TP
 (ENG: 0 / 5×10^{-4})

3. 1×10^{-3} GLP $+ 1 \times 10^{-5}$ ETZ $\xrightarrow{4 \times 10^{10}}$ ETG $-$ GLP
 (GLP: 0 / 1×10^{-5})

4. 1×10^{-5} ETG $+ 1.5 \times 10^{-3}$ 1TP $\xrightarrow{4 \times 10^{10}}$ GPP $+$ ETZ $+$ ADP $-$ ETG $-$ 1TP
 (ETG: 0 / 5×10^{-4})

5. 1×10^{-3} GPP $\xrightarrow{1 \times 10^5}$ GAP $+$ DHA $-$ GPP
 (GPP: 0)

Glycolytic phosphorylations of ADP

6. 1.3×10^{-3} DHA $+ 2 \times 10^{-4}$ DPH $\xrightarrow{2 \times 10^9}$ AGP $+$ DPN $-$ DHA $-$ DPH
 (DHA: 0 / 1×10^{-4})

7. 1.3×10^{-3} AGP $+ 2.5 \times 10^{-4}$ DPN $\xrightarrow{8 \times 10^7}$ DHA $+$ DPH $-$ AGP $-$ DPN
 (AGP: 0 / 1×10^{-4})

8. 2×10^{-4} GAP $+ 5 \times 10^{-5}$ MOD $\xrightarrow{6 \times 10^{11}}$ MOB $+$ DPH $-$ GAP $-$ MOD
 (GAP: 0 / 5×10^{-5})

9. 1×10^{-4} MOB $+ 5 \times 10^{-3}$ PIΔ $\xrightarrow{4 \times 10^8}$ DGA $+$ MOX $-$ MOB $-$ PIΔ
 (MOB: 0 / 4×10^{-3})

10. 5×10^{-5} MOX $+ 2.5 \times 10^{-4}$ DPN $\xrightarrow{6 \times 10^9}$ MOD $-$ MOX $-$ DPN
 (MOX: 0 / 1×10^{-4})

11. 2×10^{-4} DGA $+ 1 \times 10^{-3}$ ADP $\xrightarrow{1 \times 10^{10}}$ 1TP $+$ PGA $-$ DGA $-$ ADP
 (DGA: 0 / 1×10^{-4})

12. 2×10^{-4} PGA $+ 1 \times 10^{-3}$ ADP $\xrightarrow{5 \times 10^9}$ 1TP $+$ PYR $-$ PGA $-$ ADP
 (PGA: 0 / 1×10^{-4})

13. 2×10^{-3} PYR $+ 2.0 \times 10^{-4}$ DPH $\xrightarrow{5 \times 10^8}$ LAC $+$ DPN $-$ PYR $-$ DPH
 (PYR: 1×10^{-3} / 1×10^{-4})

14. 1.2×10^{-2} LAC $+ 2.5 \times 10^{-4}$ DPN $\xrightarrow{1 \times 10^7}$ PYR $+$ DPH $-$ LAC $-$ DPN
 (LAC: 1×10^{-3} / 1×10^{-4})

Oxidative phosphorylations of ADP

15. 2×10^{-3} PYR $+ 7 \times 10^{-5}$ 4DIN $\xrightarrow{2 \times 10^7}$ 4DIH $-$ PYR $-$ 4DIN
 (PYR: 1×10^{-3} / 3×10^{-5})

16. 7×10^{-5} DIH $+ 6 \times 10^{-5}$ 3X·I $\xrightarrow{7.5 \times 10^{12}}$ 3XSI $+$ DIN $-$ DIH $-$ 3X·I $-$
 $+ 5 \times 10^{-4}$
 5×10^{-4} OXY   OXY
 (DIH: 3×10^{-5} / 2×10^{-5})

17. 6×10^{-5} XSI $+ 5 \times 10^{-3}$ PIΔ $\xrightarrow{4 \times 10^8}$ XSP $-$ XSI $-$ PIΔ
 (XSI: 2×10^{-5} / 4×10^{-3})

18. 6×10^{-5} XSP $+ 1 \times 10^{-3}$ ADP $\xrightarrow{1.5 \times 10^{10}}$ 2TP $+$ X·I $-$ XSP $-$ ADP
 (XSP: 2×10^{-5} / 1×10^{-4})

19. 6×10^{-5} XSI $+ 2.5 \times 10^{-2}$ DBP $\xrightarrow{1.2 \times 10^8}$ X·I $-$ XSI
 (XSI: 2×10^{-5} / $0 \to 2.5 \times 10^{-2}$)

ATP Utilization and transfer

20. 1.5×10^{-3} 2TP $+ 2.5 \times 10^{-2}$ DBP $\xrightarrow{4 \times 10^6}$ ITP $-$ 2TP
 (2TP: 5×10^{-4} / $0 \to 2.5 \times 10^{-2}$)

21. 5×10^{-3} 1TP $+ 3.06 \times 10^{-6}$ PUE $\xrightarrow{3 \times 10^9}$ PPP $-$ 1TP $-$ PUE
 (1TP: 5×10^{-4} / 2×10^{-6})

22. 3.06×10^{-6} PPP $\xrightarrow{2 \times 10^6}$ ADP $+$ PUE $+$ PIΔ $-$ PPP
 (PPP: 1×10^{-6})

Fig. 8. Chemical equations for the metabolic sequence in ascites tumor cell metabolism written in terms of the abbreviations used for the digital computer solution. The figures over the arrows give the reaction velocity constants; those to the lower left of the components give the maximum concentrations used (corresponding to the maximum scale of the graphical data; cf. Fig. 9); and those to the upper left, the initial concentrations. Where the initial concentration is zero but increases to a given value, the zero is followed by an arrow and the appropriate concentration.

abscissa have elapsed, the system has achieved a steady state (the values of the abscissa can be taken approximately as seconds). At this time, the oxygen trace (O) indicates a slow respiration, the phosphate level ($) is constant, mitochondrial pyridine nucleotide (H) is about 70% reduced, the mitochondrial ATP (V) is at ~50% of its maximal level, and cytoplasmic ATP (C) is about 25%

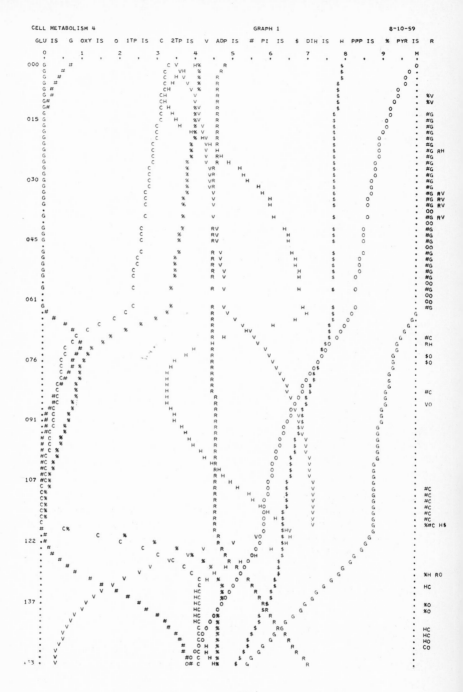

maximal. Pyruvate (R) is about 45% maximal and the concentration of the intermediate in ATP utilization (%) is about 36% maximal. The ADP (#) concentration is so low that it does not appear on this scale of the graph. It is, however, the rate-determining intermediate in this state of metabolism and the rate of ATP utilization by the phosphate-utilizing enzymes may be termed the rate-determining step.

GLUCOSE-ACTIVATED METABOLISM

Glucose (G) which has been zero up to time units 61 is suddenly raised to its maximal concentration and appears on the top of the graph. There follows a rapid glucose utilization as indicated by the downward slope of this curve which continues for approximately 20 time units. Thereafter, there is progressive inhibition of glucose utilization and the rate has fallen almost to zero by 100 time units. Activation of oxygen utilization is indicated by the increased downward slope of the oxygen trace (O) and there is a concurrent activation of phosphate utilization ($). Mitochondrial reduced pyridine nucleotide (H) is oxidized on addition of glucose, in accordance with the spectrophotometric observations; this is due to an abrupt rise of the ADP concentration (#), indicated at the bottom of the trace. There are concurrent decreases of cytoplasmic ATP (C) and increases in mitochondrial ATP (V) due to oxidative phosphorylation. Since the cytoplasmic ATP is expended the concentration of the intermediate in ATP utilization (%) also falls abruptly. Pyruvate shows only a small increase during this state of metabolism in accordance with the analytical data. As the ATP in the cytoplasm is expended, the ADP level falls as does the respiratory rate. Mitochondrial reduced pyridine nucleotide again increases in a way closely following that of the spectroscopic cycle of the experimental data. Thus, by 110 time units, the metabolism is inhibited and ADP is fully in control of the system.

EFFECT OF "UNCOUPLING AGENTS"

The addition of the uncoupling agent which allows the transfer of ATP from the mitochondria to the cytoplasm causes an abrupt

---

FIG. 9. A plot of the digital computer solution for three states of metabolism in an ascites tumor cell suspension. The numbers on the abscissa represent a time scale (approximately seconds). In the interval 0–062, there is metabolism of endogenous substrate; from 062–118, the activated and inhibited phases of glucose and oxygen metabolism caused by glucose addition; from 118–153, the reaction of glucose and oxygen metabolism by addition of an uncoupling agent. The identity of the components represented by the various curves can be determined from Table I, and the maximum concentrations of the various chemicals from Fig. 8. For other details, see text (DC-10(1)).

decrease of trace V and an abrupt rise of the trace C (cytoplasmic ATP). Simultaneously, there is an increase in the concentration of the intermediate in ATP utilization (%) and a restitution of the rates of glucose and oxygen utilization. Phosphate utilization proceeds at a rapid rate. In accordance with the experimental data, there is an abrupt rise in the rate of pyruvate formation, since, under these conditions, glycolysis is fully activated. ADP (#) rises to a steady-state value and the efficacy of the glycolytic enzyme system in maintaining the ATP level is indicated by the constant steady-state value of cytoplasmic ATP (C).

The graph of Fig. 9 is only one of five such graphs in which concentrations of reactants are plotted. Other graphs detailing the kinetics of intermediates in glucose phosphorylation, glycolytic phosphorylation, the interaction of dihydroxyacetone-phosphate dehydrogenase and glyceraldehyde 3-phosphate dehydrogenase, and oxidative phosphorylation are described in detail elsewhere (Chance and Hess, 1959f). In addition, it is possible to compare in detail the properties of the computer representation with those of the intact cell; for example, the stoichiometric ratios of the rates of utilization of glucose, oxygen, and phosphate are compared with those of a tumor cell suspension containing 0.17 gram cells per milliliter. Satisfactory stoichiometric and kinetics correlations are obtained.

Discussion

In complex chemical systems where detailed data are available on the concentrations of intermediates in the chemical system and on the metabolic flux through the system, it is possible to construct according to the law of mass action, accurate computer representations of such data which will show closely similar kinetic responses to changes in the concentrations of metabolites. In the case of the ascites tumor cell, it has been found that a model of great simplicity can be employed which is wholly based on the law of mass action and which involves the compartmentation of only two components (ATP and DPNH) between the cytoplasm and the mitochondria. As the detailed comparison of the properties of the living cell and those of the computer solution proceed, it will undoubtedly be necessary to include a more elaborate chemical system and possibly to introduce further limitations on the nature of the interactions involved. Among the elaborations of the computer solution that are being considered are, first, the inclusion of portions of the pentose-phosphate shunt, particularly transketolase and transaldolase; second, the inclusion of sufficient reverse reactions so that the formation of glucose from lactate is possible; third, the introduction of more elements of the Krebs cycle into the mitochondrial oxidation system, particularly fatty acid oxidation.

In the light of these data, it is now possible to examine certain generalizations concerning the relative activities of glucose phosphorylation and glycolytic phosphorylations in other cell types. The interesting data of Racker, which indicate the great preponderance of the glyceraldehyde 3-phosphate dehydrogenase and the 1,3-diphosphoglycerate kinase relative to hexokinase are particularly interesting in this respect. It should be noted in our solution that there is approximately five times as much glyceraldehyde 3-phosphate dehydrogenase as hexokinase; the velocity constant for the interactions of this enzyme with its substrate (6×10^{11}) is almost 100 times greater than that for hexokinase, a result in general agreement with that obtained by Racker's analyses (1960). The significant feature, however, of the computer solutions and of our experimental data on the intact ascites cell is that hexokinase can produce ADP much more rapidly than the glycolytic system can rephosphorylate it. An explanation of this apparent discrepancy is afforded by the fact that Racker's assays were made with higher values of the substrate concentrations for the dehydrogenase relative to those available for hexokinase than in the living cell. Thus, the conditions under which there is a low concentration of glyceraldehyde 3-phosphate available to its dehydrogenase are apparently more characteristic of the living cell. In short, enzymatic assays of extractable enzymatic activities from various types of cells do not in themselves tell the activity of that system inside the cell; it is therefore essential to make observations of the kind indicated by Figs. 3, 4, and 5 in which direct tests of the effectiveness of these pathways can be made in the intact cell.

A second consideration of the direct experimental and computer studies is the effect of the ATP concentration on the relative glycolytic and oxidative activities. One of the salient features of the oxidative phosphorylation system is its apparent insensitivity to ATP concentration. The phosphorylation rate and efficiency appear to be constant at ATP/ADP values approaching 10^4. On the other hand, the glycolytic phosphorylations are readily reversible reactions in which the ATP/ADP ratio can have a dominant effect upon the flux through them. It is therefore possible that the rate of glycolysis relative to the rate of respiration can be controlled by the cytoplasmic ATP concentration. A high level would slow down lactate production and eventually lead to glucose production, and vice versa. A part of the mechanism employed here is a regulation of the exchange of ATP between the mitochondria and the cytoplasm. Ascites tumor cells are characterized by a high retention of ATP by the mitochondria from glucose phosphorylating enzymes, leading to a low ATP concentration in the cytoplasm. According to the suggestion made above, these would be appropriate conditions for rapid lactate formation and these cells have a relatively high rate of lactate formation. If, on the other hand, there were less retention of ATP by the mitochondria, then indeed one would expect a diminished lactate formation, and glucose or glycogen accumulation, as occurs in the liver cell.

It would be useful to compare ATP retention in mitochondria isolated from ascites tumor cells and in those isolated from liver cells, since the extent to which Pasteur and Crabtree effects might be demonstrable would depend upon this property. From the simple diagrams of Figs. 6 and 7 it can be seen that the absence of this property would cause glucose and oxygen utilization to continue without interruption. Furthermore, some of the activating effects of the uncoupling agent would not be observed without such retention of ATP.

Although these regulations observed in ascites tumor cells under specified short-term conditions are not proposed as a general mechanism for metabolic regulations of all cells, it would be of interest to determine the extent to which they could be observed in other cells. A start in this direction has been made with the comparative study of yeast cells where the inhibition of oxygen metabolism following glucose addition is scarcely detectable. In addition, it is recognized that yeast cells show no measurable long-term Crabtree effect, i.e., an inhibition of respiration in the presence of glucose, although they do show significant Pasteur effects. Since any significant ATP retention by the mitochondria is unlikely in yeast cells, some other mechanism must be responsible for the Pasteur reaction in this material. Phosphate control of the relative glycolytic and respiratory activities is discussed in some detail by Racker et al. (1960), Racker and Wu (1959) and Lynen et al. (1959) and appears to be a reasonable explanation. It should be remembered, however, that metabolism may be controlled in many ways, and that no system of control demonstrated for a particular cell under a particular metabolic condition is known to apply generally throughout nature. It is, therefore, essential to confine the discussion of a particular metabolic control sequence to a particular type of biological material under specified conditions.

Summary

Detailed spectrophotometric studies of respiratory enzymes and chemical analyses of metabolic intermediates in the early phases of glucose metabolism by an ascites tumor cell suspension afford a basis for a computer representation of the metabolic interactions that represent, according to the law of mass action, the metabolism of glucose and oxygen. Close agreement of the kinetics of intermediates in the intact cell and in the computer representation is obtained on the assumption of the applicability of the law of mass action and of a compartmentation of adenosine triphosphate and reduced diphosphopyridine nucleotide between the cytoplasmic and mitochondrial spaces. The significance of this type of representation and of the metabolic control mechanism in relation to other control phenomena in intact cells is discussed.

REFERENCES

Chance, B. (1951). *Rev. Sci. Instr.* **22,** 643.
Chance, B. (1954). *Science* **120, 767.**
Chance, B. (1955a). *Harvey Lectures, Ser.* **49,** p. 145.
Chance, B. (1955b). *Discussions Faraday Soc.* **20,** 205.
Chance, B. (1959a). *In* "Ciba Foundation Symposium on the Regulation of Cell Metabolism" (G. E. W. Wolstenholme and C. M. O'Connor, eds.), p. 91. Churchill, London.
Chance, B. (1959b). *Ann. N.Y. Acad. Sci.* **81,** 477.
Chance, B., and Castor, L. N. (1952). *Science* **116,** 200.
Chance, B., and Hess, B. (1956). *Ann. N.Y. Acad. Sci.* **63,** 1008.
Chance, B., and Hess, B. (1959a). *Science* **129, 700.**
Chance, B., and Hess, B. (1959b). *J. Biol. Chem.* **234,** 2404.
Chance, B., and Hess, B. (1959c). *J. Biol. Chem.* **234,** 2413.
Chance, B., and Hess, B. (1959d). *J. Biol. Chem.* **234,** 2416.
Chance, B., and Hess, B. (1959e). *J. Biol. Chem.* **234,** 2421.
Chance, B., and Hess, B. (1959f). Submitted to *J. Biol. Chem.*
Chance, B., and Williams, G. R. (1955a). *J. Biol. Chem.* **217,** 383.
Chance, B., and Williams, G. R. (1955b). *J. Biol. Chem.* **217,** 439.
Harris, E. D., and Lindsey, A. J. (1948). *Nature* **162,** 413.
Ibsen, H. K., Coe, E. L., and McKee, R. W. (1958). *Biochim. et Biophys. Acta* **30,** 384.
Johnson, M. J. (1941). *Science* **94,** 200.
Lynen, F. (1941). *Liebigs Ann. Chem.* **546,** 120.
Lynen, F., and Koenigsberger, R. (1951). *Liebigs Ann. Chem.* **573,** 60.

Lynen, F., Hartmann, G., Netter, K. F., and Schuegraf, A. (1959). *In* "Ciba Foundation Symposium on the Regulation of Cell Metabolism" (G. E. W. Wolstenholme and C. M. O'Connor, eds.), p. 256. Churchill, London.

Racker, E. (1956). *Ann. N.Y. Acad. Sci.* **63**, 1017.

Racker, E., Wu, R., and Alpers, J. B. (1960). This volume, page 175.

Racker, E., and Wu, R. (1959). *In* "Ciba Foundation Symposium on the Regulation of Cell Metabolism" (G. E. W. Wolstenholme and C. M. O'Connor, eds.), p. 205. Churchill, London.

Wu, R., and Racker, E. (1959). *J. Biol. Chem.* **234**, 1036.

Yang, C. C., and Legallais, V. (1954). *Rev. Sci. Instr.* **25**, 801.

Bibliography of the Published Work of Jesse P. Greenstein

The following list, collected by Drs. Herbert A. Sober and Milton Winitz, includes Jesse Greenstein's biography of Miescher (ref. 78), his obituary of Brand (ref. 219), and several of the book reviews he wrote over the years. The list also includes a number of abstracts of his early papers which were published in the Proceedings of the American Society of Biological Chemists. Abstracts of later papers presented at national meetings, such as those which were published in Federation Proceedings, are not included.

1. Electrometric Determinations of the Dissociation of Glycocoll and Simple Peptides. *J. Gen. Physiol.*, **14**, 255 (1930). With P. H. Mitchell.
2. Studies of the Peptides of Trivalent Amino Acids. I. Titration Constants of Histidyl-histidine and of Aspartylaspartic Acid. *J. Biol. Chem.*, **93**, 479 (1931).
3. Studies of the Peptides of Trivalent Amino Acids. II. Titration Constants of Tyrosyl-tyrosine and of Glycyltyrosine. *J. Biol. Chem.*, **95**, 465 (1932).
4. The Titration Constants of α, β-Diaminopropionic Acid and Their Relation to the Constants of Various Isomers. *J. Biol. Chem.*, **96**, 499 (1932).
5. Synthese von Peptiden des d-Lysine: Lysyl-d-glutaminsaure und d-Lysyl-l-histidin. *Ber.* **65**, 1692 (1932). With M. Bergmann and L. Zervas.
6. Studies of the Peptides of Trivalent Amino Acids. III. The Apparent Dissociation Constants, Free Energy Changes, and Heats of Ionization of Peptides Involving Arginine, Histidine, Lysine, Tyrosine and Aspartic and Glutamic Acids and the Behavior of Lysine Peptide toward Nitrous Acid. *J. Biol. Chem.*, **101**, 603 (1933).
7. Studies of Multivalent Amino Acids and Peptides. I. The Synthesis of Certain Tetravalent Amino Acids and Their Derivatives. *J. Biol. Chem.*, **109**, 529 (1935).
8. Studies of Multivalent Amino Acids and Peptides. II. The Synthesis of Certain Derivatives of Lysyl-Glutamic Acid. *J. Biol. Chem.*, **109**, 541 (1935).
9. Studies of Multivalent Amino Acids and Peptides. III. The Dielectric Constants and Electrostriction of the Solvent in Solutions of Tetrapoles. *J. Am. Chem. Soc.*, **57**, 637 (1935). With J. Wyman, Jr., and E. J. Cohn.
10. The Solvent Action of Neutral Salts upon Peptides in Solutions of Low Dielectric Constant. *Proc. Am. Soc. Biol. Chemists* (1935). With E. J. Cohn and T. L. McMeekin.
11. Studies of Multivalent Amino Acids and Peptides. IV. The Apparent Dissociation Constants of α-Aminotricarballylic Acid and of Glycyl α-Aminotricarballylic Acid. *J. Biol. Chem.*, **110**, 619 (1935). With N. R. Joseph.
12. Studies of Multivalent Amino Acids and Peptides. V. Cystine Cyamidene. *J. Biol. Chem.*, **112**, 35 (1935).

13. Studies of Multivalent Amino Acids and Peptides. VI. The Action of Proteolytic Enzymes on Certain Synthetic Substrates. *J. Biol. Chem.*, **112**, 517 (1936).

14. Further Studies of Dielectric Constant and Electrostriction of Amino Acids and Peptides. *J. Am. Chem. Soc.*, **58**, 463 (1936). With J. Wyman, Jr.

15. On a Relation between the Dissociation Constants of Substituted Aliphatic Acids and the Distance between the Dissociating and the Substituted Groups. *J. Am. Chem. Soc.*, **58**, 1314 (1936).

16. The Synthesis of Isocitric Acid from Citric Acid. *Proc. Am. Soc. Biol. Chemists* (1936).

17. The Effect of Certain Substituted Dithio Acids on the Blood Sugar of Rabbits. *Proc. Am. Soc. Biol. Chemists* (1936). With H. B. Friedgood.

18. Studies in the Physical Chemistry of Amino Acids, Peptides, and Related Substances. VIII. The Relation between the Activity Coefficients of Peptides and Their Dipole Moments. *J. Am. Chem. Soc.*, **58**, 2365 (1936). With E. J. Cohn, T. L. McMeekin, and J. H. Weare.

19. Studies of Multivalent Amino Acids and Peptides. VII. Derivates of d l-α-Aminotricarballylic Acid. *J. Biol. Chem.*, **116**, 463 (1936).

20. Studies of Multivalent Amino Acids and Peptides. VIII. The Synthesis of Bisanhydro-l-Cystinyl-l-Cystine and Other Diketopiperazines of Cystine. *J. Biol. Chem.*, **118**, 321 (1937).

21. The Synthesis of Crystalline l-Cysteinyl-l-Cysteine Hydrochloride. *Proc. Am. Soc. Biochemists* (1937).

22. Peptides, Peptidases and Diketopiperazines. *In* "Chemistry of the Amino Acids and Proteins" (C. L. A. Schmidt, ed.), Chapter VI. C. C. Thomas, Springfield, Illinois (1938).

23. Studies of Multivalent Amino Acids and Peptides. IX. The Synthesis of l-Cystinyl-l-Cystine. *J. Biol. Chem.*, **121**, 9 (1937).

24. A Synthesis of Homoarginine. *J. Org. Chem.*, **2**, 1 (1937).

25. Studies of Multivalent Amino Acids and Peptides. X. Cystinyl Peptides as Substrates for Aminopolypeptidase and Dipeptidase. *J. Biol. Chem.*, **124**, 255 (1938).

26. The Polarity of Aminocyclohexane Carboxylic Acids. *Proc. Am. Soc. Biol. Chemists* (1938). With J. Wyman, Jr.

27. Alicyclic Amino Acids. *J. Am. Chem. Soc.*, **60**, 2341 (1938). With J. Wyman, Jr.

28. Studies on the Physical Chemistry of Cystinyl Peptides. *J. Biol. Chem.*, **125**, 515 (1938). With J. Wyman, Jr. and F. W. Klemperer.

29. Sulfhydryl Groups in Proteins. I. Egg Albumin in Solutions of Urea, Guanidine, and Their Derivatives. *J. Biol. Chem.*, **125**, 501 (1938).

30. Aspartylhistidine. *J. Biol. Chem.*, **128**, 245 (1939). With F. W. Klemperer.

31. Sulfhydryl Groups in Proteins. II. Edestin, Excelsin, and Globin in Solutions of Guanidine Hydrochloride, Urea, and Their Derivatives. *J. Biol. Chem.*, **128**, 233 (1939).

32. Book Review—"Fortschritte der Biochemie" by F. Haurowitz. *J. Am. Chem. Soc.*, **61**, 2211 (1939).

33. Studies of Multivalent Amino Acids and Peptides. XI. The Synthesis of Diglycyl-l-Cystine. *J. Biol. Chem.*, **128**, 241 (1939).

34. Denaturation of Myosin. *J. Am. Chem. Soc.,* **61,** 1613 (1939). With J. T. Edsall and J. W. Mehl.

35. Further Studies on the Physical Chemistry of Cystine Peptides. *J. Biol. Chem.,* **129,** 681 (1939). With F. W. Klemperer and J. Wyman, Jr.

36. Sulfhydryl Groups in Proteins. III. The Effect on Egg Albumin of Various Salts of Guanidine. *J. Biol. Chem.,* **130,** 519 (1939).

37. The Effect of Denaturing Agents on Myosin. I. Sulfhydryl Groups as Estimated by Porphyrindin Titration. *J. Biol. Chem.,* **133,** 397 (1940). With J. T. Edsall.

38. Sulfur Groups in Proteins and the Problem of Denaturation. *Nucleus,* **17,** 155 (1940).

39. Effect of Salts on the Physical Properties of Sodium Thymonucleate. *Proc. Am. Soc. Biol. Chemists* (1940).

40. Sulfhydryl Groups in the Liver Nucleoprotein of the Calf and Rabbit. *Proc. Am. Soc. Biol. Chemists* (1940).

41. Chemical Studies on the Components of Normal and Neoplastic Tissues. I. Viscosity and Streaming Birefringence of Sodium Thymonucleate. *J. Natl. Cancer Inst.,* **1,** 77 (1940). With W. V. Jenrette.

42. Chemical Studies on the Components of Normal and Neoplastic Tissues. II. The Nucleoprotein Fraction of Normal Animal Liver. *J. Natl. Cancer Inst.,* **1,** 91 (1940). With W. V. Jenrette.

43. Chemical Studies on the Components of Normal and Neoplastic Tissues. III. The Composition and Amphoteric Properties of the Nucleoprotein Fraction of the Jensen Rat Sarcoma. *J. Natl. Cancer Inst.,* **1,** 367 (1940). With J. W. Thompson and W. V. Jenrette.

44. Chemical Studies on the Components of Normal and Neoplastic Tissues. IV. The Melanin-Containing Pseudoglobulin of the Malignant Melanoma of Mice. *J. Natl. Cancer Inst.,* **1,** 377 (1940). With F. C. Turner and W. V. Jenrette.

45. Chemical Studies on the Components of Normal and Neoplastic Tissues. V. The Relative Arginase Activity of Certain Tumors and Normal Control Tissues. *J. Natl. Cancer Inst.,* **1,** 687 (1941). With W. V. Jenrette, G. B. Mider, and J. White.

46. The Relative Arginase Activity of Certain Tumors and Normal Control Tissues. *J. Biol. Chem.,* **137,** 795 (1941). With W. V. Jenrette, G. B. Mider, and J. White.

47. Sulfhydryl Groups of Serum Albumin, Serum and Milk. *J. Biol. Chem.,* **136,** 795 (1940).

48. The Depolymerization of Thymonucleic Acid by an Enzyme System in Normal and Cancerous Hepatic and Mammary Tissues and in the Milk and Sera of Several Species. *J. Natl. Cancer Inst.,* **1,** 845 (1941).

49. Physical Changes in Thymonucleic Acid Induced by Proteins, Salts, Tissue Extracts, and Ultraviolet Irradiation. *Cold Spring Harbor Symposia Quant. Biol.,* **9,** 236 (1941).

50. The Relative Activity of Xanthine Dehydrogenase, Catalase and Amylase in the Normal and Cancerous Hepatic Tissues of the Rat. *J. Natl. Cancer Inst.,* **2,** 17 (1941). With W. V. Jenrette and J. White.

51. Effects of Ultraviolet Radiation on Sodium Thymonucleate. *J. Natl. Cancer Inst.,* **2,** 23 (1941). With A. Hollaender and W. V. Jenrette.

52. The Liver Catalase Activity of Tumor-Bearing Rats and the Effect of Extirpation of the Tumors. *J. Biol. Chem.*, **141**, 327 (1941). With W. V. Jenrette and J. White.

53. The Liver Catalase Activity of Tumor-Bearing Rats and the Effect of Extirpation of the Tumors. *J. Natl. Cancer Inst.*, **2**, 283 (1941). With W. V. Jenrette and J. White.

54. The Relative Enzymatic Activity of Certain Mouse Tumors and Normal Control Tissues. *J. Natl. Cancer Inst.*, **2**, 293 (1941). With W. V. Jenrette, G. B. Mider, and H. B. Andervont.

55. Ribonuclease and Thymonucleodepolymerase. *J. Natl. Cancer Inst.*, **2**, 301 (1941). With W. V. Jenrette.

56. Note on the Composition of the Nucleoprotein Fraction of Normal Liver and of the Transplanted Hepatic Tumor in the Rat. *J. Natl. Cancer Inst.*, **2**, 305 (1941). With W. V. Jenrette and J. White.

57. The Liver Catalase Activity of Tumor-Bearing Mice and the Effect of Spontaneous Regression and of Removal of Certain Tumors. *J. Natl. Cancer Inst.*, **2**, 345 (1942). With H. B. Andervont.

58. A Method of Evaluating Thymonucleodepolymerase Activity in Normal and Tumor Tissues. *J. Natl. Cancer Inst.*, **2**, 357 (1942).

59. Distribution of Acid and Alkaline Phosphatase in Tumors, Normal Tissues, and the Tissues of Tumor-Bearing Rats and Mice. *J. Natl. Cancer Inst.*, **2**, 511 (1942).

60. Titration of the Liver Catalase Activity of Normal and of Tumor-Bearing Rats and Mice. *J. Natl. Cancer Inst.*, **2**, 525 (1942).

61. The Reactivity of Porphyrindin in the Presence of Denatured Proteins. *J. Biol. Chem.*, **142**, 175 (1942). With W. V. Jenrette.

62. Kidney and Blood Catalase Activity of Tumor-Bearing Animals. *J. Natl. Cancer Inst.*, **2**, 589 (1942). With J. W. Thompson and H. B. Andervont.

63. Note on the Enzymatic Activity of a Transplanted Adenocarcinoma of the Glandular Stomach of a Mouse. *J. Natl. Cancer Inst.*, **2**, 631 (1942).

64. Comparative Enzymatic Activity of Transplanted Hepatomas and of Normal, Regenerating and Fetal Liver. *J. Natl. Cancer Inst.*, **3**, 7 (1942). With J. E. Edwards, H. B. Andervont, and J. White.

65. Sulfhydryl Groups in Normal and Tumorous Hepatic Tissue Extracts Before and After Addition of Salts. *J. Natl. Cancer Inst.*, **3**, 61 (1942).

66. The Creatine and Creatinine Content of Transplanted Hepatomas and of Normal and Regenerating Liver. *J. Natl. Cancer Inst.*, **3**, 287 (1942).

67. The Incubation of Citrulline and Ammonia with Normal and Neoplastic Hepatic Tissues. *J. Natl. Cancer Inst.*, **3**, 293 (1942).

68. Electrophoretic Patterns, Colloid Osmotic Pressure and Viscosity of Serum Denatured by Ultraviolet Radiation. *J. Biol. Chem.*, **146**, 663 (1942). With B. D. Davis and A. Hollaender.

69. Further Studies of the Liver Catalase Activity of Tumor-Bearing Animals. *J. Natl. Cancer Inst.*, **3**, 397 (1943).

70. Note on the Copper Content of the Tissues of Tumor-Bearing Animals. *J. Natl. Cancer Inst.*, **3**, 405 (1943). With J. W. Thompson.

71. Tumor Enzymology. *J. Natl. Cancer Inst.*, **3**, 419 (1943).

72. Recent Progress in Tumor Enzymology. *Advances in Enzymol.*, **3**, 315 (1943).

73. Degradation of Cystine by Normal Liver but Not By Transplanted Hepatomas. *J. Natl. Cancer Inst.,* **3,** 491 (1943).

74. Peptides, Peptidases and Diketopiperazines. Addendum to "Chemistry of the Amino Acids and Proteins" (C. L. A. Schmidt, ed.), Chapter VI. C. C. Thomas, Springfield, Illinois (1943).

75. Depolymerases for Yeast and for Thymus Nucleic Acids in Normal and Neoplastic Tissues. *J. Natl. Cancer Inst.,* **4,** 55 (1943).

76. Note on the Colloid Osmotic Pressure of the Serums of Rats Bearing the Transplanted Jensen Sarcoma. *J. Natl. Cancer Inst.,* **4,** 63 (1943). With J. W. Thompson.

77. The Colloid Osmotic Pressure of Mixtures of Protein and Thymus Nucleate. *J. Biol. Chem.,* **150,** 107 (1943).

78. Friedrich Miescher, 1844-1895, Founder of Nuclear Chemistry. *Sci. Monthly,* **57,** 523 (1943).

79. Enzymatic Activity of Normal Adult, Regenerating, Fetal and Neoplastic Tissues of the Rat. *J. Natl. Cancer Inst.,* **4,** 271 (1943). With J. W. Thompson.

80. Range in Activity of Several Enzymes in Normal and Neoplastic Tissues of Mice. *J. Natl. Cancer Inst.,* **4,** 275 (1943). With J. W. Thompson.

81. Note on the Liver Catalase Activity of Pregnant Mice and of Mice Bearing Growing Embryonic Implants. *J. Natl. Cancer Inst.,* **4,** 283 (1943). With H. B. Andervont.

82. A Transplantable Osteogenic Sarcoma Originating in a C3H Mouse. *J. Natl. Cancer Inst.,* **4,** 389 (1944).

83. Nucleoproteins. *Advances in Protein Chem.,* **1,** 209 (1944).

84. The Chemistry of Protein Denaturation. *Chem. Revs.,* **34,** 157 (1944). With H. Neurath, F. W. Putnam, and J. C. Erickson.

85. Book Review—"Biochemie der Tumoren" by H. v. Euler and B. Skarzyński. *Cancer Research,* **4,** (1944).

86. The Chemistry of the Proteins and Amino Acids. *Ann. Rev. Biochem.,* **13,** 117 (1944). With H. Neurath.

87. Chemical Studies on Human Cancer. I. Cytochrome Oxidase, Cytochrome C, and Copper in Normal and Neoplastic Tissues. *J. Natl. Cancer Inst.,* **5,** 55 (1944). With J. Werne, A. B. Eschenbrenner, and F. M. Leuthardt.

88. Esterase (Butyric Esterase) Activity of Normal and Neoplastic Mouse Tissues. *J. Natl. Cancer Inst.,* **5,** 31 (1944).

89. Note on the Cystine Oxidase Activity in Normal and Neoplastic Tissues of the Mouse. *J. Natl. Cancer Inst.,* **5,** 39 (1944).

90. Comparative Oxidase Activity of Melanotic and Amelanotic Melanomas. *J. Natl. Cancer Inst.,* **5,** 35 (1944). With G. Algire.

91. Chapter on the Chemistry of Mammary Tumors in the Mouse. *Am. Assoc. Advance. Sci. Monograph* (1944). By members of the staff of the National Cancer Institute.

92. Esterase Activity of Blood Serum of Four Strains of Mice. *J. Natl. Cancer Inst.,* **5,** 29 (1944). With M. B. Shimkin and H. B. Andervont.

93. Enzymes in Normal and Neoplastic Tissues in Symposium on Cancer. *Occasional Publ. Am. Assoc. Advance. Sci.* (1945).

94. Biochemistry of Malignant Tissues. *Ann. Rev. Biochem.,* **14,** 643 (1945).

95. Cystine and Cysteine in the Water Extractable Proteins of Rat and Rabbit Tissues. *J. Biol. Chem.*, **156**, 349 (1944). With F. M. Leuthardt.
96. Sulfur Distribution in Extracts of Normal and Neoplastic Animal Tissues. *J. Natl. Cancer Inst.*, **5**, 111 (1944). With F. M. Leuthardt.
97. Book Review—Advances in Enzymology, Vol. IV. *Cancer Research*, **5**, 62 (1945).
98. The Degradation of Cystine Peptides by Tissues. I. Exocystine Desulfurase and Dehydropeptidase in Rat Liver Extracts. *J. Natl. Cancer Inst.*, **5**, 209 (1944). With F. M. Leuthardt.
99. The Degradation of Cystine Peptides by Tissues. II. Distribution of Exocystine Desulfurase and Dehydropeptidase in Tissue Extracts of Various Species. *J. Natl. Cancer Inst.*, **5**, 223 (1944).
100. The Degradation of Cystine Peptides by Tissues. III. Absence of Exocystine Desulfurase and Dehydropeptidase in Tumors. *J. Natl. Cancer Inst.*, **5**, 249 (1945). With F. M. Leuthardt.
101. Degradation of Cystine Peptides by Tissues—A New Aspect of Protein Catabolism. *Science*, **101**, 19 (1944). With F. M. Leuthardt.
102. Effect of Nucleates on the Rate of Methylene Blue Decolorization in Tissue Extracts. *J. Biol. Chem.*, **157**, 753 (1945). With H. W. Chalkley.
103. The Influence of Nucleic Acid on Dehydrogenase Systems—A Contribution to the Problem of Gene Mechanism. *Ann. Missouri Botan. Garden*, **32**, 179 (1945). With H. W. Chalkley.
104. Book Review—Outline of the Amino Acids and Proteins. *J. Am. Chem. Soc.* **67**, 885 (1945).
105. Desaminases for Ribosenucleic and Desoxyribosenucleic Acids. *J. Natl. Cancer Inst.*, **6**, 61 (1945). With H. W. Chalkley.
106. Desaminases for Ribosenucleic and Desoxyribosenucleic Acids. *Arch. Biochem. Biophys.* **7**, 451 (1945). With H. W. Chalkley.
107. Effect of Nucleates on Dehydrogenase Systems. *J. Natl. Cancer Inst.*, **6**, 119 (1945). With H. W. Chalkley.
108. Effect of Sodium Bicarbonate, Pyruvate, and Diphosphopyridine Nucleotide (DPN) on Dehydrogenase Activity. *J. Natl. Cancer Inst.*, **6**, 143 (1945). With H. W. Chalkley.
109. Note on the Enzymatic Activity of Normal and Neoplastic Tissues of the Rat. *J. Natl. Cancer Inst.* **6**, 317 (1946). With F. M. Leuthardt.
110. Effect of Bicarbonate and Diphosphopyridine Nucleotide (DPN), on Dehydrogenase Activity in Liver Extracts. *J. Biol. Chem.*, **160**, 371 (1945). With H. W. Chalkley.
111. Book Review—Advances in Enzymology, Vol. V. *Cancer Research*, **6**, 46 (1946).
112. Tumor Enzymology. *Actualite Rev. Med.*, *Brussels* (1946).
113. Enzymatic Activity in Primary and Transplanted Rat Hepatomas. *J. Natl. Cancer Inst.*, **6**, 211 (1946). With F. M. Leuthardt.
114. The Degradation of Cystine Peptides by Tissues. IV. Dehydropeptidase Activity in Normal and Neoplastic Tissues. *J. Natl. Cancer Inst.*, **6**, 197 (1946). With F. M. Leuthardt.
115. Note on Some Aspects of the Effect of Nucleates in Primary and Transplanted Rat Hepatomas. *J. Natl. Cancer Inst.*, **6**, 207 (1946). With H. W. Chalkley.

116. Enzymatic Hydrolysis of Benzoylarginineamide in Normal and Neoplastic Tissues. *J. Natl. Cancer Inst.*, **6**, 203 (1946). With F. M. Leuthardt.

117. Protective Effect of Thymus Nucleate on the Heat Coagulation of Proteins. *J. Natl. Cancer Inst.*, **6**, 219 (1946). With C. E. Carter.

118. Dehydropeptidase Activity in Tissues. *J. Biol. Chem.*, **162**, 175 (1946). With F. M. Leuthardt.

119. Thymus Nucleate and the Heat Coagulation of Egg Albumin. *J. Biol. Chem.* With C. E. Carter (*Proc. Am. Soc. Biol. Chemists,* 1945).

120. Thymus Nucleate and the Heat Coagulation of Tissue Extracts. *J. Biol. Chem.* With C. E. Carter (*Proc. Am. Soc. Biol. Chemists,* 1946).

121. Enzymatic Desamination and Dephosphorylation of Ribosenucleic and Desoxyribosenucleic Acids. *J. Natl. Cancer Inst.*, **7**, 9 (1946). With C. E. Carter, H. W. Chalkley, and F. M. Leuthardt.

122. Studies on the Enzymatic Degradation of Nucleic Acids. *J. Natl. Cancer Inst.*, **7**, 29 (1946). With C. E. Carter.

123. Book Review—Advances in Protein Chemistry, Vol. II. *Science,* **103**, 210 (1946).

124. The Enzymatic Desamination, Dephosphorylation and Degradation of Nucleic Acids to Dialyzable Substances. *Arch. Biochem.*, **11**, 307 (1946).

125. Neutral β-Glycerophosphatase Activity in Normal and Neoplastic Tissues. *J. Natl. Cancer Inst.*, **7**, 1 (1946). With F. M. Leuthardt.

126. Activity of Phosphatases in Fresh and Dialyzed Extracts of Normal Mouse Liver and of Mouse Hepatoma. *J. Natl. Cancer Inst.*, **7**, 47 (1946). With C. E. Carter and F. M. Leuthardt.

127. Spectrophotometric Determination of Dehydropeptidase Activity in Normal and Neoplastic Tissues. *J. Natl. Cancer Inst.*, **7**, 51 (1946). With C. E. Carter.

128. Influence of α-Keto Acids in the Desamidation of Amino Acid Amides. *J. Natl. Cancer Inst.*, **7**, 57 (1946). With C. E. Carter.

129. Enzymatic Desamidation of Glutamine in the Presence of Pyruvate Furnished By Concomitant Reactions. *J. Natl. Cancer Inst.*, **7**, 269 (1947). With J. M. Goncalves.

130. Studies on the Effect of Pyruvate on the Desamidation of Glutamine, Asparagine and Related Compounds. *J. Natl. Cancer Inst.*, **7**, 275 (1947). With V. E. Price.

131. Desamidation of Amino Acid Amides in Rat Liver Extracts of Varying Concentration. *J. Natl. Cancer Inst.*, **7**, 281 (1947). With J. M. Goncalves and V. E. Price.

132. Desamidation of Glutamine and Asparagine in Normal and Neoplastic Hepatic Tissues. *J. Natl. Cancer Inst.*, **7**, 285 (1947). With M. Errera.

133. A Spectrophotometric Method for the Determination of Dehydropeptidase Activity. *J. Biol. Chem.*, **165**, 725 (1946). With C. E. Carter.

134. The Influence of α-Keto Acids on the Desamidation of Amino Acid Amides. *J. Biol. Chem.*, **165**, 741 (1946). With C. E. Carter.

135. Acceleration of Enzymatic Desamidation of Glutamine By Several Inorganic Anions. *J. Natl. Cancer Inst.*, **7**, 433 (1947). With C. E. Carter.

136. Effects of Acidity and of Heating on the Capacity of Rat Liver Extracts to Desamidate Glutamine and Asparagine. *J. Natl. Cancer Inst.*, **7**, 437 (1947). With M. Errera.

137. Enzymatic Hydrolysis of Acetyldehydroalanine. *J. Natl. Cancer Inst.*, **7,** 433 (1947). With J. M. Goncalves and V. E. Price.

138. Enzymatic Hydrolysis of α,α-Diglycylaminopropionic Acid Hydrochloride. *J. Natl. Cancer Inst.*, **8,** 25 (1947). With J. M. Goncalves.

139. Note on the Enzymatic Hydrolysis of α,α-Diglycylaminopropionic Acid in Normal and Neoplastic Rat Hepatic Tissues. *J. Natl. Cancer Inst.*, **8,** 29 (1947). With M. de Mingo.

140. Rate of Appearance of Ammonia in Digests of Rat Kidney Extracts with Isomeric Peptides. *J. Natl. Cancer Inst.*, **8,** 31 (1947). With J. M. Goncalves and V. E. Price.

141. Presence of Dehydropeptidase I and II Activity in Plant Material. *J. Natl. Cancer Inst.*, **8,** 35 (1947). With F. M. Leuthardt.

142. Spectral and Chemical Properties of Pyruvoylglycine. *J. Natl. Cancer Inst.*, **8,** 39 (1947). With M. Errera.

143. Enzymatic Degradation of Ribosenucleic Acid and Desoxyribosenucleic Acid with an Addendum on the Effect of Nucleates on the Heat Stability of Proteins. *Cold Spring Harbor Symposia Quant. Biol.* (1947). With C. E. Carter and H. W. Chalkley.

144. Effect of X-rays on Thymus Nucleic Acid. *Cold Spring Harbor Symposia Quant. Biol.* (1947). With B. Taylor and A. Hollaender.

145. A New Synthesis of Chloroacetyldehydroalanine. *Arch. Biochem.*, **14,** 249 (1947). With V. E. Price.

146. Dehydropeptidase Activity in Certain Animal and Plant Tissues. *J. Biol. Chem.*, **171,** 477 (1947). With V. E. Price.

147. Ammonia Nitrogen from Digests of Isomeric Peptides in Kidney Homogenate Digests. *Science,* **106,** 369 (1947). With J. M. Goncalves and V. E. Price.

148. Enzymatic Hydrolysis of α,α-Di(glycylamino) propionic Acid. *Arch. Biochem.*, **16,** 1 (1948). With J. M. Goncalves.

149. Effect of Keto Acids on Desamidation of Glutamine. *Arch. Biochem.*, **15,** 449 (1947). With M. Errera.

150. Note on the Ultraviolet Absorption Spectra of Keto Acids and of Keto Acid Peptides. *Arch. Biochem.*, **15,** 445 (1947). With M. Errera.

151. Effect of X-Radiation on Sodium Thymus Nucleate. *Arch Biochem.*, **16,** 19 (1948). With B. Taylor and A. Hollaender.

152. Desamidation of Homologous Amino Acid Amides in Normal and Neoplastic Tissues. *J. Natl. Cancer Inst.*, **8,** 71 (1947). With M. Errera.

153. Note on the Benzoylargineamidase Activity in Extracts of Rat Liver and Hepatoma. *J. Natl. Cancer Inst.*, **8,** 77 (1947). With F. M. Leuthardt.

154. "Biochemistry of Cancer," Approx. 400 pp. Academic Press, New York (1947).

155. Chemistry of Melanomas. *Special Publ. N.Y. Acad. Sci.,* **4,** 433 (1948).

156. *N*-Acylated and *N*-Methylated Glycyldehydroalanine. *J. Biol. Chem.*, **173,** 337 (1948). With V. E. Price.

157. Further Studies on α,α-Di(acylamino)propionic Acids. *Arch. Biochem.*, **17,** 51 (1948). With V. E. Price and M. Errera.

158. Effect of Phosphate and Other Anions on the Enzymatic Desamidation of Various Amides. *Arch. Biochem.*, **17,** 105 (1948). With F. M. Leuthardt.

159. Effect of Added Phosphate on Glutamine Desamidation in Tumors. *J. Natl. Cancer Inst.*, **8**, 161 (1948). With F. M. Leuthardt.
160. Dehydropeptidase Activity of Normal and Pathological Human Sera. *J. Natl. Cancer Inst.*, **8**, 169 (1948). With A. Meister.
161. Dehydropeptidases. *Advances in Enzymol.*, **8**, 117 (1948).
162. Addition Reactions of Dehydropeptides. *Arch. Biochem.*, **19**, 467 (1948). With I. Z. Eiger.
163. Ammonia Produced from Cystine Peptides and Dehydropeptides. *Arch. Biochem.*, **18**, 377 (1948). With F. M. Leuthardt.
164. The Possible Multiple Nature of Dehydropeptidase I. *J. Biol. Chem.*, **175**, 953 (1948). With V. E. Price and F. M. Leuthardt.
165. Derivatives of α,α-Di(glycylamino)propionic Acid. *J. Biol. Chem.*, **175**, 963 (1948). With V. E. Price.
166. Enzymatic Hydrolysis of Analogous Saturated and Unsaturated Peptides. *J. Biol. Chem.*, **175**, 969 (1948). With V. E. Price.
167. Enzymatic Hydrolysis of α,γ-Diketo Acids. *J. Biol. Chem.*, **175**, 573 (1948). With A. Meister.
168. Acetylated Dehydroamino Acids. *Arch. Biochem.*, **18**, 383 (1948). With V. E. Price.
169. Carcinogens. *In* "Encyclopedia of Chemical Technology" (R. E. Kirk and D. F. Othmer, eds.), Vol. III. Interscience, New York (1949).
170. Liver Glutaminases. *J. Biol. Chem.*, **178**, 483 (1949). With V. E. Price.
171. Phosphate-Activated Glutaminase in Kidney and Other Tissues. *J. Biol. Chem.*, **178**, 495 (1949). With M. Errera.
172. Keto Acid-Activated Glutaminase and Asparaginase. *J. Biol. Chem.*, **178**, 695 (1949). With V. E. Price.
173. Preparation of L- and D-Alanine by Enzymic Resolution of Acetyl-DL-Alanine. *J. Biol. Chem.*, **178**, 503 (1949). With P. J. Fodor and V. E. Price.
174. Resolution of Several Amino Acids. *J. Biol. Chem.*, **179**, 1169 (1949). With V. E. Price and J. B. Gilbert.
175. Enzymatic Hydrolysis of Saturated and Unsaturated Tripeptides. *J. Biol. Chem.*, **180**, 193 (1949). With V. E. Price and P. J. Fodor.
176. Effect of Anions on the Non-enzymatic Desamidation of Glutamine. *J. Biol. Chem.*, **180**, 209 (1949).
177. Resolution of Racemic Phenylalanine, Tyrosine, and Tryptophan. *J. Biol. Chem.*, **180**, 473 (1949). With J. B. Gilbert and V. E. Price.
178. Effect of Thymus Nucleate on the Thermal Coagulation of Albumin Solutions. *J. Biol. Chem.*, **182**, 457 (1950).
179. Enzymatic Resolution of Racemic Lysine, Norleucine, Norvaline, and α-Aminobutyric Acid. *J. Biol. Chem.*, **182**, 451 (1950). With J. B. Gilbert and P. J. Fodor.
180. The Separation of Dehydropeptidase and Analogous L- and D-Peptidases. *J. Biol. Chem.*, **181**, 535 (1949). With V. E. Price, A. Meister, and J. B. Gilbert.
181. Separation of Enzymatic Activities toward Chloroacetylalanine, Chloroacetylalanylglycine and Glycylalanine. *J. Biol. Chem.*, **181**, 549 (1949). With P. J. Fodor.
182. Some Biochemical Aspects of Tumors. Proceedings of the Papal Academy of Science (Rome) (1949).

183. The Neoplastic Transformation as a Biological Fractionation of Related Enzyme Systems. *J. Natl. Cancer Inst.*, **10**, 271 (1949). With P. J. Fodor and V. E. Price.

184. A Resolution of Histidine, Cystine and Alanine by Asymmetric Enzymatic Hydrolysis of the Racemic Amides. *J. Biol. Chem.*, **184**, 55 (1950). With V. E. Price and R. Kingsley.

185. The Enzymatic Hydrolysis of L- and D-Amino Acid Amides by Mushroom Preparations. *Arch. Biochem.*, **26**, 92 (1950). With V. E. Price, L. Levintow and R. B. Kingsley.

186. Preparation and Enzymatic Hydrolysis of Three New Homologous Dehydropeptides. *J. Biol. Chem.*, **184**, 633 (1950). With L. Levintow, S.-C. J. Fu, and V. E. Price.

187. Tumor Enzymology. *In* "The Enzymes" (J. B. Sumner and K. Myrbäck, eds.), Vol. II, Part 2, p. 1131. Academic Press, New York (1952). With A. Meister.

188. Configuration of Isomeric Allothreonines by Enzymatic Resolution. *J. Am. Chem. Soc.*, **72**, 2812 (1950). With L. Levintow.

189. The Present Status of Cancer Research. *Science Counselor*, **13** (1950).

190. Preparation and Properties of α,α-Di(acylamino)aliphatic Acids. *Arch. Biochem.*, **28**, 440 (1950). With S.-C. J. Fu, L. Levintow, and V. E. Price.

191. Preparation of D-Ornithine, D-Citrulline and D-Arginine. *J. Biol. Chem.*, **188**, 643 (1951). With L. Levintow.

192. Preparation of the Four Stereoisomers of Isoleucine. *J. Biol. Chem.*, **188**, 647 (1951). With L. Levintow, C. G. Baker, and J. White.

193. A Resolution of Glutamic Acid. *Arch. Biochem. Biophys.*, **31**, 77 (1951). With L. Levintow and R. B. Kingsley.

194. Alkali-Catalyzed Ring Closure of Pyruvoylglycine. *Arch. Biochem. Biophys.*, **31**, 83 (1951). With S.-C. J. Fu and V. E. Price.

195. Further Studies on Pyruvoyl Amino Acids. *Arch. Biochem. Biophys.*, **32**, 365 (1951). With S.-C. J. Fu.

196. Cation Activation of Desoxyribonuclease. *Arch. Biochem. Biophys.*, **32**, 414 (1951). With T. Miyaji.

197. Optical Purity of Amino Acid Enantiomorphs. *J. Biol. Chem.*, **192**, 535 (1951). With A. Meister, L. Levintow, and R. B. Kingsley.

198. An Enzymatic Resolution of Proline. *J. Biol. Chem.*, **193**, 81 (1951). With D. Hamer.

199. Preparation of the Optical Isomers of Analogous Cyclohexyl- and Phenyl-Substituted Amino Acids. *J. Am. Chem. Soc.*, **74**, 551 (1952). With D. Rudman and A. Meister.

200. Specificity of Amino Acid Acylases, *J. Biol. Chem.*, **194**, 455 (1952). With S. M. Birnbaum, L. Levintow, and R. B. Kingsley.

201. Effect of Cancer on Liver Enzymes. *J. Am. Med. Assoc.*, **148**, 697 (1952).

202. Stereoisomers of Hydroxyproline. *J. Biol. Chem.*, **195**, 383 (1952). With D. S. Robinson.

203. Glycyl Dehydropeptides of Leucine, Valine and Isoleucine. *J. Biol. Chem.*, **195**, 849 (1952). With A. Meister.

204. Preparation of the Optical Isomers of Arginine, Histidine and S-Benzylcysteine by Asymmetric Enzymic Hydrolysis of Their Acetyl Derivatives. *Arch. Biochem. Biophys.*, **39**, 108 (1952). With S. M. Birnbaum.

205. Optical Enantiomorphs of Isovaline. *J. Am. Chem. Soc.*, **74**, 4701 (1952). With C. G. Baker, S.-C. J. Fu, S. M. Birnbaum, and H. A. Sober.

206. Optical Enantiomorphs of α,β-Diaminopropionic Acid. *J. Biol. Chem.*, **198**, 335 (1952). With S. M. Birnbaum, R. J. Koegel, and S.-C. J. Fu.

207. Enzymatic Susceptibility of Corresponding Chloroacetyl and Glycyl-L-Amino Acids. *J. Biol. Chem.*, **198**, 507 (1952). With K. R. Rao, S. M. Birnbaum, and R. B. Kingsley.

208. Enzymatic Resolution of α,γ-Diaminobutyric Acid. *J. Biol. Chem.*, **199**, 207 (1952). With S.-C. J. Fu, K. R. Rao, and S. M. Birnbaum.

209. L-Isoleucine, D-Isoleucine, L-Alloisoleucine and D-Alloisoleucine. *Biochem. Preparations*, **3**, 84 (1953). With S. M. Birnbaum and L. Levintow.

210. Optical Enantiomorphs of Homoserine and Homocystine. *Arch. Biochem. Biophys.*, **42**, 212 (1953). With S. M. Birnbaum.

211. Conversion of β-Chloroacetyl-L-Diaminopropionic Acid to L-2-Ketopiperazine-5-Carboxylic Acid. *J. Biol. Chem.*, **201**, 547 (1953). With R. J. Koegel, S. M. Birnbaum, C. G. Baker, and H. A. Sober.

212. Method of Enzymatic Resolution of Amino Acids. U.S. Patent 2,616,828 (1952). With L. Levintow.

213. Purification and Properties of an Aminopeptidase from Kidney Cellular Particulates. *J. Biol. Chem.*, **202**, 1 (1953). With D. S. Robinson, and S. M. Birnbaum.

214. Optical Enantiomorphs of α-Aminoadipic Acid. *J. Am. Chem. Soc.*, **75**, 1994 (1953). With S. M. Birnbaum and M. C. Otey.

215. Enzymatic Susceptibility of Comparable N-Acylated L-, D- and Dehydro-Amino Acids. *J. Biol. Chem.*, **203**, 1 (1953). With K. R. Rao and S. M. Birnbaum.

216. Resolution of the Racemic α-Amino Derivatives of Heptylic, Caprylic, Nonylic, Decylic and Undecylic Acids. *J. Biol. Chem.*, **203**, 333 (1953). With S. M. Birnbaum and S.-C. J. Fu.

217. Optical and Enzymatic Characterization of Amino Acids. *J. Biol. Chem.*, **204**, 307 (1953). With S. M. Birnbaum and M. C. Otey.

218. Optical Enantiomorphs of Tertiary Leucine. *J. Biol. Chem.* **205**, 221 (1953). With N. Izumiya, S.-C. J. Fu, and S. M. Birnbaum.

219. Erwin Brand: 1891-1953. *Science*, **119**, 144 (1954). With O. E. Reynolds.

220. Solubilized Kidney Glutaminase I. *Arch. Biochem. Biophys.*, **49**, 245 (1954). With M. C. Otey and S. M. Birnbaum.

221. "Biochemistry of Cancer," 2nd ed. Academic Press, New York (1954).

222. Peptidases in Renal and Hepatic Tissues. *Bull. Israeli Acad. Sci.*, **4**, 6 (1954). With S. M. Birnbaum.

223. The Resolution of Racemic α-Amino Acids. *Advances in Protein Chem.*, **9**, 121 (1954).

224. Studies on Polycysteine Peptides and Proteins. I. Isomeric Cystinylcystine Peptides. *Arch. Biochem. Biophys.*, **52**, 203 (1954). With N. Izumiya.

225. Studies on Polycysteine Peptides and Proteins. II. Apparent Dissociation Constants and Ultraviolet and Infrared Absorption Spectra of Isomeric Cystinylcystine Peptides. *Arch. Biochem. Biophys.*, **53**, 501 (1954). With M. C. Otey.

226. Studies on Diastereoisomeric α-Amino Acids and α-Hydroxy Acids. I. Preparation of the Four Optical Isomers of α-Aminotricarballylic Acid

and Their Conversion to the Corresponding Isocitric Acid Lactones. *J. Am. Chem. Soc.,* **77,** 707 (1955). With N. Izumiya, M. Winitz, and S. M. Birnbaum.

227. Studies on Diastereoisomeric α-Amino Acids and corresponding α-Hydroxy Acids. II. Contribution of the Asymmetric α and β Carbon Atoms to the Molar Rotations of the Diastereomeric α-Aminotricarballylic Acids and Corresponding Isocitric Acids. *J. Am. Chem. Soc.,* **77,** 716 (1955). With M. Winitz and S. M. Birnbaum.

228. Influence of Optically Active Acyl Groups on the Enzymatic Hydrolysis of *N*-Acylated-L-amino Acids. *J. Am. Chem. Soc.,* **76,** 6054 (1954). With S.-C. J. Fu and S. M. Birnbaum.

229. Studies on Diastereoisomeric α-Amino Acids and corresponding α-Hydroxy Acids. III. Configuration of the β-Asymmetric Center of Isoleucine. *J. Am. Chem. Soc.,* **77,** 3106 (1955). With M. Winitz and S. M. Birnbaum.

230. Studies on Diastereoisomeric α-Amino Acids and Corresponding α-Hydroxy Acids. IV. Rotatory Dispersion of the Asymmetric α- and ω-carbon Atoms of Several Diastereoisomeric Amino Acids. *J. Am. Chem. Soc.,* **77,** 3112 (1955). With M. C. Otey, M. Winitz, and S. M. Birnbaum.

231. Saturation of Acetyldehydroalanine with Benzylamine. *J. Am. Chem. Soc.,* **77,** 4412 (1955). With S.-C. J. Fu.

232. Separation of the Three Isomeric Components of Synthetic α,ε-Diaminopimelic Acid. *J. Am. Chem. Soc.,* **77,** 1916 (1955). With E. Work, M. Winitz, and S. M. Birnbaum.

233. Studies on Diastereoisomeric α-Amino Acids and Corresponding α-Hydroxy Acids. V. Infrared Spectra. *J. Am. Chem. Soc.,* **77,** 5708 (1955). With R. J. Koegel, M. Winitz, S. M. Birnbaum, and R. McCallum.

234. Studies on Carcinogenic Amines. I. L- and D-Amino Acid Derivatives of 2-Aminofluorene, 4-Aminobiphenyl and 4,4'-Diaminodiphenyl, and Their Susceptibility to Hydrolysis by Tissue Homogenates. *J. Am. Chem. Soc.,* **77,** 5721 (1955). With M. Winitz and S. M. Birnbaum.

235. The *In Vivo* Effect on Liver Catalase by a Tumor. *J. Natl. Cancer Inst.,* **15,** 1603 (1955).

236. Studies on Polycysteine Peptides and Proteins. III. Configurations of the Peptides of L-Cystine Obtained by Oxidation of L-Cysteinyl-L-cysteine. *J. Am. Chem. Soc.,* **78,** 373 (1956). With R. Wade and M. Winitz.

237. A Simplified Preparation of D-Arginine. *Arch. Biochem. Biophys.,* **60,** 496 (1956). With S. M. Birnbaum and M. Winitz.

238. Book Review—Annual Review of Biochemistry, Vol. 24. *J. Am. Chem. Soc.,* **78,** 1075 (1956).

239. Studies on Diastereoisomeric α-Amino Acids and Corresponding α-Hydroxy Acids. VI. Rotatory Dispersion of Copper Complexes. *J. Am. Chem. Soc.,* **78,** 1602 (1956). With M. Winitz, N. Izumiya, and S. M. Birnbaum.

240. A Water Soluble Synthetic Diet. *Arch. Biochem. Biophys.,* **63,** 266 (1956). With S. M. Birnbaum and M. Winitz.

241. Studies on Diastereoisomeric α-Amino Acids and Corresponding α-Hydroxy Acids. VII. Influence of β-Configuration on Enzymic Susceptibility. *J. Am. Chem. Soc.,* **78,** 2423 (1956). With M. Winitz, L. Bloch-Frankenthal, N. Izumiya, S. M. Birnbaum, and C. G. Baker.

242. Some Biochemical Characteristics of Morphologically Separable Cancers. *Cancer Research,* **16,** 641 (1956).

243. Cobalt Ion Activation of Renal Acylase I. *J. Am. Chem. Soc.,* **78,** 4636 (1956). With R. Marshall and S. M. Birnbaum.

244. Book Review—Currents in Biochemical Research 1956. *J. Am. Chem. Soc.,* **78,** 5455 (1956).

245. Collected Lectures in Japan (I-IV, inclusive) 1956. Auspices of Japanese Biochemical Society.
    I. Nutrition of Amino Acids and the Role of Arginine in Ammonia Toxicity.
    II. The Action of Stereospecific Enzymes on Isomeric Amino Acids and Peptides.
    III. The Preparation and Properties of Cyclic Peptides of Cystine.
    IV. Enzymic Aspects of Cancer Research.

246. Studies on the Metabolism of Amino Acids and Related Compounds *In Vivo.* I. Toxicity of Essential Amino Acids, Individually and in Mixtures, and the Protective Effect of L-Arginine. *Arch. Biochem. Biophys.,* **58,** 253 (1955); **64,** 319 (1956). With P. Gullino, M. Winitz, S. M. Birnbaum, J. Cornfield, and M. C. Otey.

247. Studies on the Metabolism of Amino Acids and Related Compounds *In Vivo.* II. Effect of Toxic Doses of Essential Amino Acids on Blood Sugar, Liver Glycogen, and Muscle Glycogen Levels. *Arch. Biochem. Biophys.,* **64,** 333 (1956). With M. Winitz, P. Gullino, and S. M. Birnbaum.

248. Studies on the Metabolism of Amino Acids and Related Compounds *In Vivo.* III. Prevention of Ammonia Toxicity by Arginine and Related Compounds. *Arch. Biochem. Biophys.,* **59,** 302 (1955); **64,** 342 (1956). With M. Winitz, P. Gullino, S. M. Birnbaum, and M. C. Otey.

249. Studies on the Metabolism of Amino Acids and Related Compounds *In Vivo.* IV. Blood Ammonia and Urea Levels Following Intraperitoneal Administration of Amino Acids and Ammonium Acetate, and the Effect of Arginine Thereon. *Arch. Biochem. Biophys.,* **62,** 236 (1956); **64,** 355 (1956). With J. P. du Ruisseau, M. Winitz, and S. M. Birnbaum.

250. Studies on the Metabolism of Amino Acids and Related Compounds *In Vivo.* V. Effects of Combined Administration of Nonprotective Compounds and Subprotective Levels of L-Arginine-HCl on Ammonia Toxicity in Rats. *Arch. Biochem. Biophys.,* **64,** 368 (1956). With M. Winitz, J. P. du Ruisseau, M. C. Otey, and S. M. Birnbaum.

251. Percarbobenzoxylation of Arginine. *Arch. Biochem. Biophys.,* **65,** 573 (1956). With L. Zervas and M. Winitz.

252. Studies on Arginine Peptides. I. Intermediates in the Synthesis of *N*-Terminal and *C*-Terminal Arginine Peptides. *J. Org. Chem.,* **22,** 1515 (1957). With L. Zervas and M. Winitz.

253. Studies on Diastereoisomeric α-Amino Acids and Corresponding α-Hydroxy Acids. VIII. Configuration of the Isomeric Octopines. *J. Am. Chem. Soc.,* **79,** 652 (1957). With N. Izumiya, R. Wade, M. Winitz, M. C. Otey, S. M. Birnbaum, and R. J. Koegel.

254. Preparation and Properties of the Isomeric Forms of α-Amino- and

α,ϵ-Diaminopimelic Acid. *J. Am. Chem. Soc.,* **79,** 648 (1957). With R. Wade, S. M. Birnbaum, M. Winitz, and R. J. Koegel.

255. Preparation and Properties of the Isomeric Forms of Cystine and *S*-Benzylpenicillamine. *J. Am. Chem. Soc.,* **79,** 4538 (1957). With R. Marshall, M. Winitz, and S. M. Birnbaum.

256. Studies on the Metabolism of Amino Acids and Related Compounds *In Vivo.* VI. Free Amino Acid Levels in the Tissues of Rats Protected Against Ammonia Toxicity. *Arch. Biochem. Biophys.,* **68,** 161 (1957). With J. P. du Ruisseau, M. Winitz, and S. M. Birnbaum.

257. Studies on the Metabolism of Amino Acids and Related Compounds *In Vivo.* VII. Ammonia Toxicity in Partially Hepatectomized Rats and the Effect of L-Arginine-HCl Thereon. *Arch. Biochem. Biophys.,* **71,** 458 (1957). With J. P. du Ruisseau, M. Winitz, and S. M. Birnbaum.

258. ϵ-Lysine Acylase. *Arch. Biochem. Biophys.,* **69,** 56 (1957). With W. K. Paik, L. Bloch-Frankenthal, S. M. Birnbaum, and M. Winitz.

259. Studies on Diastereomeric α-Amino Acids and Corresponding α-Hydroxy Acids. IX. Configuration of the Isomeric γ-Hydroxy-glutamic Acids. *J. Am. Chem. Soc.,* **79,** 6192 (1957). With L. Benoiton, M. Winitz, and S. M. Birnbaum.

260. Quantitative Nutritional Studies with Water-Soluble, Chemically Defined Diets. I. Growth, Reproduction and Lactation in Rats. *Arch. Biochem. Biophys.,* **72,** 396 (1957). With S. M. Birnbaum, M. Winitz, and M. C. Otey.

261. Quantitative Nutritional Studies with Water-Soluble, Chemically Defined Diets. II. Nitrogen Balance and Metabolism. *Arch. Biochem. Biophys.,* **72,** 417 (1957). With S. M. Birnbaum and M. Winitz.

262. Quantitative Nutritional Studies with Water-Soluble, Chemically Defined Diets. III. Individual Amino Acids as Sources of "Non-Essential" Nitrogen. *Arch. Biochem. Biophys.,* **72,** 428 (1957). With S. M. Birnbaum and M. Winitz.

263. Quantitative Nutritional Studies with Water-Soluble, Chemically Defined Diets. IV. Influence of Various Carbohydrates on Growth, with Special Reference to D-Glucosamine. *Arch. Biochem. Biophys.,* **72,** 437 (1957). With M. Winitz and S. M. Birnbaum.

264. Quantitative Nutritional Studies with Water-Soluble, Chemically Defined Diets. V. Role of the Isomeric Arginines in Growth. *Arch. Biochem. Biophys.,* **72,** 448 (1957). With M. Winitz and S. M. Birnbaum.

265. A Synthesis of L-Arginyl-L-Arginine. *Arch. Biochem. Biophys.,* **75,** 290 (1958). With L. Zervas, T. Otani, and M. Winitz.

266. Studies on the Metabolism of Amino Acids and Related Compounds *In Vivo.* VIII. Influence of the Route of Administration of L-Arginine·HCl on Protecting Rats Against Ammonia Toxicity. *Arch. Biochem. Biophys.,* **76,** 430 (1958). With P. Gullino, S. M. Birnbaum, and M. Winitz.

267. The Use of Amino Acid Oxidases for the Small-Scale Preparation of the Optical Isomers of Amino Acids. *J. Am. Chem. Soc.,* **80,** 953 (1958). With J. R. Parikh, M. Winitz, and S. M. Birnbaum.

268. Quantitative Nutritional Studies with Water-Soluble, Chemically Defined Diets. VI. Growth Studies on Mice. *Arch. Biochem. Biophys.,* **78,** 245 (1958). With S. M. Birnbaum, M. E. Greenstein, and M. Winitz.

269. Preparation and Disulfide Interchange Reactions of Unsymmetrical Open-Chain Derivatives of Cystine. *J. Am. Chem. Soc.,* **81**, 1729 (1959). With L. Zervas, L. Benoiton, E. Weiss, and M. Winitz.

270. The Enzymic Resolution of β-Methylaspartic Acid with Acylase II. *Arch. Biochem. Biophys.,* **81**, 434 (1959). With L. Benoiton, S. M. Birnbaum, and M. Winitz.

271. Studies on Diastereomeric α-Amino Acids and Corresponding α-Hydroxy Acids. X. The Preparation of β-Hydroxy-β-Methylaspartic Acid. *J. Am. Chem. Soc.,* **81**, 1726 (1959). With L. Benoiton, M. Winitz, R. F. Colman, and S. M. Birnbaum.

272. Quantitative Nutritional Studies with Water-Soluble, Chemically Defined Diets. VII. Nitrogen Balance in Normal and Tumor-Bearing Rats Following Forced-Feeding. *Arch. Biochem. Biophys.,* **81**, 439 (1959). With T. Sugimura, S. M. Birnbaum, and M. Winitz.

273. Quantitative Nutritional Studies with Water-Soluble, Chemically Defined Diets. VIII. The Forced-Feeding of Diets Each Lacking in One Essential Amino Acid. *Arch. Biochem. Biophys.,* **81**, 448 (1959). With T. Sugimura, S. M. Birnbaum, and M. Winitz.

274. Quantitative Nutritional Studies with Water-Soluble, Chemically Defined Diets. IX. Further Studies on D-Glucosamine Containing Diets. *Arch. Biochem. Biophys.* **83**, 521 (1959). With T. Sugimura, S. M. Birnbaum, and M. Winitz.

275. Studies on Arginine Peptides. II. Synthesis of L-Arginyl-L-Arginine and Other N-Terminal Arginine Dipeptides. *J. Am. Chem. Soc.,* **81**, 2878 (1959). With L. Zervas, T. Otani, and M. Winitz.

276. Book Review—Causation of Cancer, *Brit. Med. Bull.,* **14**, No. 2; *J. Am. Chem. Soc.,* in press (1959).

277. A Synthesis and Resolution of DL-Serine. *Arch. Biochem. Biophys.,* **83**, 1 (1959). With S. Akabori, T. T. Otani, R. Marshall, and M. Winitz.

278. The Solid-State Infrared Absorption of the Optically Active and Racemic Straight-Chain α-Amino Acids. *Ann. N.Y. Acad. Sci.,* **69**, 94 (1957). With R. J. Koegel, R. A McCallum, M. Winitz, and S. M. Birnbaum.

279. Quantitative Nutritional Studies with Water-Soluble, Chemically Defined Diets. X. Formulation of a Nutritionally Complete Liquid Diet. *J. Natl. Cancer Inst.* **24**, in press (1960).

280. Dehydropeptidases; Pancreatic Carboxypeptidase; Renal Aminopeptidase; Glutaminase; Amino Acid Amidase. *In* "The Biochemist's Handbook." E. and F. N. Spon, Ltd. London, England. In press (1960). With M. Winitz and S. M. Birnbaum.

281. "The Chemistry of the Amino Acids," Three Volumes. John Wiley and Sons, New York (1960). With M. Winitz.

AUTHOR INDEX

A

Abrams, R., 168, *171*
Acs, G., 86, 92, *107*
Ada, G. L., 159, *170*
Akabori, S., 10, *28*
Alexander, H. E., 159, *170*
Allan, B. J., 51, 52, *58*
Allard, C., 111, 115, *118*
Allen, E., 86, *107*, 162, *172*
Alm, R. S., 69, 73, *83*
Anderson, S. G., 159, *170*
Ando, T., 44, *58*
Andrejew, A., 116, *118*
Anfinsen, C. B., 33, *40, 41,* 81, *83*
Anson, M. L., 43, *58*
Åqvist, S. E. G., 81, *83*
Ashmore, J., 111, 114, *118*
Astrachan, L., 169, *173*
Auerbach, V. H., 111, *118,* 151, *172*
Awapara, J., 126, *145*
Ayengar, P., 138, *144*
Azari, P. B., 67, 68, *84*

B

Baker, C. G., 11, *28*
Barban, S., 112, *118*
Barnett, S. R., 124, *144*
Barnum, C. P., 167, 168, *170*
Barry, J. M., 134, *144*
Bartlett, G. R., 26, *28*
Barton, A. D., 162, *172*
Baumann, C. A., 113, *118*
Beck, W. S., 185, *188*
Behrens, O. K., 102, *106*
Beiser, S. M., 153, *170*
Bendich, A., 153, 155, *170*
Benitez, H. B., 158, *170*
Bennett, L. L., 113, *118*
Berg, C. P., 23, *28*
Berg, P., 86, 89, 93, *106,* 162, *170*
Bergenstal, D. M., 69, *84*
Bergmann, F. H., 162, *170*
Bergquist, A., 151, *173*

Bessman, S. P., 133, 140, *145*
Bharadwaj, T. P., 161, *172*
Bhargava, P. M., 161, 162, 167, *170*
Bickford, R. C., 126, *144*
Biesele, J. J., 149, *172*
Bigelow, C. C., 33, *40*
Bird, H. H., 159, *171*
Birnbaum, S. M., 14, 16, 18, 20, 22, 23, *28, 29,* 126, *144*
Birns, M., 111, *118*
Black, S., 63, *83*
Bloch, K., 85, 89, *106, 107*
Block, M. A., 126, *144*
Block, R. J., 23, *28*
Blumenfeld, O. O., 33, *40*
Boardman, N. K., 62, *83,* 161, *170*
Bock, R. M., 73, *83*
Boedtker, H., 159, *171*
Bollman, J. L., 126, *144*
Bollum, F. J., 148, *171, 173*
Boman, H. G., 69, 71, *83*
Bonner, D. M., 151, *171*
Borges, P. R. F., 130, *145*
Borsook, H., 85, *106*
Bovard, F. C., 86, *107*
Boxer, G. E., 111, *118*
Boyer, P. D., 87, 90, *106*
Brachet, J., 157, 158, *171*
Brockman, R. W., 113, *118*
Brown, F., 159, *171*
Brown, R. A., 159, *171*
Brumm, A. F., 148, *173*
Buchanan, J. M., 134, 139, 142, *144, 145*
Burke, W. T., 140, *144*
Burnet, M., 114, *118*
Busch, H., 133, *144, 145*

C

Caldwell, A. L., 121, *145*
Calvin, M., 36, 37, *40*
Canellakis, E. S., 148, 168, *171*
Cantero, A., 111, 115, *118*

Cardini, C. E., 134, *145*, 183, *188*
Carlisle, C. H., 32, *40*
Carruthers, C., 121, *145*
Carter, C. E., 169, *173*
Castelfranco, P., 87, 90, 91, 93, 98, *106, 107*
Castor, B., 194, *211*
Castor, L. N., 175, *188*
Cha, C. Y., 31, 33, 34, *40*
Chance, B., 115, *118,* 175, *188,* 191, 192, 193, 194, 195, 196, 197, 208, *211*
Chang, J. P., 165, *171*
Chanin, M., 124, 126, *144, 145*
Chantrenne, H., 85, 86, *106*
Chargaff, E., 151, 158, 159, 164, 167, 169, *170, 171, 173*
Chin, L. E., 134, *144*
Christensen, H. N., 135, *144*
Clark, W. H., Jr., 111, *118*
Clowes, G. H. A., 121, *145*
Coe, E. L., 193, 196, 197, *211*
Cohen, E., 43, 45, 46, *59*
Cohen, P. P., 85, *106,* 113, *118*
Cohen, S., 73, 74, *83*
Cohen, S. S., 148, *171*
Cohn, M., 151, *171*
Coleman, J. E., 51, 52, 53, *58*
Colter, J. S., 159, *171*
Commoner, B., 159, *171*
Consden, R., 122, *144*
Cook, J. L., 74, *84*
Coombs, T. L., 48, 49, 50, *59*
Cordes, E., 161, 162, *173*
Cori, C. F., 176, 180, 183, *188*
Cori, G. T., 176, 183, *188*
Countryman, J. L., 169, *173*
Cowdry, E. V., 121, *145*
Crawford, I. P., 78, 79, *83*
Crick, F. H. C., 158, 159, *171*
Crosbie, G. W., 163, 164, *171*

D

Darnell, J. E., Jr., 134, 140, *144*
Davidson, J. N., 163, 164, 167, 169, *171, 172, 173*
Davie, E. W., 44, *59,* 91, 92, *106, 107*
Davis, B. D., 10, *29*
Dawson, R. M. C., 126, *144*
Deeley, E. M., 149, *173*

de Lamirande, G. 111, 115, *118*
DeMoss, J. A., *106*
Dent, C. E., 122, *144*
Desoer, C., 151, *173*
Denber, C. G., 10, *29*
Dewey, D. L., 10, *28*
Dieckmann, M., 162, *170*
Dodgen, C. L., 126, *144*
Donovan, J. W., 33, 34, 35, *40*
Doty, P., 55, *59,* 159, 162, *171*
Dounce, A. L., 124, *144*
Dubnoff, J. W., 85, *106*
du Ruisseau, J., 126, *144*
du Vigneaud, V., 23, *28,* 102, *106*

E

Eagle, H., 112, *118,* 134, 140, *144, 145*
Eiseman, B., 126, *144*
Edmonds, M., 168, *171*
Eisenberg, H., 159, *172*
Elkins-Kaufman, E., 56, 57, *58*
Elliott, W. H., 85, 87, *106*
Elson, D., 159, 164, 169, *171*
Essner, E., 111, *118*

F

Fahey, J. L., 65, 73, *83*
Farber, E., 111, *118*
Feeney, R. E., 67, 68, *84*
Field, E. O., 74, *83*
Fischer, E. H., 57, *58*
Fiscus, J., 149, 151, *172*
Fitch, R. H., 176, *189*
Flaks, J. G., 148, *171*
Fling, M., 151, *172*
Flock, E. V., 126, *144*
Fohn, C. H., 111, *118*
Ford, C. E., 148, *171*
Foulds, L., 112, *118*
Fraenkel-Conrat, H., 159, *171*
Frankel, S., 121, 122, 138, 140, *145*
Franklin, R. E., 159, *171*
Franklin, R. M., 159, *171*
Freed, J. J., 149, *171*
Freedman, A. D., 134, *144*
Freer, R. M., 124, *144*
Fresco, J. R., 159, *171*
Frieden, C., 54, *58*
Friedmann, B. F., 111, *118*

Fruton, J. S., 98, *107*
Fujii, S., 98, *107*
Fujioka, H., 44, *58*
Furth, J., 114, *118*

G

Gawehn, K., 176, 184, 185, *189*
Geiduschek, E. P., 155, *171*
Geissler, A. W., 176, 184, 185, *189*
Georgiev, G. P., 163, *174*
Gierer, A., 159, *171*
Ginoza, W., 159, *171*
Gladner, J. A., 44, *59*
Glassman, E., 86, *107*
Goldman, A., 126, *144*
Goldstein, L., 167, *171*
Goldthwait, D. A., 134, 142, *144*
Gordon, A. H., 122, *144*
Goulian, M., 65, *83*
Graff, S., 134, *144*
Graham, O. L., 133, *145*, 149, 151, *172*
Greco, A., 79, 80, 81, *83*
Green, N. M., 44, *58*
Greenbaum, A. L., 151, *171*
Greenberg, D. M., 139, *145*
Greenberg, G. R., 134, 142, *144*, 148, *173*
Greenfield, R. E., 63, 78, *84*
Greenstein, J. P., 9, 10, 13, 14, 16, 18, 20, 22, 23, *28, 29*, 43, 50, *58, 59*, 109, 110, 111, 117, *118*, 124, 126, *144*, 147, *171*, 175, *188*
Griffin, A. C., 125, *145*, 148, 149, 151, *172*
Grindlay, J. H., 126, *144*
Grollman, A. P., 151, *171*
Gross, A. L., 149, 151, 152, 153, *172*
Guth, L., 124, *145*
Gutter, F. J., 63, 65, 71, 74, 75, 76, 77, *83, 84*

H

Haddow, A., 114, *118*
Hall, B. D., 162, *171*
Hamerton, J. L., 148, *171*
Handler, P., 134, *145*
Hanes, C. S., 135, *144*

Harbers, E., 168, *172*
Harrington, W. F., 32, 33, 36, *40, 41*
Harris, E. D., 194, *211*
Harris, I. J., 44, *59*
Hart, R. G. F., 159, *171*
Hartman, P. E., 187, *188*
Hartman, S. C., 134, 142, *144*
Hartmann, G., 180, *188*, 210, *212*
Haselkorn, R., 159, *171*
Hauenstein, J. D., 32, 33, 34, *41*
Hauschka, T. S., 148, *171*
Hecht, L. I., 86, *106, 107*, 158, 162, 168, *171, 172*
Heidelberger, C., 167, 168, *172, 173*
Henry, C., 159, *171*
Herbert, E., 168, *172*
Hermans, J., Jr., 31, 36, 37, *40*
Hertz, R., 69, *84*
Hess, B., 115, *118*, 191, 193, 194, 196, 197, 208, *211*
Hilmoe, R. J., 64, *84*
Hird, F. J. R., 135, *144*
Hirohata, R., 102, *107*
Hirs, C. H. W., 31, *40*
Hjertén, S., 63, 65, 71, *83, 84*
Hoagland, M. B., 86, 89, 90, *106*, 162, *172*
Hoberman, H. D., 125, *144*
Hogeboom, G. H., 87, *107*
Holley, R. W., 86, *106*
Holtzer, A., 155, *171*
Horowitz, N. H., 151, *172*
Hoskins, J. M., 159, *173*
Hoffa, Y., 161, 163, 167, 169, *173*
Humphrey, G. F., 167, *173*
Hungerford, D. A., 149, *171*
Huppert, J., 159, *172, 173*
Huseby, R. A., 167, 168, *170*
Hutchinson, W. D., 74, *84*
Hvidt, A., 32, 33, *40*

I

Iacobellis, M., 126, *144*
Ibsen, H. K., 193, 196, 197, *211*
Imamura, H., 102, *106*
Ingram, V. M., 151, *172*
Isherwood, F. A., 135, *144*
Itano, H. A., 74, *83, 84*

J

Jackson, R. W., 23, *28*
Jaffe, J. J., 148, *171*
Jelinek, B., 124, 126, 140, *144, 145*
Jencks, W. P., 86, *106*
Johnson, I. S., 112, *118*
Johnson, J. M., 176, *189*
Johnson, M. J., 202, *211*
Josse, J., 148, *172*
Junge, B., 57, *58*

K

Kägi, J. H. R., 55, *59*
Kahler, H., 176, *188, 189*
Kalyankar, G. D., 85, 100, *106, 107*
Kaper, J. M., 159, *172*
Kaplan, 132
Kaplan, H. S., 152, 164, *173*
Karasek, M., 90, 93, *107*
Karp, G. W., 151, *173*
Kawaniski, Y., 44, *58*
Kay, E. R. M., 167, *173*
Keller, E. B., 86, 89, 98, *106, 107*
Keller, P. J., 43, 45, 46, *59*
Kendo, K., 102, *107*
Kennedy, E. P., 116, *119*
Kenney, F. T., 151, *172*
Keynan, A., 134, *145*
Khorana, H. G., 64, *84*
Kielley, R. K., 116, *118*
Kihara, H., 140, *145*
Kingdom, H. S., 92, *107*
Kingsley, R. B., 13, *28*
Kirby, K. S., 156, *172*
Kit, S., 125, 133, 145, 148, 149, 151, 152, 153, 155, 159, *172*
Klein, G., 112, *118*, 149, *172*
Klug, A., 159, *171*
Knox, W. R., 151, *172*
Koch, G., 159, *170*
Koenigsberger, R., 197, *211*
Köningsberger, V. V., 91, *106*
Koeppe, O. J., 87, *106*
Kondo, N., 153, *172*
Kornberg, A., 148, *172*
Kornberg, S. R., 148, *172*
Koshland, D. E., Jr., 87, *107*
Kowalsky, A., 87, *107*

Krakow, J. S., 148, *171*
Krebs, H. A., 85, 87, *107*
Kretchner, N., 151, *172*
Krimsky, I., 177, 185, *188*
Krishnaswamy, P. R., 90, 91, 92, 93, *107*
Kuff, E. L., 87, *107*
Kunkel, H. G., 74, *83*

L

Lagerkvist, U., 134, *145*
Laird, A. K., 162, *172*
Landan, B. R., 111, 114, *118*
Langer, L., 87, *107*
Laskowski, M., Jr., 33, 34, 35, *40*
Lavik, P. S., 113, *118*
Law, L. W., 113, *118*
Leahy, J., 162, *172*
Lederberg, J., 151, *172*
Legallais, V., 194, *212*
Lehninger, A. L., 151, *171*
Leibman, K. C., 168, *172*
Leloir, L. F., 134, *145*, 183, *188*
LePage, G. A., 167, 168, *173*
Leupold, U., 151, *172*
Levan, A., 149, *172*
Levenberg, B., 134, 139, 142, *144, 145*
Levin, Ö., 63, 71, *84*
Levintow, L., 13, *28*, 85, 87, 88, *107*, 134, *145*
Levy, M., 33, *40*, 112, *118*
Leyon, H., 161, *172*
Lichtenheld, F. R., 126, *144*
Liles, R. H., 161, *172*
Lin, E. C. C., 151, *172*
Linderstrøm-Lang, K., 33, 35, *40*
Lindsey, A. J., 194, *211*
Ling, N. S., 73, *83*
Lipmann, F., 86, 90, 91, 92, *106, 107*
Litt, M., 159, *171*
Littaner, U. Z., 159, *172*
Loftfield, R. B., 86, *107*
Logan, R., 167, *172*
Loosli, J. K., 23, *28*
Love, R., 161, *172*
Lowe, I. P., 124, 142, 143, *145*
Luchsinger, W. W., 87, *106*
Lynen, F., 180, *188*, 197, 202, 210, *211, 212*

M

Maas, W. K., 85, *107*
McCoy, P. F., 65, *83*
McGilvery, R. W., 85, *106*
McHenry, E. W., 130, *145*
McIndoe, W. M., 169, *172*
McKee, R. W., 193, 196, 197, *211*
McMaster-Kaye, R., 161, 164, *172*
Mandeles, S., 85, 89, *107*
Mandelkern, L., 32, *41*
Mann, F. C., 126, *144*
Mantsavinos, R., 148, *171*
Markham, R., 64, *84*
Marshak, A., 167, *173*
Martin, A. J. P., 122, *144*
Marvin, H. N., 126, *145*
Maver, M. E., 79, 80, 81, *83*
Medes, G., 111, *118*
Meister, A., 13, *28*, 85, 86, 87, 88, 89,
    90, 91, 92, 93, 98, 100, *106*, *107*, 134,
    139, 140, *145*
Miller, E. C., 113, *118*
Miller, J. A., 113, 114, *118*
Miller, L. L., 140, *144*
Minagawa, T., 161, *173*
Moldave, K., 85, 89, 91, 98, *106*, *107*,
    134, 140, *144*, *145*
Mole R. H., 148, *171*
Moore, P. R., 113, *118*
Moore, S., 31, *40*, *41*, 62, 63, *84*
Morrison, M., 74, *84*
Mountain, I. M., 159, *170*
Moyed, H. S., 86, *107*
Moyer, A. W., 159, *171*
Muntwyler, E., 126, *144*
Murray, M. R., 158, *170*

N

Naora, H., 168, *173*
Naora, Hatsuko, 168, *173*
Narita, K., 10, *28*
Netter, K. F., 180, *188*, 210, *212*
Neurath, H., 43, 44, 45, 46, 47, 48, 49,
    50, 52, 55, 56, 57, *58*, *59*
Nohara, H., 86, *107*
Novelli, G. D., 85, 93, *106*, *107*
Novikoff, A. B., 111, *118*
Nyhan, W. L., 133, *145*

O

O'Brien, J. R. P., 74, *83*
Ofengand, E. J., 86, *106*, 162, *170*
Ogata, K., 86, *107*
Olson, M. E., 139, *145*
Ono, T., 102, *107*
Osawa, S., 153, 161, 163, 167, 169, *172*,
    173
Osofsky, H., 126, *144*
Otey, M. C., 14, 18, 20, *28*
Ottesen, M., 33, *40*
Ozawa, G., 130, *145*

P

Pahl, H. B., 153, 155, *170*
Palade, G. E., 162, 167, *173*
Pardee, A. B., 151, *174*
Parks, R. E., Jr., 112, *118*
Parr, C. W., 73, *84*
Partridge, S. M., 63, *83*
Patterson, A. R. P., 168, *173*
Patterson, E. K., 149, *173*
Paul, J., 112, *118*
Peabody, R. A., 134, 142, *144*
Pearson, E. S., 112, *118*
Perske, W. F., 112, *118*
Peterson, E. A., 63, 64, 65, 71, 73, 74,
    75, 76, 77, 79, 80, 82, *83*, *84*
Piez, K. A., 134, *145*
Pitot, H. C., 111, *118*
Plaut, W., 167, 168, *171*, *173*
Podber, E., 149, *173*
Pol, E. H., 64, *84*
Polli, E. E., 151, 152, 153, 155, *173*
Porath, J., 63, *84*
Potter, V. R., 111, 113, 114, *118*, 133,
    144, 148, 167, 168, *171*, *172*, *173*
Preiss, J., 134, *145*, 162, *170*
Price, V. E., 63, 78, *84*
Pucher, G. W., 10, *29*
Putnam, F. W., 44, *59*

R

Rabinovitz, M., 139, *145*
Racker, E., 175, 177, 180, 181, 185, *188*,
    189, 191, 193, 196, 197, 199, 202, 209,
    210, *212*
Rafn, M. L., 135, *144*

Ragland, R. S., 149, 151, *172*
Ramasarma, G. B., 138, 140, *144, 145*
Rands, D. G., 32, 33, *41*
Rechcigl, M., Jr., 23, *28*
Reem, G. H., 151, *172*
Reid, E., 161, 162, *173*
Reisfeld, R. A., 69, *84*
Reynafarge, B., 111, *118*
Rhodes, M. B., 67, 68, *84*
Richards, B. M., 149, *173*
Richter, G., 168, *173*
Roberts, E., 121, 122, 124, 125, 126, 130, 131, 132, 133, 134, 135, 136, 138, 140, 141, 142, 143, *144, 145*
Robertson, W. van B., 176, *188*
Ronzoni, E., 140, *145*
Rose, W. C., 14, 23, *29*
Rosenberg, A. J., 116, *118*
Rosenkranz, H. S., 155, *170*
Rosoff, M., 155, *170*
Ross, G. A. L., 130, *145*
Rouser, G., 124, 130, 140, *145*
Rupley, J. A., 46, 47, 48, 49, 50, 54, 55, 56, 57, *59*
Rusch, H. P., 113, *118*
Russell, W. O., 165, *171*
Rustad, R. C., 168, *173*

S

Sanders, F. K., 159, *172, 173*
Sayre, F. W., 141, *145*
Schachfer, D., 85, *107*
Schellman, J., 32, 33, 36, *40*
Scheraga, H. A., 31, 32, 33, 34, 35, 36, 37, 38, 39, *40, 41*
Schildkraut, C. L., 31, 35, *41*
Schneider, J. H., 167, *173*
Scholtissek, C., 167, *173*
Schramm, G., 159, *171*
Schuegraf, A., 180, *188*, 210, *212*
Schulze, H. O., 112, *118*
Schweet, R., 162, *172*
Schweet, R. S., 86, *107*, 161, 162, *173*
Schwerin, P., 133, 140, *145*
Schwert, G. W., 44, 56, *59*
Scott, J. F., 86, *106*, 158, 162, 168, *171*
Scouloudi, H., 32, *40*
Sealock, R. R., 23, *28*
Sela, M., 33, *41*

Sellers, R. F., 159, *171*
Shane, M., 14, *29*
Sharon, N., 90, *106*
Shearer, G. B., 159, *171*
Shigeura, H. T., 167, *173*
Shonk, C. E., 111, *118*
Shooter, K. V., 152, 153, 155, *173*
Shugar, D., 32, *41*
Siekevitz, P., 162, 167, *173*
Simkin, J. L., 161, 162, 167, *170*
Simonsen, D. G., 125, 126, 131, 132, 133, 134, 135, *145*
Singer, B., 159, *171*
Singer, S. J., 74, *84*
Sinsheimer, R., 159, *173*
Skipper, H. E., 113, *118*
Slater, T. F., 151, *171*
Smellie, R. M. S., 163, 164, 167, *171, 173*
Smith, E. L., 44, *59*
Smith, K. C., 152, 161, 162, 164, *173*
Smith, L. C., 14, *29*
Snell, E. E., 140, *145*
Snoke, J. E., 85, 89, *107*
Sober, H. A., 11, *28*, 63, 64, 65, 71, 73, 74, 75, 76, 77, 79, 80, 81, 82, *83, 84*
Somerville, R., 148, *173*
Sorof, S., 113, *118*
Spackman, D. H., 31, *41*
Speck, J. F., 85, 87, *107*
Staehelin, M., 64, 82, *84*
Steere, R. L., 159, *172*
Stein, E. A., 57, *58*
Stein, W. H., 31, *40, 41*, 62, 63, *84*
Steinfeld, J. L., 73, *83*
Stent, G. S., 158, *173*
Stephenson, M. L., 86, *106, 107*, 158, 162, 168, *171, 172*
Stepka, W., 122, *144*
Sterling, W. R., 78, *84*
Stevens, A. L., 64, *84*
Stevens, B. M., 161, 162, *173*
Steward, F. C., 122, *144*
Stewart, D. L., 159, *171*
Stickland, L. H., 185, *188*
Stockell, A., 44, *59*
Strauss, B., 161, *173*
Strecker, H. J., 134, *145*
Strode, C., 159, *171*

Strong, L. C., 148, *173*
Stulberg, M. P., 90, *106*
Sugimura, T., 20, *29*
Sumerwell, W., 57, *58*
Suntzeff, V., 121, *145*
Swift, H., 161, *173*
Swingle, S. M., 63, *84*

T

Taggart, J. V., 85, *107*
Takagi, Y., 168, *172*
Takaka, K., 161, 163, 167, 169, *173*
Tanaka, K. K., 131, 132, 133, 134, 135, *145*
Tanaka, T., 131, 132, 133, 134, 135, *145*
Tanford, C., 32, 33, 34, 37, *41*
Tannenberg, W. J., 134, *144*
Taylor, J. H., 161, 164, *172, 173*
Tener, G. M., 64, *84*
Tessman, I., 159, *173*
Thompson, E. O. P., 44, *59*
Thompson, J. W., 176, *189*
Tiselins, A., 63, 69, 71, 73, *83, 84*
Tishkoff, G. H., 122, 124, 138, *144, 145*
Trent, L. W., 164, 169, *171*
Tyner, E. P., 167, *173*

U

Uzman, L. L., 151, *173*

V

Vallee, B. L., 43, 44, 46, 48, 49, 50, 51, 52, 53, *58, 59*
Van Damme, O., 159, *170*
Van Etten, C., 23, *28*
Vermund, H., 168, *170*
Vickery, H. B., 10, *29*
Vinograd, J., 74, *84*
Voegtlin, C., 176, *189*
Vogel, H. J., 167, *173*
Volkin, E., 169, *173*

W

Waelsch, H., 133, 134, 140, *145*
Wagner, B., 161, *173*
Wagner, R. P., 151, *173*
Waisman, H. A., 111, *118*

Walker, D. L., 112, *118*
Walker, P. M. B., 149, *173*
Wallenins, G., 74, *83*
Warburg, O., 115, 116, *119*, 175, 176, 184, 185, *189*
Weber, G., 111, 114, *118*
Weber, R. E., 32, 37, *41*
Webster, L. D., Jr., 92, *107*
Wecker, E., 159, *171, 173*
Weinhouse, S., 111, 115, 116, *118, 119*, 148, *173*, 175, *186*, 201
Weiss, S. B., 86, 92, *107*
Weissburger, E. K., 113, *119*
Weissburger, J. H., 113, *119*
Westlund, L. E., 69, *83*
White, J. M., 130, *145*
Wildman, S. G., 159, *173*
Williams, G. R., 194, 195, *211*
Williams, H. H., 23, *28*
Williams, R. C., 159, *171*
Williams, R. J. P., 58, *59*, 69, 73, *83*
Williams-Ashman, H. G., 116, *119*
Winnick, R. E., 85, 100, *107*
Winnick, T., 85, 100, *107*
Winitz, M., 9, 10, 14, 16, 18, 20, 22, 23, *28, 29*, 126, *144*
Womack, M., 14, *29*
Wong, G. K., 98, *107*
Woods, P. S., 164, *173*
Work, E., 10, *28*
Work, T. S., 161, 162, 167, *170*
Wretlind, K. A., 23, *29*
Wright, N. G., 63, *83*
Wu, R., 175, 177, 179, 180, 181, 182, 184, *188, 189*, 193, 196, 197, 210, *212*
Wyckoff, M. M., 63, 65, 71, *84*
Wyttenbach, C., 87, *107*

Y

Yamada, T., 158, *174*
Yang, C. C., 193, *212*
Yang, J. T., 55, *59*
Yanofsky, C., 78, 79, *83*, 151, *174*
Yates, R. A., 151, *174*

Z

Zachau, H. G., 86, *107*
Zaitlin, M., 161, *170*

Zajdela, F., 116, *118*
Zalokar, M., 164, 167, *174*
Zamecnik, P. C., 86, 89, 90, 98, *106,*
107, 158, 162, 168, *171, 172*

Zbarsky, I. B., 163, *174*
Zimmerman, S. B., 148, *172*
Ziondrou, C., 98, *107*
Zubay, G., 158, *174*

SUBJECT INDEX

A

Acyl adenylates
  as intermediates in activation of
    amino and fatty acids, 86, 90
Adenosine 5′-monophate-2′(3′)-amino
    acid ester, structure, 90
Adenosine 5-phosphate (AMP)
  effect on glycolysis of ascites tumor
    cells, 181
Acylase(s), renal
  resolution of racemic amino acids
    with, 11, 12, 13, 28, 43
  stereospecifity, 4
Adenosine 5′-diphosphate (ADP)
  glutamine synthesis and, 87, 88
  spectroscopic and respiratory re-
    sponses of ascites tumor cells
    to, 194, 195-196
Adenosine 5′-triphosphate (ATP)
  glycolysis in tumor cells and, 177-
    179, 181, 188
  role in biosynthesis of peptide
    bonds, 85
  synthesis from amino acyl adeny-
    lates, and tryptophan-activat-
    ing enzymes 90, 93-99
  inhibition of, 94
β-Alanyl-activating enzyme
  from chick pectoral muscle, 100
    specificity of, 102
    synthesis of adenosine 5′-triphos-
      phate from, 104
    of β-alanyl peptides from, 100-
      105
β-Alanyl peptides, *see* also Carnosine
    and Anserine
  synthesis, enzymatic, 100-105
Albumin
  chromatography, 71
Amidase, renal
  resolution of racemic amino acids
    with, 11, 12, 13, 28
D-Amino acid oxidase
  inhibition by sodium benzoate, 26-27

role in conversion of D-amino acids
  to L-isomers 24, 26, 27
Amino acids
  activation, peptide bond synthesis
    and, 85-107
  enzymatic resolution of racemic, 10-
    13, 28, 43
    purity, 13
    yield, 13
  essential, replacement of L- by D-
    isomers, 23
  free, see also individual compounds
    in healthy and tumor tissues
      effect of sterile autolysis on,
        136-138
      experimental variations, 126
    free, in tumor cells and host tissues,
      122, 123, 126-130
      comparative studies, 142-143
      effect of tumor growth, 126-130
      effect of tumor regression on,
        130-132
    metabolic conversion of D- into L-
      isomers, 24-27
      rate-limiting step, 25, 26, 27
      role of amino acid oxidase, 24,
        26
    metabolism in plant and animal
      tumors, 143
    nutritional value, optical rotation
      and, 20-22, 23, 24-25
    optically pure, large-scale prepara-
      tion, 9-13
Amino acyl adenylates
  enzyme-bound, formation, 98-99
  formation of ATP from 93-99
    structural requirements, 93
  as intermediates in biological pep-
    tide bond synthesis, 99, 106
  in protein synthesis, 86, 106
  preparation, 91-92
  reactivity, 98
  reaction with proteins and nucleic
    acids, 98

γ-Amino butyryl peptides
synthesis of, 103
α-Amylase
of *Bacillus subtilis,* stability and
metal content, 57
Animals
germ-free, chemically defined diets
as food for, 22, 23, 28
Anticancer agents, *see* also individual
compounds
effective, requirements, 142
Anserine
biosynthesis, 85, 100
occurrence, 102
Ascites tumor cells
ADP utilization, pathway of, 199-
200
carbohydrate metabolism in, 177-
179
cytochromes of, 193, 194-195
Ehrlich, proteins of, 134
free amino acid patterns, in, effect
of growth on, 127
glucose utilization by
inhibition of, 197, 200
reversibility of, by uncoupling
agents, 197-200
lactate formation in, 191
metabolic activity of diploid and
tetraploid, 149-150
DNA content and, 150
quantitative relationships in, 149,
150, 170
metabolic control in, 191-212
digital computer representation,
202-212
essential features of, 200
model for, 203, 208
metabolic control sequence, 200-202
metabolic response to glucose and
uncoupling agents, 191, 195-
197
respiration in mitochondria of,
175
Yoshida, effect of glutamine inhibitors on, 138-139
free amino acids in, 130-132
effect of chemicals on, 132
of X-irradiation on, 132

B

Benzoylglycine
biosynthesis, 85, 89
Brain
amino acid pattern, effect of sterile
autolysis on, 136
enzymes of carboyhdrate metabolism in, 185

C

C 1498 leukemia
amino acid pattern during growth
and regression of, 130
Calcium phosphate gels
as adsorbents in protein chromatography, 62-63
Cancer
cells, *see* Cancer, cells,
genetic concept, DNA and, 151-
157
relationships between enzymes,
genes and, 147-151
Squamous cell, free amino acid pattern, 122
Carbohydrate metabolism
in chicken leucocytes, 184-185
in HeLa cells, 179-184
effect of adenosine monophos-
phate and inorganic phos-
phate on, 182
Carboxypeptidase A, *see* Carboxypeptidase, pancreatic
Carboxypeptidase, pancreatic
activity, zinc content and, 48-50
behavior towards phenylacetate, 56-
57, 58
formation, 43
isolation, 43
labeled with Zn[65], 46-48
metal-free, restoration of activity
by metals other than zinc, 49-
53
as metalloenzyme, 43, 44, 46, 53-54
molecular structure, 44
occurrence, 45, 58
properties, 44
of metal-free and native, 54-56, 58
relation between structure and function of, 43-58

resolution of racemic amino acids with, 11, 12, 13, 28, 43
stability, metal content and, 57, 58
stereospecificity, 43
substrate specificity, 44-45
zinc in, 46
Carcinogenesis
biochemical theories of, 113-117
deletion theory, 113-115, 117
theory of impaired respiration, 115-116
rate-limiting enzymatic changes in, 148
Carcinogens
reaction with key cellular proteins, 113, 114
Carnosinase
hydrolysis of β-alanylpeptides by, 101
Carnosine
biosynthesis, enzymatic, 85, 100-105
occurrence, 102
synthesis, enzymatic
from β-alanyl adenylate, 102-103
nonenzymatic 103
Cells
cancer, distribution of RNA in, 162
fermentative character of, 191
glycolysis in, 115
number and structure of chromosomes in, 147, 148-149, 170
Cellulosic ion exchangers
as adsorbents in protein chromatography, 62, 63
Chromatin complex
carcinogenesis and, 148
Chromatography
of DNA from normal neoplastic tissues, 152-157, 158
effect of anion exchanger, 155-156
preparation of sample, 156
of protein mixtures, 61-83
adsorbents for, 62-63
elution, gradient, 68, 69-83
stepwise, 67-69
disadvantages, 68-69
mechanism, 63-67

Chromosomes
effect of neoplasia on number and structure of, 147, 148-149
genetic aspects, 151
Cobalt
activity of carboxypeptidase and, 49 ff.
Colitis, ulcerative
chemically defined diets in treatment of, 22, 23, 28
Computer, digital
representation of metabolic control pattern in ascites tumor cells by, 202-211
effect of uncoupling agents, 207-208
glucose-activated metabolism, 207
Crabtree effect
in tumor cells, 186, 188, 200
Cytochromes
of ascites tumor cells, 193, 194-195
Cytoplasm
RNA of, heterogeneity of, 161

D

Deoxyribonucleic acids (DNA)
chromosomal, interaction of RNA and, 159
effect of preparation on molecular size and properties of, 155
genetic concept of cancer and, 151-157
metabolism of ascites tumor cells and, 149, 150
molecular structure, 159, 170
of normal and neoplastic tissues, 151-157
chromatographic fractionation, 152-157
differences between, 152, 156-157, 170
synthesis, enzymatic switchpoints for control of, 160
Diets
chemically defined, water-soluble, 13-28
applications of, 22-27, 28
composition, 14-15, 28

effect of nonessential amino acids on growth of weanling rats, 16-20
nutritional studies with, 16-28
Diphosphopyridine nucleotide biosynthesis, glutamine and, 134

E

E-39 (2,5 di-*n*-propoxy-3,6-bis ethylenimino benzoquinone), 134
effect on amino acid patterns of tumor cells, 132, 134
Egg white proteins
separation on cellulosic ion exchanger, 67-68
Endopeptidase
from procarboxypeptidase, 45-46, 58
Enzyme-forming systems (EFS)
function of RNA in, 157-161
origin of, 147
Enzymes, see also specific compounds
activity, in tumor tissues, 109 ff
as compared with normal tissues, 110
amino acid-activating,
activity, sulfhydryl groups and, 105
glycolytic, in brain homogenates, 185
in ascites tumor cells, 177-179
in HeLa cells, 179-180, 187
liver, effect of neoplasia on, 147-148
relationships between cancer, genes and, 147-151
respiratory, in tumor tissues, 175

F

Fatty acids
aetivation, 86

G

Genes
relationships between enzymes, cancer and, 147-151
Glucose
metabolic response of Ehrlich ascites tumor cells to, 191

phosphorylation, 209-210
utilization by ascites tumor cells, 179, 195-197
L-Glutamic acid
microbial synthesis, 10
Glutaminase
phosphate-activated of tumors, 141
renal, 141-142
active site, 141- 142
Glutamine
biosynthesis, 85, 86, 87-89
optical specificity, 87
possible mechanism, 87
in blood of man and experimental animal, 139-140
formation of hydroxamic acids from, optical rotation and, 87, 88
intracellular virus biosynthesis and, 140
metabolism, enzymes of, 141-142
role in cellular metabolism, 134
in tumor and host tissues, 127-139
effect of aulolysis on, 136, 138
inhibitors of, attempted preparation of potent, 141-142
liberation by anticancer drugs, 132, 134
metabolism of, 132-135
chemotherapeutic implications, 138-140
possible sources of, 134, 135
γ-L-Glutamylhydrazide
effect on tumor cells, 138-139
γ-Glutamyl phosphate
as intermediate in glutamine synthesis, 87
Glycolysis
anaerobic, in brain slices, 185
comparative biochemistry, 185-186
glutamine and, 134
in human leucocytes, 185
hexokinase as limiting factor, 185
in tumor cells, 115
inorganic phosphate as rate-limiting factor, 178, 187
Greenstein, Jesse P.
bibliography of published works, 213-227
obituary, 1-8

H

HeLa cells
carbohydrate metabolism in, 179-184
effect of change in growth medium on, 182
Hemoglobin(s)
chromatography, 73-78
effect of urea, 76, 78
heterogeneity, demonstrated by, 73-74, 78
pathological, 74
subunit structure, 74-75
Hepatocarcinogenesis
enzyme deletion and, 114-115
Histidine
peptides of, synthesis, 100, 102

K

Kwashiorkor
chemically defined diets in treatment of, 22, 23, 25

L

Lactic acid
aerobic formation, in growing tissue culture cells, 179
in tumor tissues, 175, 176-179, 180
mechanism of, 188
Leucocytes
chicken, carbohydrate metabolism in, 184-185
Liver
amino acid pattern, in effect of sterile autolysis on, 136
Liver tumors
enzyme activity and, 110-111
enzyme loss in, 147-148
L-Lysine
microbial synthesis, 10

M

Magnesium
adenosine 5'-triphosphate synthesis and, 98
peptide bond synthesis and, 85

Man
quantitative metabolic studies with chemically defined diets, 22
Marine organisms
free amino acids in, 142-143
Mercaptalbumin,
chromatography, 72, 73
Metabolism
cellular, control substance for, 192-193
factors affecting, 151
genetic aspects, 150-151
phosphate control of glycolytic and respiratory activities, 210
rate-limiting factors, 191-192
nature and distribution of participating enzymes, 193
Metals
in carboxypeptidase and procarboxypeptidase, 46-54
Methionine-activating enzyme
yeast, formation of L-methionyl adenylate from, 93
Mitochondria
affinity for ADP, 197, 199, 200, 210
Murphy lymphosarcoma (ascites)
free amino acid patterns, 127-129
Muscle
β-alanyl peptides in, 102
Mutation
conversion of normal to neoplastic cell due to, 114

N

Nitromin, 134
effect on amino acid patterns of tumor cells, 132
Nucleases
chromatography, 79-83
heterogeneity demonstrated by, 81 ff.
Nucleoproteins
carcinogenesis and, 114
Nucleus
as primary site of RNA synthesis, 164-169
from studies with isotopic precursors, 164-167
RNA of, heterogeneity of, 161

O

Oligophrenic phemylpyruvica
  chemically defined diets in treatment of, 23
Ophidine (β-alanyl-2-methylhistidine)
  occurrence, 102

P

Pancreas
  acinar cells, as source of carboxypeptidase, 45
Parenteral feeding
  chemically defined diets and, 22, 28
Pasteur effect, 180
  in brain slices, 185
  in lactate formation in HeLa cells, 180
  in tumor cells, 179, 186, 188
  in yeast cells, 210
Peptide bonds
  biosynthesis, amino acid activation and, 85-107
    amino acyl adenylates as intermediates in, 99
    possible mechanism, 85-86
    role of adenosine 5'-triphosphate, 85
Phenylacetylglutamine
  biosynthesis, mechanism, 89
Phosphate
  inorganic, peptide bond synthesis and, 85
  as rate-limiting-factor in glycolysis in tumor tissues, 178, 180, 181
Phosphorylase
  activity, in HeLa cells, 180, 181-182, 183
Phosphorylation
  glycolytic, 209-210
Polio virus
  synthesis by HeLa cells, glutamine and, 134
Polyadenylic acid
  enzymatic hydrolysis, 64
    chromatographic separation of digest, 65
Poly-γ-benzyl-L-glutamate
  molecular structure, thermal transition, 36

Procarboxypeptidase, 43
  in pancreas juice, 45, 46
  conversion to carboxypeptidase, 45-46
  isolation, 45
Proteins
  biosynthesis, possible mechanism, 86
  cellular, reaction with carcinogens, 113-114
  internal interactions in, 31, 32
  mixtures of, chromatography of, 61-83

R

Respiration
  cellular, carcinogenesis and, 114-116
Ribonuclease
  abnormal carboxyl and tyrosyl groups in, 32-36
  determination of amino acid sequence in, 31, 32
  of disulfide bridges in, 31, 32
  internal hydrogen bonding in, 31-41
    experiments aimed at demonstration of, 32-39, 40
      effect of deuterium-hydrogen substitution on stability of hydrogen bonds, 32, 36-37, 40
      kinetics of deuterium-hydrogen exchange, 32, 35-36, 40
      optical rotation, 32, 37-39, 40
      titrations in a denaturing solvent, 32-35, 40
      ultraviolet difference spectra, 32, 33, 37, 40
    number of bonds, 36
  internal interactions in, 34, 35
  model of, 31, 32, 38, 39-40
  molecular size and shape, 32
  molecular structure, 32
    thermal transition, 32, 36, 37-39
Ribonucleic acid
  base composition, in normal and tumor tissues, 163-164
  biosynthesis, nucleus as primary site of, 164-169
  common P donor for cytoplasmic and nuclear, 168-ix

complexes with amino acids, 86
cyloplasmic, 161
 independent synthesis, 168, 169
 function in enzyme-forming systems, 157-161
  genetic aspects, 157-158, 159
  possible mode of, 158
 heterogeneity of, 161-162
 interaction with chromosomal DNA, 159
 molar base ratios of, in normal and tumor tissues, 160-161, 170
 molecular structure, 159, 170
 ribosomal, enzymes and, 162
  properties of, 162
 transfer-, properties of, 162
Ribonucleoproteins
 nuclear, composition, 163
  in RNA tumor cells, 163
  relation to microsomal ribosomes, 163

S

Sarkomycin, 134
 effect on amino acid patterns of tumor cells, 132
Sea anemones, resemblance of amino acid patterns in tumors and, 143
Serum
 chromatography, electrophoresis of chromatogram, 65, 66
  of normal human, 70-71
  of pathological, 69
Sodium benzoate
 detoxification, 27
 inhibition of D-amino acid oxidase by, 26-27
Space travel
 chemically defined diets as potential food supply for, 22, 23, 28

T

Tissue cultures
 effect on cellular metabolism and enzyme activities, 112
Tissues
 animal, permeability to glutamine and glutamic acid, 133

free amino acids in healthy tissues, 121-130
 constancy of, 125-126
 normal, lactic acid formation in, 175-176
 RNA base ratios of normal and tumor, 160-161
 sterile autolysis, 135-136
  effect on amino acid pattern of healthy and tumor, 135-138
 tumor, aerobic lactic acid formation in, 175-176, 180, 188
Tobacco mosaic virus, plant chloroplast as site of synthesis, 161
Transphosphorylase
 drug resistance in tumors and, 113
Trypsin
 role in activation of procarboxypeptidase, 45-46
Tryptophan
 biosynthesis in *E. coli,* enzymes catalyzing, 78
Tryptophan-activating enzyme
 pancreatic, 90
  active site, 96-97
  affinity for L-tryptophanyl adenylate, 94
  formation of adenosine 5'-triphosphate and, 93-99
 specificity of, 96
Tryptophan-ribonucleic acid complex, preparation, 99
Tryptophan synthetase
 chromatography of, 78-79
Tryptophanyl adenylate, formation, enzymatic, 90-91
L-Tryptophanyl adenylate
 formation of adenosine 51'triphosphate from, 95-98
Tumors
 abnormal enzymatic and metabolic patterns in, 147, 149-151
 biochemical changes in growing, 112-113
 development of drug resistance in, 113
 difference in amino acid metabolism in plant and animal, 143

free amino acid patterns in, 121-125
effect of growth and regression on,
130-132
glutamine in, effect of autolysis on,
136-138
metabolic role, 133-135
impaired respiration in, 175
lactate formation in, 175, 176, 180
possible significance of, 186-187
transplantable, glutamine inhibitors
in chemotherapy of, 138

V

Virus(es)

effect on lactate formation in growing tissue culture cells, 179
intracellular biosynthesis, glutamine
and, 140

X

X-irradiation, effect on free amino
acid patterns of Yoshida sarcoma, 132

Z

Zinc, in carboxypeptidase, 46-54
in pancreatic carboxypeptidase, 44,
46-54